LORD'S & COMMONS

Also edited by John Bright-Holmes

The Joy of Cricket

LORD'S & COMMONS

Cricket in novels and stories

Edited by
John Bright-Holmes

ANDRE DEUTSCH

First published 1988 by
André Deutsch Limited
105-106 Great Russell Street, London WC1B 3LJ

British Library Cataloguing in Publication Data

Lords and commons: cricket in novels and stories.
1. English literature. Special subjects: Cricket – Anthologies
I. Bright-Holmes, John
820.8′0355

ISBN 0 233 98284 1

Printed in Great Britain by
WBC Print Ltd, Bristol

Contents

Editor's Introduction

When I began assembling fictional accounts of cricket, I became fascinated by their vividness and variety but was still conscious of a contradiction. Does anyone, I wondered, want to read untrue tales of a game when, nearly every day of the week, they can play, watch or read about the real thing? Also, was there enough cricket fiction? And new material as well?

Most earlier collections of cricket writing carry their meed of fiction with authors like Conan Doyle, P.G. Wodehouse and E.W. Hornung; with the farcical humour of *England, Their England* and the symbolic intensity of *The Go-Between*; while there are many stirring school stories from *Tom Brown's Schooldays* onwards. I recall too the late Rowland Bowen explaining 'the golden age of cricket' through the Edwardian country-house cricket match in E.R. Eddison's *A Fish Dinner in Memison*. Pride of place amongst my predecessors must go, however, to Gerald Brodribb, who has updated his valuable booklet 'Cricket in Fiction' (1950) for inclusion in this volume; and to Leslie Frewin who, in the late 1960s, produced two volumes of *The Best of Cricket's Fiction*. Without their work, mine would have taken me infinitely longer.

In the twenty years since Mr Frewin's collection some fine and very interesting new writing has emerged, but before I describe it and the arrangement of this book, it is worth asking, what is the nature of cricket fiction? Is there really such an animal? If so, what form or forms does it take? Broadly speaking, I have found seven categories:

1. Cricket novels – where cricket itself is the subject and mainspring of the book, such as *The Cricket Match* by Hugh de Selincourt.

2. The novel which is not about cricket, but includes an important element or episode which does concern cricket. *England, Their England* and *The Go-Between* are examples, each with its 'set-piece'.
3. Story collections by one author.
4. Individual stories.
5. School novels and stories. These can be included in the previous categories; but there is so much written, both for adults and for younger readers, that they form a natural class of their own, which is reflected in the arrangement of this book.
6. Magazine serials.
7. Novels or stories which contain brief, passing references to the game.

For the purpose of this anthology, the last category has been largely ignored. If you search diligently in Thackeray's *The Newcomes*, for example, you will find some very brief early references to cricket being played at school. Similarly, on a more substantial level, you will find episodes of cricket in Iris Murdoch's *The Sandcastle*, in E.M. Forster's *Maurice*, in Kingsley Amis's *Take a Girl like You*; or set at Lord's as in Galsworthy's *To Let*, and even, as in Robert Graves's story *The Shout*, at an asylum's cricket ground. However, from the cricket enthusiast's rather special point of view, these episodes are treated, quite correctly in context, as little more than background or scenery. It takes a George Meredith to indulge the subject effectively and briefly.

What I have been looking for, therefore, are cricket passages out of novels or stories, or complete stories, which are substantial enough in themselves to involve, inform and entertain the reader and which allow the game sufficient space and detail to develop its own character. As I read, I found often that the most colourful and effective writing came from the 'school' stories. 'Willingly to school', therefore, the second section of this book, provides possibly the most satisfying part of the collection with the different approaches of Helen Mathers, Talbot Baines Reed, P.G. Wodehouse (compare St Dominic's with Wrykyn), and

E.F. Benson all representing a sort of age of innocence. The school plot thickens with E.W. Hornung's *Fathers of Men*, and Alec Waugh's *The Loom of Youth*; and it receives its first-world-war shock from Bruce Marshall's *Prayer for the Living* which leaves the reader with one of the most resonant images in writing about cricket. After that, and except for the evergreen Bunter, everything is destined for change, even Eton *v.* Harrow.

The other two parts of the book are divided between a 'Lord's', or first-class cricket, section; and a 'commons' group which concentrates on village cricket in all its variety. In the first section Jeffrey Archer offers an intriguing and ironic story of the University match, and Ted Dexter and Clifford Makins an account of a great innings played under unique pressure, both at Lord's; while Mike Marqusee portrays a torrid tour in India, and George Macdonald Fraser revives the 'middle Ages' of cricket through a remarkable hat-trick by his 'hero', Flashman. In the 'commons' section J.C. Snaith's *Willow the King* seems to me to rival Hugh de Selincourt, given that Snaith, who had played first-class cricket, is writing some twenty-five years earlier and describing a higher class of game (and wicket). Before that, J.L. Carr's *A Season in Sinji* is an example, like *The Go-Between*, of a novel which successfully integrates cricket into its narrative thrust.

For while there is a great deal of good writing in this book, it is true to say that sport in general, and cricket in particular, are not commensurately represented in English novels and literature considering how large they loom in daily life. The reason is partly technical. It is not easy, in the course of what Bernard Malamud – who wrote a mythic novel *The Natural* set in the world of baseball – calls 'a fiction' to take narrative time out to describe a game. If a game is worth describing it needs, as I have said, detail and space; and if the story-line is not to sag, it should avoid large-scale interruptions. This is why so many episodes of cricket in fiction take the compromise form of set-pieces which tend to stand out or apart from the book itself.

The 'Willingly to school' section of this book is arranged chronologically. Both the 'Lord's' and the 'commons' sections run, instead, chronologically backwards, starting with the most recent writing or settings. Generally, the cricket itself is the governing factor here so that when Stanley Shaw, writing in 1985, is describing the fifth Test of 1902, he is placed beside C.B. Fry. How rare it is, though, that the closed world of first-class cricket is penetrated in fiction, although two pre-1939 novels – Dudley Carew's *The Son of Grief* and Bruce Hamilton's *Pro* – also succeed where few others have trod.

Around the time that I was making my final choice for this book, a correspondence appeared in *The Independent* about the rarity of cricket fiction. I was surprised, but in the circumstances also rather pleased, that most of the suggestions offered were well-known hardy annuals. Now that I have completed this selection, I am delighted at its quality and range. I have deliberately included several of the hardy annuals, partly because old friends are best and have a right to be present, partly because they will always make new friends. On the other hand several of the items might not have been easy for readers to track down, amongst which I include the Australian, Dal Stivens's stories and also the rewarding early chapters of J.D. Beresford's *The Hampdenshire Wonder* even though it appeared as long ago as 1911. In sum, and so far from my being short of material as I had originally feared, I have collected enough to fill two volumes the size of the present one, and with no loss of quality. So, if any reader notices 'glaring' omissions, it may be because of the richness of the material and the difficulty of selection; it may also be that I am holding my fire for a possible second innings, should readers wish for a further volume.

Does the 'untruth' of cricket fiction ultimately matter? Can it be as absorbing as real match accounts? The answer is surely 'yes', provided that it offers its own authenticity. The point about (good) fiction, after all, is not that it is untrue but that it is truer than true. Just as Mike Marqusee's *Slow Turn* reveals much about the pressures of first-class professional cricket (and the psychology of slow bowling), so Stanley Shaw's re-creation of the Hirst/Rhodes 'we'll get 'em in singles' stand brings fresh light and perspective to the history of the game. All the pieces in this book contribute to this effect – they renew our understanding and love of the game, and enrich it. If cricket in fiction needs any justification it lies here; but cricket is also a part of life and so a natural subject for the novelist or storyteller.

This seems to contradict a remark of Robert Louis Stevenson: 'Cricket is a game if you like, but not a game of play. You cannot tell yourself a story about cricket.' But I like to think that this whole book disproves what Stevenson is apparently saying; and, in doing so, I hope it will give you, the reader, the same pleasure that I have enjoyed while compiling it.

John Bright-Holmes
February 1988

Editor's Acknowledgements

Several people have helped me while I have been collecting the material for this book, most notably Gerald Brodribb who, in addition to placing his researches generously at my disposal, also lent me many books from his library.

I would also like to thank the following for help and encouragement in various ways: David Ballheimer; David Frith; Stephen Green (Lord's); Stephen Green (British Library); Miriam Hodgson; Gerald Howat (and his *Village Cricket*); Michael Meyer; Ian Morley-Clarke; James McNeish; Tom Rosenthal; Ion Trewin; and James Wright.

I must also express my appreciation of E.W. Padwick's *A Bibliography of Cricket* (Library Association; second edition, 1984).

PART ONE

LORD'S AND OTHER FIRST-CLASS OCCASIONS

THE CENTURY

A Story by
Jeffrey Archer

The author himself has written about this story: 'I took my theme from three different cricket matches. Lovers of Wisden *will have to do some considerable delving to uncover them.'*

'Life is a game,' said A.T. Pierson, thus immortalising himself without actually having to do any real work. Though E.M. Forster showed more insight when he wrote 'Fate is the Umpire, the Hope is the Ball, which is why I will never score a century at Lord's.'

When I was a freshman at University, my room mate invited me to have dinner in a sporting club to which he belonged called Vincent's. Such institutions do not differ greatly around the Western world. They are always brimful of outrageously fit, healthy young animals, whose sole purpose in life seems to be to challenge the opposition of some neighbouring institution to ridiculous feats of physical strength. My host's main rivals, he told me with undergraduate fervour, came from a high-thinking, plain-living establishment which had dozed the unworldly centuries away in the flat, dull, fen country of England, cartographically described on the map as Cambridge. Now the ultimate ambition of men such as my host was simple enough: in whichever sport they aspired to beat the 'Tabs' the select few were rewarded with a Blue. As there is no other way of gaining this distinction at either Oxford or Cambridge, every place in the team is contested for with considerable zeal. A man may be selected and indeed play in every other match of the season for the University, even go on to represent his country, but if he does not play in the Oxford and Cambridge match, he cannot describe himself as a Blue.

My story concerns a delightful character I met that evening when I dined as a guest at Vincent's. The undergraduate to whom I refer was in his final year. He came from that part of the world that we still dared to describe in those days (without a great deal of thought) as the colonies. He was an Indian by birth, and the son of a man whose name in England was a household word, if not a legend, for he had captained Oxford and India at cricket, which meant that outside of the British Commonwealth he was about as well known as Babe Ruth is to the English. The young man's father had added to his fame by scoring a century at Lord's when captaining the University cricket side against Cambridge. In fact, when he went on to captain India against England he used to take pride in wearing his cream sweater with the wide dark blue band around the neck and waist. The son, experts predicted, would carry on in the family tradition. He was in much the same mould as his father, tall and rangy with jet-black hair, and as a cricketer, a fine right-handed batsman and a useful left-arm spin bowler. (Those of you who have never been able to comprehend the English language let alone the game of cricket might well be tempted to ask why not a fine right-arm batsman and useful left-handed spin bowler. The English, however, always cover such silly questions with the words: Tradition, dear boy, tradition.)

The young Indian undergraduate, like his father, had come up to Oxford with considerably more interest in defeating Cambridge than the examiners. As a freshman, he had played against most of the English county sides, notching up a century against three of them, and on one occasion taking five wickets in an innings. A week before the big match against Cambridge, the skipper informed him that he had won his Blue and that the names of the chosen eleven would be officially announced in *The Times* the following day. The young man telegraphed his father in Calcutta with the news, and then went off for a celebratory dinner at Vincent's. He entered the Club's dining room in high spirits to the traditional round of applause afforded to a new Blue, and as he was about to take a seat he observed the boat crew, all nine of them, around a circular table at the far end of the room. He walked across to the captain of boats and remarked: 'I thought you chaps sat one behind each other.'

Within seconds, four thirteen-stone men were sitting on the new Blue while the cox poured a jug of cold water over his head.

'If you fail to score a century,' said one oar, 'we'll use hot water next time.' When the four oars had returned to their table, the cricketer rose slowly, straightened his tie in mock indignation, and as he passed the crew's table, patted the five-foot one inch, 102-pound cox on the head and said, 'Even losing teams should have a mascot.'

This time they only laughed but it was in the very act of patting the cox on the head that he first noticed his thumb felt a little bruised and he commented on the fact to the wicket-keeper who had joined him for dinner. A large entrecôte steak arrived and he found as he picked up his knife that he was unable to grip the handle properly. He tried to put the inconvenience out of his mind, assuming all would be well by the following morning. But the next day he woke in considerable pain and found to his dismay that the thumb was not only black but also badly swollen. After reporting the news to his captain he took the first available train to London for a consultation with a Harley Street specialist. As the carriage rattled through Berkshire, he read in *The Times* that he had been awarded his Blue.

The specialist studied the offending thumb for some considerable time and expressed his doubt that the young man would be able to hold a ball, let alone a bat, for at least a fortnight. The prognosis turned out to be accurate and our hero sat disconsolate in the stand at Lord's, watching Oxford lose the match and the twelfth man gain his Blue. His father, who had flown over from Calcutta especially for the encounter, offered his condolences, pointing out that he still had two years left in which to gain the honour.

As his second Trinity term approached, even the young man forgot his disappointment and in the opening match of the season against Somerset scored a memorable century, full of cuts and drives that reminded *aficionados* of his father. The son had been made Secretary of cricket in the closed season as it was universally acknowledged that only bad luck and the boat crew had stopped him from reaping his just reward as a freshman. Once again, he played in every fixture before the needle match, but in the last four games against county teams he failed to score more than a dozen runs and did not take a single wicket, while his immediate rivals excelled themselves. He was going through a lean patch, and was the first to agree with his captain that with so much talent around that year he should not be risked against Cambridge. Once again he watched Oxford lose the Blues match and his opposite number the Cambridge Secretary, Robin Oakley, score a faultless century. A man well into his sixties sporting an MCC tie came up to the young Indian during the game, patted him on the shoulder, and remarked that he would never forget the day his father had scored a hundred against Cambridge: it didn't help.

When the cricketer returned for his final year, he was surprised and delighted to be selected by his fellow team-mates to be Captain, an honour never previously afforded to a man who had not been awarded the coveted Blue. His peers recognised his outstanding work as Secretary and knew if he could reproduce the form of his freshman year he would undoubtedly not only win a Blue but go on to represent his country.

The tradition at Oxford is that in a man's final year he does not play cricket until he has sat Schools, which leaves him enough time to play in the last three county matches before the Varsity match. But as the new captain had no interest in graduating, he by-passed tradition and played cricket from the opening day of the summer season. His touch never failed him for he batted magnificently and on those rare occasions when he did have an off-day with the bat, he bowled superbly. During the term he led Oxford to victory over three county sides, and his team looked well set for their revenge in the Varsity match.

As the day of the match drew nearer, the cricket correspondent of *The Times* wrote that anyone who had seen him bat this season felt sure that the young Indian would follow his father into the record books by scoring a century against Cambridge:

but the correspondent did add that he might be vulnerable against the early attack of Bill Potter, the Cambridge fast bowler.

Everyone wanted the Oxford captain to succeed, for he was one of those rare and gifted men whose charm creates no enemies.

When he announced his Blues team to the press, he did not send a telegram to his father for fear that the news might bring bad luck, and for good measure he did not speak to any member of the boat crew for the entire week leading up to the match. The night before the final encounter he retired to bed at seven although he did not sleep.

On the first morning of the three-day match, the sun shone brightly in an almost cloudless sky and by eleven o'clock a fair sized crowd were already in their seats. The two captains in open-necked white shirts, spotless white pressed trousers and freshly creamed white boots came out to study the pitch before they tossed. Robin Oakley of Cambridge won and elected to bat.

By lunch on the first day Cambridge had scored seventy-nine for three and in the early afternoon, when his fast bowlers were tired from their second spell and had not managed an early breakthrough, the captain put himself on. When he was straight, the ball didn't reach a full length, and when he bowled a full length, he was never straight; he quickly took himself off. His less established bowlers managed the necessary breakthrough and Cambridge were all out an hour after tea for 208.

The Oxford openers took the crease at ten to six; forty minutes to see through before close of play on the first day. The captain sat padded up on the pavilion balcony, waiting to be called upon only if a wicket fell. His instructions had been clear: no heroics, bat out the forty minutes so that Oxford could start afresh the next morning with all ten wickets intact. With only one over left before the close of play, the young freshman opener had his middle stump removed by Bill Potter, the Cambridge fast bowler. Oxford were eleven for one. The captain came to the crease with only four balls left to face before the clock would show six-thirty. He took his usual guard, middle and leg, and prepared himself to face the fastest man in the Cambridge side.

Potter's first delivery came rocketing down and was just short of a length, moving away outside the off stump. The ball nicked the corner of the bat – or was it pad? – and carried to first slip, who dived to his right and took the catch low down. Eleven Cambridge men screamed 'Howzat'. Was the captain going to be out – for a duck? Without waiting for the umpire's decision he turned and walked back to the pavilion, allowing no expression to appear on his face though he continually hit the side of his pad with his bat. As he climbed the steps he saw his father, sitting on his own in the members' enclosure. He walked on through the Long Room, to cries of 'Bad luck, old fellow' and 'Better luck in the second innings' from large-bellied old Blues.

The next day, Oxford kept their heads down and put together a total of 181 runs, leaving themselves only a twenty-seven run deficit. When Cambridge batted for a second time they pressed home their slight advantage and the captain's bowling figures ended up as eleven overs, no maidens, no wickets, forty-two runs. He took his team off the field at the end of play on the second day with Cambridge standing at 167 for seven, Robin Oakley the Cambridge captain having notched up a respectable sixty-three not out, and he looked well set for a century.

On the morning of the third day, the Oxford quickies removed the last three Cambridge wickets for nineteen runs in forty minutes and Robin Oakley ran out of partners, and left the field with eighty-nine not out. The Oxford captain was the first to commiserate with him. 'At least you notched a hundred last year,' he added.

'True,' replied Oakley, 'so perhaps it's your turn this year. But not if I've got anything to do with it!'

The Oxford captain smiled at the thought of scoring a century when his team only needed 214 runs at a little under a run a minute to win the match.

The two Oxford opening batsmen began their innings just before midday and remained together until the last over before lunch when the freshman was once again clean bowled by Cambridge's ace fast bowler, Bill Potter. The captain sat on the balcony nervously, padded up and ready. He looked down on the bald head of his father, who was chatting to a former captain of

England. Both men had scored centuries in the Varsity match. The captain pulled on his gloves and walked slowly down the pavilion steps, trying to look casual; he had never felt more nervous in his life. As he passed his father, the older man turned his sun-burned face towards his only child and smiled. The crowd warmly applauded the captain all the way to the crease. He took guard, middle and leg again, and prepared to face the attack. The eager Potter who had despatched the captain so brusquely in the first innings came thundering down towards him hoping to be the cause of a pair. He delivered a magnificent first ball that swung in from his legs and beat the captain all ends up, hitting him with a thud on the front pad.

'Howzat?' screamed Potter and the entire Cambridge side as they leaped in the air.

The captain looked up apprehensively at the umpire who took his hands out of his pockets and moved a pebble from one palm to the other to remind him that another ball had been bowled. But he affected no interest in the appeal. A sigh of relief went up from the members in the pavilion. The captain managed to see through the rest of the over and returned to lunch nought not out, with his side twenty-four for one.

After lunch Potter returned to the attack. He rubbed the leather ball on his red-stained flannels and hurled himself forward, looking even fiercer than he had at start of play. He released his missile with every ounce of venom he possessed, but in so doing he tried a little too hard and the delivery was badly short. The captain leaned back and hooked the ball to the Tavern boundary for four, and from that moment he never looked as if anyone would prise him from the crease. He reached his fifty in seventy-one minutes, and at ten past four the Oxford team came into tea with the score at 171 for five and the skipper on eighty-two not out. The young man did not look at his father as he climbed the steps of the pavilion. He needed another eighteen runs before he could do that and by then his team would be safe. He ate and drank nothing at tea, and spoke to no one.

After twenty minutes a bell rang and the eleven Cambridge men returned to the field. A minute later, the captain and his partner walked back out to the crease, their open white shirts flapping in the breeze. Two hours left for the century and victory. The captain's partner only lasted another five balls and the captain himself seemed to have lost that natural flow he had possessed before tea, struggling into the nineties with ones and twos. The light was getting bad and it took him a full thirty minutes to reach ninety-nine, by which time he had lost another partner: 194 for seven. He remained on ninety-nine for twelve minutes, when Robin Oakley the Cambridge captain took the new ball and brought his ace speed man back into the attack.

Then there occurred one of the most amazing incidents I have ever witnessed in a cricket match. Robin Oakley set an attacking field for the new ball – three slips, a gully, cover point, mid off, mid on, mid wicket and a short square leg, a truly vicious circle. He then tossed the ball to Potter who knew this would be his last chance to capture the Oxford captain's wicket and save the match; once he had scored the century he would surely knock off the rest of the runs in a matter of minutes. The sky was becoming bleak as a bank of dark clouds passed over the ground, but this was no time to leave the field for bad light. Potter shone the new ball once more on his white trousers and thundered up to hurl a delivery that the captain jabbed at and missed. One or two fielders raised their hands without appealing. Potter returned to his mark, shining the ball with even more relish and left a red blood-like stain down the side of his thigh. The second ball, a yorker, beat the captain completely and must have missed the off stump by about an inch; there was a general sigh around the ground. The third ball hit the captain on the middle of the pad and the eleven Cambridge men threw their arms in the air and screamed for leg before wicket but the umpire was not moved. The captain jabbed at the fourth ball and it carried tentatively to mid on, where Robin Oakley had placed himself a mere twenty yards in front of the bat, watching his adversary in disbelief as he set off for a run he could never hope to complete. His batting partner remained firmly in his crease, incredulous: one didn't run when the ball was hit to mid on unless it was the last delivery of the match.

The captain of Oxford, now stranded fifteen yards from safety, turned and looked at the captain of Cambridge, who held the ball in his hand. Robin Oakley was about to toss the ball to the wicket-keepr who in turn was waiting to remove the bails and send the Oxford captain back to the pavilion, run out for ninety-nine, but Oakley hesitated and, for several seconds the two gladiators stared at each other and then the Cambridge captain placed the ball in his pocket. The Oxford captain walked slowly back to his crease while the crowd remained silent in disbelief. Robin Oakley tossed the ball to Potter who thundered down to deliver the fifth ball, which was short, and the Oxford captain effortlessly placed it through the covers for four runs. The crowd rose as one and old friends in the pavilion thumped the father's back.

He smiled for a second time.

Potter was now advancing with his final effort and, exhausted, he delivered another short ball which should have been despatched to the boundary with ease but the Oxford captain took one pace backwards and hit his own stumps. He was out, hit wicket, bowled Potter for 103. The crowd rose for a second time as he walked back to the pavilion and grown men who had been decorated in two wars had tears in their eyes. Seven minutes later, everyone left the field, drenched by a thunderstorm.

The match ended in a draw.

from A QUIVER FULL OF ARROWS
1981

BYRON'S FAULTLESS STROKEPLAY

by

Ted Dexter and Clifford Makins

The Test match at Lord's began dramatically on the Thursday morning with some very hostile Australian fast bowling. Two wickets fall cheaply, then the England captain, Abbott, is felled by a kicking delivery from Fitzgerald and carried off. Later Fitzgerald collapses suddenly when about to bowl and is also carried off. He dies. By the time of the fourth day's play another death has occurred, the President of MCC, no less. The mystery is now being investigated not only by the police but by the narrator, Jack Stenton, an ex-England captain who is writing for a daily paper.

It is a commonplace that the Monday morning of a Test match normally suffers its share of the weekend hangover. There is none of the pent-up, pin-drop atmosphere of the first session on a Thursday. Batsmen, bowlers, fielders, even the captains, take quite a time to adjust to the existing tactical situation. The Australian captain, Hunt, like his opposite number, Abbott, was no great live-wire, no tactical genius, but he was tremendously sound and capable and unflappable. God knows what depth of feelings he had about Fitzgerald but he, Hunt, was the impeccable pro and was not one to worry too much about the loss of the world's finest fast bowler, let alone our MCC President. How was it, then, that one man, without the slightest hint of planning or calculation, revealed himself the complete master of the Australian attack as the new week, overcast with cloud and misfortune, got under way?

Had Julia's party been on the Sunday night, a simple explanation was there for anyone to deduce. Batsmen often thrive on the relaxation of a night's boozing, whether or not they also manage to add sexual to social intercourse. Bowlers, in the same situation, tend to flatter for a few overs and then sag at the knees. But in the Australian case there was, as far as I could see, no sign of sagging or flagging. All the usual signs of Australian bounce were there, from the concerted appeals for unlikely catches to the catapult throws to the wicket-keeper from the boundary, even when the umpire had already signalled and the batsman stopped running. Only against such a standard background of the highest class is it really possible to judge the greatness of an innings.

Exceptional circumstances, extreme field placings, bad-tempered bowlers, can all come to the aid of the best of batsmen but Byron's 134 which ended on the stroke of three o'clock, just less than half-way through one day's play, was inflicted on a composed opposition who were not the least unnerved at what he was doing. In fact, there were periods when they had every right to feel pleased with themselves. Branston, when I checked with the BBC's leading TV scorer and statistician, had much more of the strike, played and missed a good deal at the swinging ball and generally kept the fielders in a state of eager anticipation. The scoreboard, that advanced by 179 to a massive 329 for 1 before the partnership was broken, was kept busy simply because Byron never missed a scoring opportunity from the first ball he received.

Byron started the day with 8 to his name, picked up in the last half-hour on Saturday night. It had been just too early for the night watchman business. Under Abbott, this was normally Rippon's job. But I knew that the acting captain, Kirkstead, never much cared for this convention, and Byron, left to his own devices, would never have wanted that sort of protection which, anyway, so often proves to be futile and self-defeating. 'There's nothing worse', Byron had once said to me, 'than to see some tail-ender trying to play like a batsman, often doing his best to run out his partner and giving the bowler a whole lot of unnecessary encouragement.'

This was an innings with no playing-in period, with none of the usual answers posed by fresh bowlers on a newly cut and mown pitch. Play the line and let anything wide on the off-side go by; restrict the back-lift for a while remembering not to cut and hook at the same time; duck and sway away from the short balls and be prepared to take one in the ribs if there is no other way out. These are the standard defence mechanisms of the experienced player while, for want of a better description, he gets his eye in. Unlike tennis players who enjoy a knock-up on court, the Test batsman, even after net practice, is still forced to use the first few overs in the middle as a warm-up.

Bowlers, not being the fools they sometimes look, vary their own policy accordingly. On their side of the equation they don't expect to be punished if they pitch short, even with a ball 62 overs old. And so the Australian bowlers, on this Monday morning in the hot and humid conditions that had persisted all along, were merely going through the normal routine when Byron moved straight into top gear with six boundaries off the first ten balls he received. May I say that modern cricket journalism has a ludicrous fascination with such precise mathematical formulae and, much against my inclinations, it has become a habit to note the exact length and breadth of particular passages of play.

One of Byron's cover drives, replayed later on TV in slow motion as a textbook stroke to the half volley, and described as such by the commentator, was in fact nothing of the sort. The ball was a perfect length, hit on the rise with no foot movement other than a light, preliminary step nearer the line with the back foot. The poise, the balance, the swing of the bat and the judgement of length were faultless. It is one of the mysteries of batting that minimal footwork normally spells suicide early in an innings, whereas a well-set batsman can hit the ball to all parts without any apparent need for large movements forward or back or sideways. Hunt, however, was shrewd enough to realise that Byron's start was no mere flash in the pan. With the new ball due well before lunch he sensibly switched to Flinders' leg-spin and Lytton's seamers, and both had their moral successes against Branston.

Byron, on the other hand, made them look not exactly incompetent, but something even worse perhaps – terribly ordinary. Sweeps, square cuts, late cuts, and one superb straight bat pull for six off Flinders were all produced with the minimum of ostentation and with maximum effect by a master of his craft.

Unluckily I missed seeing Sobers' 254 for a World Team in Australia. It was after this that Bradman said, 'I believe that Gary Sobers' innings was probably the best ever seen in Australia. The people who saw Sobers have enjoyed one of the historic events of cricket. They were privileged to have such an experience.'

At the time I don't think I felt privileged watching Byron. Envious, fascinated, perhaps a little surprised, but no more than that. It was probably the ex-player in me made progressively insensitive by the stints of journalism.

By the time Hindmarsh and Eyre took the new ball, Byron was past his fifty and past Branston despite starting three and a half hours after him. It was then, poised for the kill, that he seemed to stand back and contemplate what he had accomplished. I don't know whether he suddenly felt perverse, or was simply taking a rest, but he definitely stepped aside and allowed the dust to settle. In fact, his was still a copybook performance against the new ball, making sure that Abbott would not need to face up before lunch, but he had been in such total command that it was impossible not to feel disappointed when the flow was interrupted. No innings is perfect, of course, no more than a round of golf in the low sixties is perfect. Every low round ever played could be lower.

At lunch the score stood at 265 for 1; Byron 95, and Branston 80, having added only 22 to his overnight 58. There were 6 extras . . . .

And at 2.10 it started all over again.

Branston entered another tedious, sticky patch; he was getting near seven hours in the making of his hundred. Byron needed only two scoring strokes to reach his and for the first time gave a hint of impatience at what was going on at the other end. He started to farm the strike. Once again the innings took flight revealing the ruthless artist and the master craftsman. Hunt, though unruffled, suggested that there might be an odd scratch or two on the surface of his composure. The keen edge of the Australian effort was slightly blunted. Difficult to describe but only too easy to detect had you been there.

Then, pushing the last ball of an over at just the right pace into the mid-wicket area, Byron called for a run and was answered initially by Branston. Suddenly the young Notts left-hander sensed danger. He stopped. He knew then right enough what to do. He knew he ought to go on and be run out himself but self-preservation made him turn sharply. He reached the safety of his own crease a split-second before Byron.

Branston, a picture of guilt and misery, stared speechless in Byron's direction but saw no more than the man's broad shoulders receding towards the pavilion. Byron had never broken stride, never bothered to look at the umpire. He just trotted on, in, then out of sight, taking the huge crowds so much by surprise that the richly deserved standing ovation never materialised. The greatest exhibition of faultless stroke play I ever saw was over.

from TESTKILL
1977

A VERY PERSONAL FORM OF ATTACK

by

Mike Marqusee

'Exactly how I made the transition from might-be to has-been remains a mystery.' David Stott – 'DTS' in the dressing-room – is a left-handed bat who, after ten years in county cricket, is on a sponsored tour of India. There are political complications which he does not understand, even less so when he himself is assaulted in the streets of Madras just before a crucial match. Strangely, though, there seems to be some connection with the team's captain, Robin Barnett, a distinguished but unpopular player, and his grandiose plans for the future.

One of the key qualities of Mike Marqusee's novel Slow Turn *lies in its analysis of the psychology of, and the sense of personal hostility in high-class spin bowling.*

The haze in the air cleared in the afternoon and though the heat was intense the atmosphere was more comfortable, at least for the spectators. Out in the middle Robin resumed command. He lost another partner (bowled Chaughiri, caught at short leg), but hardly blinked an eye. For him the occasion was one to relish, and he swung his bat in an arrogant full arc. He disdained easy singles now, which didn't make life any easier for his partners. Fours rolled off his bat to all corners of the field. Even the wily Chaughiri suffered, though as always Robin treated him with respect. It was an innings of deliberation, as much a part of his Grand Prix plans as the elaborate charade he'd ben playing with the press. This was his answer to the old men who had dumped him unceremoniously in the off-season while he was toiling on a second-string tour of India. Between balls he patted invisible rough spots in the pitch, ignored everyone (including his batting partner), and managed to act as if he was alone and unobserved – in front of fifty thousand people.

I left the balcony and sought distraction in the old newspapers scattered around the dressing room. But all I found were cricket reports and articles about the disturbances in Madras, articles that made even less sense to me after talking to Lakshmi the evening before. I returned to the balcony, put my feet up on the white-painted railing, and watched, from under a large, flopping sun hat, tiny figures play out a finicky, infinitesimal drama in the centre of a baking concrete oval.

Robin moved inexorably towards his century. The crowd cheered for him, the same crowd that would bay for his blood if he gave any of their bowlers half a chance. Meanwhile, other batsmen came and went, concluding the pitch was impossible and Chaughiri unfathomable. Dour Donald Blackburn joined him and had limited success pushing the ball off his legs. But the show was Robin's. At tea he was 123 not out and returned through the members' enclosure to rapt applause. Cuthbert and Narayan stood in their places and roared 'Well played', and 'Good show'. We all clapped him into the dressing room. Kidleigh gave him a cup of his special tea and babbled about the umpires and the wicket. Robin said nothing. Sweat matted his thinning grey hair and dripped from the refined point of his nose. His gloves were soaked through and he tossed them aside with a wet thud. Dougie Fraser, our coach, suddenly softened by the spectacle of the exhausted captain, replaced them with a pair of new ones, clean and dry, from Robin's kit.

From the balcony I watched the milling, stretching, jabbering crowd. Suddenly I caught a flash of long brown hair, a swirl of white blouse and brown arms. I leaned over and shouted.

'Lakshmi!'

The long hair fell aside and above the white blouse was revealed an unfamiliar, middle-aged face. It disappeared in the crowd.

'That your bird then?'

I whirled around. Kidleigh had sneaked up behind me.

'Didn't know you fancied these coloured birds, DTS,' he chortled.

'Leave it out.' I spat it at him.

He backed away nervously, still wearing that stupid grin.

I looked at the crowd. How absurd to think I could pick a single woman in this sea of strange faces. I was annoyed with myself. I should have dropped Kidleigh over the railing and let the spectators tear him to pieces. Instead I had acted as if Lakshmi were some guilty secret. I had my hidden secrets, but Lakshmi was the least of them. She had probably gone to work today as usual. Why should I expect anything else?

After tea Robin batted on for twenty minutes. He seemed determined to punish the bowling and hammered thirty more runs before being caught in the covers for 155. It had been a classic innings on a slow pitch. The applause lingered after his return to the dressing room and he was forced to acknowledge it from the balcony with a raised cap – his (former) county cap.

Of course, they weren't clapping a simple display of batting, however skilful. The applause was about other things. It was about Robin's dismissal by his county club; it was about his status as captain-in-exile of the English Test side; it was about his age and the near certainty that never again would he grace the ground at Chepauk. They were as much a part of the innings as the late cuts and off drives.

Soon after Robin's dismissal Donald spooned a catch to midwicket and it was my turn in the middle. I walked down the cool concrete corridor and emerged through the small door into the glare of the sun, the noise, and fifty thousand pairs of eyes.

I had my helmet under my arm and, suddenly conscious of my bruise and red ear, I pushed it on my head and pulled it down over my face. A murmur spread through the crowd and gathered like a little wave into a gentle ripple of applause.

It was the story in the paper. I blushed. The applause continued as I stepped on to the brittle, manicured outfield and made my way to the wicket. I felt I ought to acknowledge the crowd's apparent good grace and ever so slightly I raised my bat. Embarrassed enough already (it had never occurred to me that my injuries would be of the least concern to anyone else), I was tongue-tied when Chaughiri himself came up to me.

'It's terrible for such a thing to happen to you in Madras. It's not like that, you know, not usually.' And he sighed and wandered slowly back to his mark, fingering the seam of the ball thoughtfully. Even the square-leg umpire shook my hand, said he hoped I was feeling all right and then opined that something really must be done about all this violence.

At the other end, leaning on his bat and barely suppressing a smile, Ernie beckoned to me.

'They'll clap you to the crease, but see what happens when the ball catches a nick on the pad.'

I shrugged and walked slowly back to my crease. As I did I allowed myself to become aware of the crowd surrounding us like a vast saucer brimful of humanity. They were separated from us by a sea of empty grass, not to speak of wire fences and slouching police patrols, but they seemed to bear down heavily. Go slow, go slow, I told myself, as I usually did, largely because there was no alternative. Hold out to the end of play. Keep wicket intact. Keep score ticking over. I took my guard and steadied my head to receive my first ball from Chaughiri.

Like a hovering, apparently motionless bird, it hung in the air for ages, then dropped outside my off stump and moved into my front pad, which I had luckily stretched well down the pitch.

The noise, as Ernie predicted, was deafening, though Chaughiri himself showed no interest whatsoever. For the rest of the over I attempted to conceal my inability to decide whether to play forward or back to the leg-spinner and somehow survived. I was relieved when the strike passed to Ernie at the other end.

I managed to avoid Chaughiri for a few overs and even took some easy runs off the other bowler, which made me feel better. Though the sun was beginning to set behind the top of the stand, the heat was still intense and in no time my clothes, gloves, hair were soaked with sweat. I removed the helmet and passed it to the umpire, who placed it behind the wicket keeper. Injury or no injury, it was just too hot inside the damn thing. In any case, I felt peculiarly safe out there in the middle, among fellow cricketers, and the crowd seemed far away.

One of the fielders stared at my wounds.

'You look like you've been playing West Indians, not Indians,' he said.

'I think I'll save that thing,' I answered, pointing to the discarded helmet, 'and use it off the field from now on.'

They laughed.

At the non-striker's end I watched the famous Chaughiri action close up. After a run-up of four stilted paces, he brought his right arm over from behind the small of his back in a looping arc. His wrist turned over so fast I could never make out exactly what he was doing with the ball and certainly could never read the googly. Ernie coped well enough at the other end, though his scoring was only slightly faster than mine. He played back more often than not, used a lot of bottom hand, and poked his nose at every ball as if a very nasty smell was coming from it.

It's supposed to be easier for left-handers to play leg-spin, but against Chaughiri there didn't seem to be much advantage. My sole intention was survival. Nonetheless, I clipped one off my legs for two and the next ball I sneaked past square-leg to the boundary for four. I began to relax. The longer I stayed out there, the more it felt like any other cricket match. I listened to the Indian players talk amongst themselves in their curious argot, a mixture of Tamil and English in which phrases like 'extra cover', 'well bowled', and 'good length' popped up incongruously.

I felt I had re-entered a private world, and yet here I was in front of a huge and utterly alien crowd, as public as if a spotlight had picked me out on a stage. I know some cricketers for whom the whole game is an intensely private matter. Batting especially breeds this attitude. Total concentration is required. There can be a long wait between balls and the only way to deal with it is to turn inward, to conduct a kind of dialogue with yourself. This can become all-absorbing and even block out any consciousness of the paying customers. You know they're out there, but they seem not to matter, because in the end it's you who's got to decide how to play the well-pitched-up ball, whether to step down the track, or to glance the ball away to fine-leg.

My footwork, slapdash at the best of times, was well out of

synch on this pitch. Somehow my score reached eighteen. I could hear Dougie mumbling under his breath. 'Keep your head down. Don't worry about runs. Runs will come. Concentrate.' But with each ball from Chaughiri the middle of my bat seemed to shrink and it was always a relief not to hear the clatter of stumps or the hysterical shout of appeal.

I escaped to the other end. Ernie coiled himself into his cramped, tortured-looking crouch. Chaughiri delivered. The ball hung in the air for the longest time, then turned outrageously wide of the off-stump. Ernie prodded at air, then swore. I avoided his eye. It's bad enough everyone else watching you without your team-mates looking on as well.

Ernie tapped the bat impatiently as Chaughiri flicked the ball from hand to hand like a card sharper. He turned and began his run-up, looking for all the world like a stiff-legged teenager learning to waltz.

In the air the ball looked to be a replica of the previous one. Ernie was already high into his backlift and followed through with a savage swish in the direction of mid-off.

A tiny click echoed round the ground. Chaughiri's indecipherable googly had sneaked between swinging bat and static pad and gently knocked against middle stump, barely dislodging a single bail. There was a silent split-second as the crowd craned necks to confirm what had happened, then uproar. Ernie stiffened and walked back to the pavilion with a glum, mortified stare. The cheering was prolonged and passionate. It was what the crowd wanted to see, and Chaughiri had delivered the goods with all the élan of a master magician calmly making a volunteer from the audience vanish into thin air.

The funny thing about this kind of spin bowling is how hostile it is. Its gentility, it sheer artful slowness, disguises aggression and violence. When you bat against it you are under a very personal form of attack, in which any weaknesses you might have ever displayed will be used against you. The bowler wants you and no one else; he wants you removed from the field of play and he is willing to lie, cheat and flatter to get it.

I was joined at the wicket by off-spinner Geoff Robinson. Geoff has a casual slouch on the field, like a lean, ghostly version of Clive Lloyd. As he approached me he wore a surprised look, as if amazed to find himself the object of so many foreign gazes.

'Skipper says shut 'em out for the rest of the day,' he informed me when we met in the middle.

I nodded agreement.

'How's the face?' he asked brightly, as if injecting a personal note in a business conversation.

My glove moved automatically towards the tender ridge on my forehead. 'I've got enough to worry about out here without that,' I said, and brought the hand rapidly back where it belonged.

Geoff dealt with the remainder of Chaughiri's over with rock-like immobility. Then it was my turn against a younger bowler at the other end. His gentle off-breaks looked easy enough, but somehow I couldn't get the ball off the square. Suddenly Chaughiri seemed to have blocked all the gaps. The young bowler's reward was a maiden over and a round of applause. He looked quite pleased with himself.

As the fielders switched over and arrayed themselves in their menacing spider's web of close-catching positions, there was a disturbance at the far end of the ground. A man had climbed and mounted the wire fence and held a banner aloft between outstretched hands. He shouted fiercely.

The umpire at the bowler's end muttered under his breath. The players exchanged glances. They seemed to shy away from me and Geoff, who were left baffled by the incident. On the man's banner were flamboyant, circular, swirling Tamil characters, and from his high, uncomfortable perch, he declaimed something equally incomprehensible in a loud, hoarse voice.

Within seconds a mob of police had converged on the man. Swiftly they mounted the fence to pull him down. There was confusion in the crowd, some cheers and some very aggrieved booing. The man struggled with the first policeman to reach him, flailing and twisting away to keep his banner aloft. In the meantime, a second policeman had made enough room to grab him from the other side. With a sudden lurch both policeman and demonstrator fell off the fence into the crowd beneath. The police were now separated by the fence from their comrade and the demonstrator. There were shouts and screams. Police filtered through gates into the crowd, lathis held threateningly across their chests. Five of them frog-marched the demonstrator along the aisles and out of sight under the stands.

The ground was seething. The booing and shouting came to a stop and were replaced by a furious murmur, as if the simmering cauldron of the ground was not quite ready to boil over. The police formed a neat ring around the boundary fence.

'Come,' said the umpire, looking at his watch. 'Enough time wasted. Play, please.'

Chaughiri flicked the ball in the air absent-mindedly, his eyes wandering vaguely over the agitated crowd.

'What was that all about?' I asked him.

His head tilted ambiguously and his mouth twisted into a pout.

'The banner said "Release Imprisoned Strikers",' he answered in the neutral tone of someone translating for an illiterate foreigner.

I watched Chaughiri torment Geoff Robinson while Geoff struggled to maintain his perfectly strokeless defence. But my mind was elsewhere. Arrests and disruptions at cricket grounds aren't so uncommon anywhere in the world, but now my hand unconsciously touched my damaged forehead. I kept thinking of the young man in the T-shirt. Strangest of all, I found myself worrying about Siva's party tonight. Who would be there? What would they expect of me? If Lakshmi didn't turn up, would I even bother to go? And now I was supposed to stand out here and block the ball for another thirty-five minutes. I felt I had been cast in a role I wasn't suited to play.

I felt vulnerable, and not just to Chaughiri and his close catchers and the (purportedly) unreliable umpires. For all I knew my erratic attacker might be lurking somewhere in the stands. And if he wasn't there, then perhaps someone else with the same intentions was. There had been no reason for my being attacked in the first place, so what was to prevent my being attacked again? Strange as that logic sounds, it was what I was thinking when my musings were interrupted by Geoff's breathless call for a single following an edge to third man.

I reminded myself of Robin's injunction. Chaughiri bowled one on the off-stump, nearly over-pitched, but it caught me by surprise. I met it with the bottom of a hastily-lowered bat. It dropped and spun at my feet. I picked it up and tossed it back to the bowler. The next delivery turned into me, not very fast, and I pushed it gently to the on side. Short leg pounced on it. There was no question of a run.

I played two more deliveries defensively down the pitch. I looked at my name on the scoreboard and the feeble figure next to it: 23. That had been my typical innings these last few years. A slow, somewhat chancy progress to the mid-twenties, abruptly terminated.

The next ball was short. I moved easily out of the crease, legs criss-crossing comfortably, and drove it firmly along the ground between the bowler and mid-off. A four. Scattered applause. At least they hadn't completely forgotten I was out there.

I felt better. I felt I was at last taking matters in hand.

Chaughiri seemed unconcerned. He skipped in, precariously balanced, and delivered. I followed the ball out of his hand on its high trajectory and began moving forwards to drive.

Then I saw the thing dip and swerve, as if it had a life of its own. Too late I saw the idiocy of my intended stroke. Still lurching forwards I didn't have to look behind to know the keeper had the ball in his hands and was whipping off the bails. The cheers said it all.

My exit was accompanied by the same polite applause that had greeted my entrance. It was a bad time to lose a wicket. Dougie pointedly ignored me as I showered and changed. Robin, luckily, was busy elsewhere.

'Checking his shares,' said Paul Walker, who was sipping cold tea and rocking in a chair by the balcony.

Dougie at last condescended to acknowledge my existence.

'This came for you.'

It was a typewritten note on thin, tissue-like paper: *I will pick you up in front of your hotel at seven. L. Kumbaikonam.*

I was careful to hide my delight from Dougie. He would have regarded it as unbecoming in a man who had just been comprehensively stumped.

from SLOW TURN
1986

THE DOUBLE-CROSS BAT

A story by

Ian Peebles

One of the most felicitous of writers on cricket, Ian Peebles combined considerable personal experience of the first-class game with shafts of irony and great good humour, qualities much needed by a fine bowler who 'lost' his leg-break. Only occasionally, however, did he venture into fiction, but this example, describing the progress of Professor Tube's remarkable invention, comes straight off the meat of the bat.

The consultant peered anxiously at the frail figure of Professor Tube hunched in the opposite chair.

'An obvious case of overwork,' he said. 'Too much mental strain, too much worry – too little fresh air and exercise.'

He turned over the report of his findings on the desk before him.

'I am, of course, familiar with your great work in the field of electronics,' he continued, 'and fully aware of the great loss to the national cause that even your temporary absence will be, but' – his voice grew impressively stern – 'I must advise a complete holiday for at least six months. Sun, fresh air, and exercise will no doubt work wonders. You must cease work immediately and find a complete change of interests. At the end of the summer I shall examine you again and hope to find a great improvement.'

Professor Tube received his sentence with customary meekness, and having heard a few additional cautions and a diplomatic statement of the position regarding fees, bowed himself out. An hour's journey took him home to his small country establishment in the quiet woods of Midshire.

Once settled in his arm-chair, he filled his pipe and recalled gratefully that the telephone had interrupted the consultant in the act of raising an admonitory finger on the subject of smoking. Had the blow fallen, reflected the professor, life would have been beyond endurance. As it was, endless leisure was going to prove a very uneasy state after his years of unceasing application. One small ray of hope lay in the fact that he would be able to follow the fortunes of Midshire cricket first hand, instead of glancing hastily at the scores in the stop press.

As a boy, cricket had been his greatest passion. Between spells of dissecting electric bells, plunging his parents into the gloom of fused lights, and suffering various degrees of electric shock, his entire being had been devoted to the game. School cricket, stump cricket, *Wisden*, W.G., Fry on *Batsmanship* had filled every spare moment, and it was a bitter blow when it became painfully clear that he would never himself emulate his heroes. Nature, it seemed, had patted the lad's head encouragingly, but had overlooked the rest of his anatomy. Early in life he had realised that the Crown and Lions of England would never adorn his brow and breast pocket; indeed, even the later purchase of the local club tie (Cambridge blue with silver rabbit snares) had seemed a pretentious gesture. The professor sighed as his eye travelled over the group of resplendent flannelled athletes above the mantelpiece and came to rest on a diffident figure half-hidden at the back, labelled 'Tube (scorer)'.

It was odd, he thought, that he could by sheer intellectual power harness the most tremendous forces known to man, yet be outstripped in his greatest love by any dolt with the primitive blessings of strong muscles and a keen eye.

Or could he?

His expression tensed. A blinding vision had impinged on his massive mind. He reached for paper and pencil, and began to jot down abstruse mathematical formulae. After ten minutes or so of rigid concentration, he arose, slide-rule in hand, and ascended the stairs to his lumber room at the top of the house. He emerged a moment later with a battered cricket bag and a cloud of dust. Descending to his basement laboratory, he locked himself in, and, in defiance of all medical orders, set to work.

For the following ten days his housekeeper, Mrs McGumble, happily unaware of any medical instructions, pursued a working-spell routine. She thrust meals through a hatch designed for the purpose. Nightly at nine fifteen she would announce that she was 'awa' ', and advise the professor to be likewise. Otherwise she had no contact with her employer. But she could tell from the hissing, crackling, and tapping which emerged from the hatch that he was well and happy.

Eventually in the bright sunshine of an April afternoon the inventor emerged with the fruits of his labour and genius clutched to his breast.

To outside appearance, it was just a robustly made old cricket bat, darkened to a deep mahogany shade with years of oily care. But, cunningly camouflaged from the closest observer, and known only to its owner, there lay housed in its ample bustle a combination of scientific secrets which yet may change the mode of life on this planet. It would be pointless to try to give the reader any idea of the technicalities involved, but it may be said that the principles of radar and jet propulsion were among them. If the professor's calculations proved correct, this bat, when directed roughly at any moving object, would unerringly deal it a smashing blow 'right out of the meat'. However hard a cricket ball might try to elude it by swerve or break, it must eventually meet the full face and force of this relentless blade.

The first tests made with the aid of a ball suspended from a branch on a long string proved beyond doubt that the mechanism was all its creator had hoped. The only major fault lay in the fact that the radar field at first proved too wide and strong. The professor became painfully aware of his miscalculation when the ball swung by out of his reach and the bat, having all but dislocated every joint in his arms, shot out of his hands like a rocket from a bazooka as it strove to make contact with the ball. However, a few timely adjustments to the mechanism and a liberal application of embrocation to his aching limbs soon corrected this situation, and from then on the bat confined its attention to balls within the reach of the normal batsman. The time was now ripe for more rigorous trial.

On the pretext of showing him a new television set, Tube invited a neighbour's son, a demon schoolboy bowler, round for a cup of tea. When he casually mentioned that he was thinking of taking up cricket again and would like a bit of a knock, the lad was more than willing. They repaired to the lawn. The bowler was at first inclined to be a trifle off-hand, when faced by the spectacled figure of the batsman. Twenty minutes later, having continually retrieved the ball from the outlying confines of his host's garden, the boy asked in a very chastened manner if he could have the bat for a change. The professor, modestly disclaiming any pretentions of being a bowler, cut off the mechanism by means of the concealed switch in the handle and surrendered the bat.

Satisfied that his mechanical arrangements were complete, Tube now addressed himself to the psychological aspect of his programme. The fact that a talent rather beyond the best efforts of Bradman and Jessop combined had passed unnoticed for so long would require some explanation. On the other hand, it was well known that his studies had occupied sixteen hours a day since early youth, and so he presumably never had any real opportunity to discover his abilities in other directions.

Such was the line he pursued a few days later at the local club nets, where his instant success compelled the use of composition balls for practice instead of the scarcer and more expensive leather variety. After a few evenings of practice, his team mates were as impatient as the professor for the arrival of the first match of the season.

The club was a small one, and its attainments of such a modest order that most opposing sides regarded their matches as a pleasant afternoon's preparation for more serious fixtures. The Midshire Gents, who came to open the season, having taken the field in this expansive frame of mind, were completely unprepared for the tornado which burst about their ears. Early in the evening they left the field thrashed, bruised, and unnerved, to find the entire resources of the Dog and Duck unequal to their requirements.

Their tales of woe and wonderment spread through the district during the week, but received small credence until the next Saturday, when the Bailshire Bumpkins were utterly massacred. There was now little room for doubt, and, as the season wore on, interest and alarm spread through Midshire and its adjoining counties. A month's havoc in the ranks of club cricket brought Professor Tube his just and not unexpected reward in the shape of a letter from the County Committee inviting him to play against Boffshire the following Saturday.

The professor spent Friday evening oiling his bat (internally) and cleaning his pads. Retiring early to bed, he arose the next morning and set forth. He thought that the occasion justified the extravagance of chartering the village taxi to drive him to the County ground, some miles distant.

Deposited at the Members' Gate by his taxi, the professor was greeting by the doorman with almost indecent condescension and spent some minutes convincing the man of his bona fides. At length, largely owing to his driver's indignant support, he was admitted, and found his way to the dressing-room.

The captain's reactions to his new player's appearance were much similiar to the doorman's, but the breeding of a long line of ancestors who had led the county to sterner occasions than cricket matches quickly asserted itself. He greeted the newcomer genially and, having shown him to a vacant corner of the room, departed in search of the opposing commander.

By the time the professor had donned his new utility flannels, the captain returned with the triumphant tidings that he had won the toss and proposed to bat.

'Lot of grass on that wicket,' he said thoughtfully. 'Wouldn't be surprised if Boakes and Stock were a bit awkward before lunch.' He picked up a pencil and busied himself with his list of players.

'Number seven do for you, Tube?' he said to the professor, and, without waiting for a reply, he called out to the room in general, 'Otherwise batting order as usual.'

To Professor Tube, watching the proceedings nervously from the balcony, it was soon apparent that the captain's doubts had been well founded. Encouraged by the early removal of Midshire's opening pair, Boffshire set about their opponents in earnest. At the end of an hour's play a meagre 40 runs had been scored when the fifth wicket went down with a resounding crash.

Tube pulled his batting gloves on over trembling fingers and fished his bat out of his bag. He narrowly survived a kindly colleague's persistent offers to lend him a decent bat, and set out amidst a half-hearted chorus of 'good lucks'. His appearance on the turf was greeted by a burst of applause from his local village contingent, but otherwise it still further depressed the sagging morale of the home supporters. One Boffshire bowler, earlier incapacitated by a strain, approached his captain to say that his leg was now feeling all right again.

The professor took guard, and peered apprehensively at the massive figure of Boakes, Boffshire and England fast bowler, pawing the earth in the middle distance like a maddened bull. The terrifying figure came thundering up to the crease in the manner of a Sherman tank, and Tube raised his magic bat. As Boake's branch-like arm came whistling over, Tube started to swing.

He swung a trifle late, and he felt the bat wrench his arms as it accelerated violently to meet the ball. But there was a sharp crack as the ball left the blade, and this was followed by a startled profanity as the ball hissed past the bowler's head. A thunderous burst of applause greeted a first-bounce boundary into the free stand, whence the ball was retrieved by a small boy and returned to the stupefied Boakes.

In the next hour the situation was dramatically changed. The all-conquering bowlers had been thrashed to all parts of the field, Tube had joined the immortals who had made a century on their first appearance, and the injured man's leg had suffered a severe relapse. Although the match ended on the second day, it practically assured Midshire's finances for the season. Tube was awarded his cap there and then, and invited to play in every match for the rest of the season.

From then on the professor's career was one of almost uninterrupted triumph. In the course of a few days his renown as a man of science was completely eclipsed by his fame as a cricketer. The fact that his methods were unorthodox and his fielding uncertain merely seemed to add colour to his devastating performances with the bat. Wiseacres who forecast circumstances which were bound to undo him found a completely unrationed diet in their own words, as Tube's flailing blade dispatched, with complete impartiality, balls from every type of bowling and pitch.

It was not until the second innings of the fifth match, against Spliceshire, that the great man met with failure. The opposite captain, seeking some diversion before Tube settled down, decided to switch his bowlers from one end to the other. He looked round for someone to bowl a single over in order to effect this change. His choice fell on one Oswald Clank, an unambitious and lazy veteran who regarded bowling as a most malicious form of corporal punishment. However, at the stern bidding of his captain, he pulled off his sweater, muttering some sour imprecations into it on the way, and prepared to attack his redoubtable enemy with the least expenditure of effort.

As he advanced to the wicket, the batsman alone realised that something was wrong. A small dry battery essential to the working of the mechanism had expired, and the magic had gone out of the bat. The effect was in a double sense electrical. Clank's first four balls completely beat the bat, and the fifth laid the middle stump flat on the ground. The succeeding batsman, utterly unnerved by this disaster, offered but the feeblest resistance. Clank returned a most impressive analysis.

To Tube this was but a momentary set-back, although he had an uneasy suspicion from now on that his bat might after all be in the nature of an athletic Monkey's Paw. Meanwhile, we should note, in passing, the result of his success on 'The Man Who Had Bowled Tube'.

The unfortunate Clank, after a delirious week of fame and free entertainment, including pictures in the Press and a talk on the B.B.C., found his trials unending. Driven on by his captain and exhorted by a member of the Selection Committee, who had immediately attached himself to the side, Clank bowled unceasingly. Had he read Pickwick (which he hadn't) he must inevitably have compared his lot to that of the faithful Quanko Sambo (*see page 328*) and brooded unhappily on that great player's tragic end. His pitiable pleas of ill health and torn muscles were answered by the arrival of famous specialists, whose searching questions and sinister instruments terrified his simple soul into further reluctant effort.

At length, after a month's torture, during which he took two wickets at astronomical cost and completely wrecked his team's hitherto rosy prospects of the Championship, Clank was given up in disgust by both captain and selector. The erstwhile hero was suffered to return to the peace and quiet of mid-on, there to ponder the simple problem of what to drink at the close of play, and the rather more ticklish one of who was most likely to pay for it.

Despite his misgivings about the malign influence he wielded, Tube himself remained ever in the news. While batting brilliantly on a West Country ground, he was on the point of dispatching the ball to the boundary when a swallow swooped past him. As the bat could not distinguish between one object and another, the bird was instantly banged into oblivion. The incident cost Tube his wicket, but was universally hailed as further proof of his genius. The only jarring note was supplied by a letter in the local press from the secretary of the 'Feathered Fellers League', deploring the bad example set by so great a sportsman, and seeking to excuse it as the boyish prank of a moment.

Tube was often rather embarrassed by gifts of bats from various enterprising manufacturers. As the original bat, although of stout build and texture, was showing signs of the tremendous punishment it had received, Tube constructed a second set of mechanism which he was able to incorporate in these gifts. He would accept them gratefully and, on the pretext of taking the bat home to oil and season it, he would insert the machinery in the privacy of his workshop. When all was ready he would inform the donor that he was going to try his bat out at the nets, and would be pleased if he could come along.

On one particular occasion a delighted sales manager insisted on his coming into the bar and toasting the future success of the bat. Carried away by his host's forceful yet charming manner, the professor's sales-resistance, so to speak, was broken down, and he permitted himself a double Scotch instead of his usual small cider. Quitting the bar in a slightly bemused state, he left his precious bat leaning against the wall, where it was later discovered by a member of the club.

This good man, a staunch supporter of the team and bar, picked up the sacred trophy and in doing so inadvertently pressed the switch. A little way down the bar another equally stout supporter of team and tap-room was in the act of hoisting a pint tankard to his lips amidst the pious wishes of his cronies for his future health and fortune. What followed was never clearly established for lack of any one coherent witness. From a few reluctant words of those present it seems that the batsman, in a sudden moment of aberration, lashed at his neighbour's drink, and with a mighty drive banged the tankard from his hand and through a window, roughly in the direction of mid-wicket.

In the awed silence which ensued it was apparent that Tube's bat had done more for the cause of temperance in Midshire than several quires of tracts. The subsequent sharp drop in the bar takings caused a mercenary-minded catering committee much fruitless speculation.

By the end of the season, despite having broken all available records, Professor Tube was a very tired and not very happy man. Wedded to his willow Frankenstein, he carved and banged away with a devastating monotony, yet could see no graceful escape. The professor, fundamentally an honest man, had an uneasy feeling that this deception might evoke some fearsome retribution. Before long his mental and bodily exhaustion was such that he took a match off and returned to see his medical consultant.

The consultant came as near to evincing signs of alarm as his reputation for infallibility would allow. His disapproval was obvious, and at the end of a prolonged examination accompanied by many tut-tuts and shakes of the head he motioned his patient to a chair.

'I must say you are not a very easy patient,' he said. 'I order you a rest from work and sensible exercise, and what do I find? You have completely overdone the exercise. Far too much cricket – far too much.'

He paused and looked his visitor squarely in the eye. 'You must give it up,' he said in measured tones, 'abandon it at once and return to work. At the same time you need not altogether give up moderate exercise.' He added in a kindlier manner, 'Try bowls or croquet, but not cricket.'

The professor was too tired to argue. Indeed, he found himself greatly relieved at this straightforward solution to his problem. But he decided that he would always maintain his interest in cricket if only in a purely academic fashion. Once home, he picked up the evening newspaper, anxious to see how the county had fared in his absence, and turned to the sporting page, where his eye lit on a prominently headlined item which read:

ANOTHER TUBE

> The feature of the morning's play at Seatown was a brilliant century by A. Flask, who made his first hundred in County cricket in rather less than an hour. In style Flask closely resembles the great Tube, and has the same uncanny gift of timing. Curiously enough, Flask is also a well-known scientist specialising in electronics and wireless subjects . . .

Professor Tube put down the paper and sat for some moments lost in thought. Then he arose and, picking up the croquet mallet which he had bought in London that morning, made his way to his laboratory.

from TALKING OF CRICKET
1953

THE AMAZING TEST MATCH CRIME

by

Adrian Alington

Cricket is often portrayed as farce, especially on the village green. Adrian Alington's unusual achievement was to use it as satire – not only of cricket but of a modern-day institution, a Test match with all its attendant ballyhoo and solemnities. Alington was the son of Cyril Alington, the headmaster of Shrewsbury and Eton and author, inter alia *of* Mr Evans *(see page 67).*

The ground was cleared, bells rang, the umpires appeared. And then punctually at half-past eleven the yellow-capped men of Imperia, led by the great Lethbridge, descended the pavilion steps. Photographers rushed to photograph them. In the Press-box thirty-eight journalists simultaneously wrote 'a battery of cameras'.

Then came a mighty roar, as England's opening batsmen Hugh and Crigh were seen to emerge and walk towards the wickets. Many in that vast throng must have wondered what the two said to each other during that long walk, so heavy with a sense of destiny. They would, no doubt, have been considerably astonished, if they could have overheard the conversation. For what Hugh said to Crigh was,

'How are you feeling, Bill?'

And Crigh answered, 'Well, it's an extraordinary thing, Fred, but I feel sleepy.'

'It's an even more extraordinary thing, Bill,' rejoined Hugh, 'but so do I.'

There can be few periods in our national life, so tense, so fraught with solemnity as the opening overs of a Test match. A great hush, as though Time itself waited upon the unfolding of historic events, lay over the Oval, as Hugh, having taken guard, scanned the disposition of the fieldsmen, patted the pitch, and caused the sight-screen to be moved, prepared to face the first ball. Almost at his feet crouched the four short legs, silly point and three slips who prayed that the ball might snick off the bat into their hands. Bumper, the Imperian shock bowler, began his long run from the Vauxhall end.

Nor was it only to the thousands packed about the Oval that the solemnity of these first moments communicated themselves. All over England, to the teeming millions of great cities, to the lonely shepherd, temporarily ignoring his sheep, went the voice of John Beltravers.

'Bumper is running up. One, two, three, four. Hugh waits, solid, majestic, like a king awaiting the deference of his subjects. Eighteen, nineteen. Bumper is still running. A hostile bowler, this Bumper. Tall, strongly built, full of menace. There is an enormous crowd here today. Men in panama hats, girls in bright dresses. Bumper still running. Forty-four, forty-five. Hugh still waiting like a king. The Imperian fielders in their yellow caps all crouching. Sixty-five, sixty-six. Bumper is nearing the wicket now. He's there. He BOWLS. Outside the off-stump. Hugh moves across, full of majesty, smiles contemptuously and leaves it alone. Bumper starts walking back . . .'

Half an hour passed, an hour, with the tensity undiminished, the solemn hush still unbroken. Once again at twelve-thirty the voice of John Beltravers brought news to waiting England.

'There is no score yet. Hugh not out nought, Crigh not out nought. Total nought. Grim back-to-the-wall stuff, this cricket. Every ball full of drama. The fielders still crouching there full of menace . . .'

As the minutes passed, some thoughtless members of the crowd began to shout derisive encouragement. Once or twice the little man with the dome-like forehead startled those about him by shouting 'Long live Sir Sutcliffe!' and 'Chukka and Tiffin!'; but for the most part the struggle went on in the grimmest silence. Time crept on. Twelve-forty-five. And still no score. In the pavilion, Sir Timothy could be heard maintaining that in his day England would have scored at least ten by now.

And then something did happen, the first indeed of the series of unusual incidents which were to make this match one to be long remembered in the annals of Cricket. A fast ball from Bumper inadvertently struck the edge of Hugh's bat. The ball trickled between the slips. No fieldsmen near. Hugh began to run.

The crowd began to applaud the first score of the match, but the clapping died away when it was observed that Crigh had toppled gently over and lay at full length upon the grass. A gasp of amazement went round the packed ground. What could this mean? Imperian fielders gathered about the prostrate man. Crigh lay with his eyes closed, and as they bent over him the bewildered Imperians heard the sound of a snore.

It was Lethbridge himself who put into words the idea which had formed in the minds of all.

'He seems,' said the great man, 'to be asleep.'

The umpire bent down and shook him.

'Here, come on, wake up.'

No result. The umpire, greatly astonished, turned to confer with his colleague at the other end. Then it was observed that Hugh also lay at full length upon the ground, breathing stertorously.

'Gosh,' exclaimed the astonished umpire. 'He's asleep now.'

In the strange telepathic way that news travels about a cricket ground the tidings reached the pavilion that England's opening batsmen were fast asleep.

In the pavilion Sir Timothy exclaimed indignantly,

'A man can't go to sleep while batting for England. The thing is unheard of.'

'It's this new-fangled off-theory and leg-theory,' growled R.S.V.P. Hatstock. 'I always knew a man would go to sleep one day.'

'Nonsense,' snapped Q.E.D. Marjoribanks, 'it's these timeless tests. I'm dashed if I see how fellows can be expected to keep awake.'

'If you ask me,' said P.T.O. Brown, 'it's this modern craze for averages. Men start doing mental arithmetic at the wicket and this is what happens.'

Out in the middle, meanwhile, a hasty conference was held. An excited buzz went round the Oval, as it was seen that the fieldsmen were carrying the unconscious forms of Hugh and Crigh back to the pavilion. There they were laid gently to rest.

'Well, well,' exclaimed Sir Timothy, who almost came to believe that his oft-repeated wish had come true and that at any rate a portion of the English team lay dead at his feet, 'this is quite extraordinary. Most extraordinary.'

A stout man in a trilby hat pushed his way forward.

'Let me see these men. I am a doctor.'

He bent over the prostrate men, conducted certain tests and presently said,

'As I thought. These men have been drugged.'

There was a tense silence. Only Sir Timothy found words to contradict this extraordinary suggestion.

'Nonsense. You can't be a proper doctor. This is a Test match. Men aren't drugged while playing for England.'

'Modern wickets are often doped,' said Q.E.D. Marjoribanks, 'but not modern batsmen.'

'Get some more doctors,' said Sir Timothy.

A second doctor was found who wore an M.C.C. tie, but this obviously more reliable man only confirmed the original diagnosis. Drugged!

Outside the crowd began to clap ironically. They had paid good money to see cricket and were not to be thwarted. The game must go on. With a determined look on his handsome face Norman Blood buckled on his pads and walked to the professionals' dressing-room. Here news of further disaster awaited. Little Teddy Trimmer, England's first wicket batsman, lay curled up in a corner fast asleep.

'What does this mean?' inquired Norman, staring in amazement at the unconscious man.

No one could enlighten him. Norman, having looked around his bewildered men said finally to little Croxton, the wicket-keeper,

'Feel sleepy?'

'No, Skipper. I feel fine.'

'Very well. You and I will hold the fort for England.'

A great cheer went up as it was seen that Norman Blood himself was prepared to play a captain's part at this critical moment, a still greater cheer as presently he flicked the ball away for a neat single. First Blood, jested nineteen journalists simultaneously, to England.

Gallantly for the remainder of the morning Norman and little Croxton, the wicket-keeper, battled. At the luncheon interval the score-sheet read:

Hugh, retired drugged	0
Crigh, retired drugged	0
*N.Blood, not out	7
†Croxton, not out	1
Extras	0
Total (for 0 wickets)	8

* Captain

† Wicket-keeper

from THE AMAZING TEST MATCH CRIME
1939

NORTHSHIRE v. DOWNSHIRE: first day

by

Dudley Carew

The Son of Grief *centres on Allen Peveril, an amateur turned pro and one of the leading lights of the Downshire side as an all-rounder. The book gives a vivid picture of the professional game as played in England in the 1930s, counterpointed by the 'son of grief' theme as given in Housman's lines:*

Now in Maytime to the wicket
Out I march with bat and pad:
See the son of grief at cricket
Trying to be glad.

No one would call Leedsfield a pretty ground. It was large, for opposite the pavilion were the Leedsfield Wednesday football ground and the football stands, while terracing ran down the other two sides. It was not a pretty ground, but the Leedsfield crowd was one of the most knowledgeable and sporting in the world, and Allen loved playing before it. The tented fields of the south were all very lovely in their way, but they had not the same tense atmosphere of the northern grounds which were devoted to cricket and to cricket only. Although there were still twenty minutes to go before the umpires came out, the pavilion was packed, and there were quite four thousand people along the terracing. There was a feeling of animation and expectancy in the air. Score-cards were being sold, boys with raucous voices and trays of chocolates were worming their way among the crowd, and men shouted to their acquaintances several rows away from them in broad Northshire accents.

A red face was turned up to him, and a voice said, 'Ah heard tha lost toss, lad.'

'We meant to. We like it best.'

'Ah reckon tha'll have all tha loikes afore we've finished wi' tha.'

Allen Peveril was happy. He felt he was taking part in his first real cricket match of the season. The matches in Downshire had been cold, empty, neutral affairs – Downshire came into her own towards the end of the season when her grounds were packed. This was the real beginning with the sun trying to shine, the weather warm enough to make a sweater superfluous, and a crowd that gave spirit to the game by its very presence. Ernest Day came out and joined him. 'You'll take three wickets before luncheon today, Mr Allen.' He had a painfully correct, even a pompous voice, but he was a dependable man all through, and one of the best No. 1 batsmen in the country, although he had never played in a Test Match. 'The pitch will be playing perfectly after luncheon, but you'll make it move this morning.'

'You know, Ernest, we might win this match if Bill bowls as he can and we try and play Patmore and Evans instead of trying to get out.'

'There's you and me and the skipper, and that's all as you very well know, and you,' he added reflectively, 'are none too dependable.'

'I know, and look at the runs Sammy gets against spin bowling – he's not worth ten in the two innings against those two.'

The seconds bell went, the umpires moved out towards the middle, the 'all aboard' was called by Philip, and the team flowed down the steps, through the gate and out on to the field.

'Let's start a fashion for trotting out of the pavilion like footballers,' suggested Allen to Day, 'Downshire, the "Let's Get Down to It" team. Dear me, what an extremely good idea.' Day smiled, a polite non-comprehending smile which made Allen laugh outright. He was feeling extraordinarily happy and at peace. There were no problems and no troubles in all the world.

They moved to their places. Allen and Day were first and

second slips in a field almost entirely behind the wicket, for Bill was bowling the first over at the football end and Bill, during his opening spell, was really fast. The ground was silent as Bill walked back to pace out his run. He then ran lazily up and brought his left arm over. He had got his run right, and walked back for the first ball of the match.

Allen felt a shiver of nervousness, not so much for himself as for Bill, pass through him. Bill was something of a protégé of his – he knew how well as well as how badly he could bowl, and he passionately wanted him to succeed today. Bill turned and began his run, the slips bent down, and the Northshire v. Downshire match began.

An hour and a half later Northshire had lost four wickets and only 48 runs were on the board, and the shocked, incredulous murmurs of the crowd sounded like surf beating on the rocks. Bill had not been immaculate, but the two wickets he had taken had been with beautiful balls. Allen had taken the other two. He had bowled his first four overs over the wicket and had then gone round. The pitch was responding, and the ball was both turning and popping. His first victim was l.b.w. to a ball that pitched on the off-stump and whipped viciously back, and his second caught by one of his short-legs off one that got up abruptly to the bat's shoulder.

The next man had not come out yet, and Allen was lying on his back, his hands clasped behind his head, empty of all thought, all emotion, except a floating sense of well-being and delight.

An exclamation from the umpire roused him. 'Gorblimey, I must be seeing things, and me what 'as only 'ad two pints this morning.'

Allen got up leisurely. 'What's the matter, Alf?' Alf was a character among umpires, a humorist, a born story-teller, and a great judge both of cricket and of men.

'Your eyes are younger than mine, but do I or do I not see young Taylor coming down them there pavilion steps?'

'Yes, that's Taylor all right, what about it?'

'Wot abaht it, wot abaht it?' Alf's eyes appealed frantically to heaven. 'This 'ere wicket'll be 'eaven after lunch won't it? It's five past one now, ain't it? Taylor's a left-'ander so's your off-breaks'll be leg-breaks to 'im, won't they? 'E's an 'itter and a bad starter, ain't 'e, and yet they go and send 'im in now when they've got Tommy Wills, who was brought up on your stuff, me lad, and would be 'ere till the close of play.' He sighed and closed his eyes with the air of a martyr. ' 'E only 'ad to send in Tommy to 'old 'is end up and then afterwards, as soon as young Taylor comes in, 'e 'its yer all over the field, see, 'cos the ball won't turn and ye won't know whether ye're comin' or goin'.'

'Good gracious me, Alf, how you do talk. No. 6 is his natural position, after all.'

'Exactly,' said Allen, ' 'is proper position on the card. And that's enough for you young gentlemen who go to universities and get your decrees, and then think you know something about cricket.'

'Degrees, Alf, degrees. Decrees are far more expensive.'

Taylor was coming up to them by this time, and Alf winked. Alf got a great deal of joy out of exaggerating his Cockney speech and accent, and Allen knew it. They were friends. As Taylor walked away down the pitch to take guard, Alf said, 'You've bowled well this morning, Mr Allen, you really have.'

Allen looked at Philip, and then placed his short-legs finer – they were now, of course, slips – put silly mid-on in a kind of indeterminate position which might be described as third-man close in, and waved cover-point back and more square. He had a forward short-leg and a man out wide at long-on.

As he began his run he knew that Taylor, a magnificent forcing batsman when he was in form, was nervous, and he knew, too, that he felt his responsibility keenly. He had, in a fraction of a second, a picture of Taylor in his mind's eye, a Taylor nervous, worried and enough of a cricketer to realize what a really good boundary would mean – confidence to himself, fifty on the board, the crowd's encouragement and a momentary but valuable illusion that the tide had turned. He bowled a ball with spin on it that was not quite a half-volley, and was well outside Taylor's off-stump. Taylor went out to hit it, his right foot was not quite far enough across, the spin caught the edge of the bat and cover-point, running to deep point, held the catch easily.

Allen did not hear the crowd at all, and walked up to Philip. 'What do you think, skipper? The pitch won't help me much longer, and Bill looks as though he's had enough.'

Philip bent down, picked a blade of grass and began to chew it. 'I think you'd better go on. Another wicket before lunch and they're through.'

Allen walked back to the wickets and stood by Alf. He looked up and down the pitch and said half aloud to himself, 'I can't see why this pitch can't behave itself between 11.30 and 1.15. It'll be fit for thousands of runs now.'

'No more do the groundsmen, Mr Allen,' said Alf. A sudden thought struck him, and there was deliberate mischief in his eye. 'A woman or a wicket, which is the harder to understand?' He went off into silent fits of laughter at the utter imbecility of his own joke, and then straightened out and gave Tommy Willis his guard. Allen had walked back and almost turned on his mark before he realized that he had a chance of doing the hat-trick and that his field was not placed for the ball he intended to bowl. It was too late now to do anything, but Ernest Day was the only slip he had and he could rely on him to move two yards further and deeper at an almost imperceptible movement of his left hand. Ernest made the move and Allen, bowling round the wicket, let the ball go through with his arm, but Wills smiled, covered up, let the ball smack into the wicket-keeper's hand, and Allen felt that Alf, for once, was wrong and had mistaken the moment of the game's crisis. Northshire's No. 1, beaten times without number but still immaculate, still regarding the ground at the end of every over with the lofty, inaccessible air of a conqueror, was still there, and he and Wills not only stayed together until lunch but took the score into the eighties. Privately Allen thought Philip should have rested Bill and himself and brought them back for the last over or two. Bill was decidedly wild, and two successive long-hops were hooked firmly to the square-leg boundary, while Allen had twelve runs taken off him in one over.

'They'll make two-fifty now, you see if they don't, although they don't deserve to, not with them sending young Taylor in like they did,' said Alf as he removed the bails and Allen could only grunt.

He walked back to the pavilion silently and alone; his mind was working too fast and urgently for him to talk to anyone. He felt that Alf was right, and he bitterly regretted that his bowling had lost its edge when Wills had come in. He had never looked like getting him out, or, indeed, even mildly disturbing him, and it was an established rule that if Northshire's No. 1, Beddoes, started badly he went on to make a hundred. No, they had done extremely well on paper, but Allen somehow had the feeling that the tide had ceased to run for them.

He saw by Philip's face that he was thinking much the same thing, and he went up to him and said, 'After all, skipper, we have done pretty well, you know.'

'I know. You and Bill bowled splendidly but . . .'

'Yes, it's a big "but", but then we may get a quick wicket afterwards or run one of them out or something. After all, when the innings started we'd have been pleased with anything under three hundred.'

They had reached the pavilion steps and ran up the gangway between two forests of clapping hands into the dark well of the pavilion.

Allen ate the usual cricket lunch of cold chicken and ham and fruit salad quickly, and was the first to leave the table and go back to the dressing-room. He wanted to lie down and relax for the twenty minutes of the interval that was still left. To get to the dressing-room he had to walk the whole length of the pavilion, and was besieged by the usual horde of autograph seekers. Usually Allen always signed as many as he possibly could – nothing enraged him more than the warning to autograph hunters, mostly small, intensely keen boys and girls, stuck up on some county grounds – but he was in a hurry, and brushed his way through them smilingly. He walked down the dark passage to the dressing-room and bumped into someone. 'I'm so sorry,' he said, and was going on, when a hand caught his sleeve, and a book was thrust in front of his face.

'I'm not,' said a level, colourless voice, 'in fact I meant you to bump into me. I want your autograph, and here is both the book and the pen.'

'Dear me.' His eyes were becoming used to the light and he saw that she was a woman of about his own age, richly, a little over-richly, dressed, and made up in a way which made her distinctly incongruous in the Leedsfield cricket pavilion. 'Who could refuse any request from so lovely a lady?' He took the book, scribbled his signature, and laughed. 'I don't usually talk like that. I think taking a wicket must have gone to my head.'

He gave her back the book and the pen, walked into the dressing-room, made himself as comfortable as he could on two chairs, relaxed his mind and his muscles, and forgot all about her.

The afternoon went much as Allen had felt it would. The Downshire change bowling was weak, the pitch behaved perfectly, and Beddoes and Wills settled down to a long stand. The hundred went up and the 150, and it was not until the score was 173 that Wills was run out, thanks to a brilliant throw-in from the deep. Downshire got two more wickets before tea, Bill getting one with the new ball when he went on at 200, and at tea the score was 207 for 8. Allen took the outstanding two wickets by the time the total was 215, and Downshire were left with two hours' batting at the end of the day.

Allen was lying face down on the dressing-room table being massaged when Day and a rather nondescript young pro called Stevens went out to open the Downshire innings, and he did not see the opening over bowled by Patmore, one of Northshire's fast bowlers, to Day, but he heard a lot about it from Sammy Westwood, the No. 3, who was sitting with his pads on on the balcony. The ground was silent while the first two balls were being bowled, but after the third there was a hum of comment outside, and Sammy swore blasphemously. 'Pitched on 'is own — toes and 'e'll go on doing it. 'E's not a bowler, 'e's a bumper and a — unfair one at that.'

He did go on doing it. Sammy reported that Day had ducked to the fourth and fifth, and that the sixth had gone over the wicket-keeper's head for four byes. The Downshire dressing-room was unanimous and indignant, and the only person who did not say anything was Allen, who foresaw trouble ahead for Downshire, and the fall of more than one wicket before the close of play. The other Northshire bowler, Evans, was more of Allen's type, but he could bowl really fast, and he chose to bowl fast now. He kept a length, however, but even so the balcony reported that Stevens was drawing away from him.

The masseur finished with Allen, who joined the rest of the team on the balcony just in time to see Stevens play a wild shot at a ball from Patmore that rose head high, and sky it for the wicket-keeper to trot up and make the easiest of catches.

Sammy muttered under his breath and the team murmured their encouragement as he went back to the dressing-room for his bat. Allen looked out over the ground at the sun which had lost its morning glory in the smoke of the factories, and was already in its decline. As far as his eye could reach there was sombreness, a blending of neutral greys, a shifting, perpetual haze of smoke. The green turf and the white figures underneath him seemed utterly irrelevant, an insult at the expense of poverty and want. Without thinking what he was saying he spoke out loud. 'In a hundred years, less than a hundred, our economic system will seem not so much fantastic as criminal.'

The balcony turned round in astonishment, and he realized what he had said. 'Don't mind me boys, don't mind me, just watch our Sammy hook Patmore for six.'

Yes, it was all that, but as he looked down at the faces of the shilling crowd beneath him, the cheerfulness and the humour of them seemed to him unbearable in their poignancy. Did they know, he wondered, what they missed, the simplest and loveliest terms of life, expanses of water under a clouded moon, white terraces by the sea, and a cave created by the bloom of flowers. A musical-comedy backcloth land, part of his mind jeered, they have better things than that, but they are guarded from you because you have not the wisdom to appreciate the symbols of that bottle of beer and that packet of sandwiches, that shouted remark to the batsman, poor in wit and used a thousand times, and that roar of laughter which follows it. His own life, his own experiment with it, had taught him so little.

He looked again at the game and concentrated on it. He had no faith at all in Westwood, and four times in one over from Patmore he saw him swing his bat recklessly at rising balls. Two of them went to the boundary, and the Leedsfield crowd, always generous to its opponents, applauded but the Downshire balcony was glum, and Jimmy Wright whispered into Allen's ear, 'I give 'im another two overs.'

It only needed one, for at the second ball of the next over, a ball which pitched half-way down the wicket, Westwood retreated to square-leg and swung his bat wildly at it. Ernest Day told Allen afterwards his eyes were shut. At any rate the ball soared up to a prodigious height and mid-on had only to move a yard.

There was a visible and audible stir round the ground, and Allen became aware that Philip was calling him from the balcony of the amateurs' dressing-room. He went along, and Philip said, 'Look here, if another wicket falls quickly I want you to go in instead of me. My God,' he went on in a different tone, 'did you ever see such a shot? The man oughtn't to be allowed.'

'Oh, we all know about our Sammy and fast bowling, but though I says it as shouldn't, I think even if Richards does get out you ought to go in. You and Ernest ought to stay there, and, as Ernest told me this morning, I'm not dependable.'

Philip thought for a moment. 'Yes, I think you're right, but if Ernest goes in the next quarter of an hour, then it's you, and you can play your natural game.'

Just as Allen had finished buckling on his second pad the crowd made that peculiar, indescribable noise, quite different from the noise that greets a six, or, indeed, from all other noises made by crowds, the noise that heralds the fall of a wicket.

'Who is it?' he called out.

'Ernest,' chorused the balcony.

'My God, how?'

'I don't rightly know. 'E played forward all right and ball didn't turn much, but 'e just missed it.'

Nervousness made jabs at the pit of Allen's stomach, and he knew he would experience those jabs so long as he continued to play cricket. He could not stop his hands from picking things off the table and putting them down again. He was ready, completely ready, but Ernest was no more than half-way on his walk back to the pavilion. Suddenly he remembered the expensive-looking woman, and wondered whether she had gone. He giggled out loud, and felt himself turning red, and then became, on the instant, calm and confident. He walked down the stairs and waited at the bottom because he wanted to speak to Ernest.

The pavilion gave him a polite reception, and Allen met him half-way down the passage.

'Went through the middle of my bat,' he said.

'How is it?'

'Fine. I felt like staying all day. Good luck.'

The Leedsfield crowd knew little and cared less for what some of the London papers had called the piquancy of Allen's position as a pro, but they did know he had hit hard in making sixty odd on their ground last year, and they gave him a good reception. As he clattered down the steps of the pavilion he looked at the score-board on the right and saw that they had lost their three wickets for 37 runs. He had not had any idea of the runs they had made, and now the whole day's play clicked into proportion. If it had only been Richards and not Ernest who had got out . . . Richards was a stolid, unimaginative bat, but his defence was not always as solid as it looked from the ring and as his rate of scoring suggested. Another wicket in the three-quarters of an hour left for play and a day which had begun so well for Downshire would end disastrously. He was thinking hard, and did not notice the joke with which the Northshire wicket-keeper greeted him, with the result that ever afterwards his relations with that wicket-keeper were never quite the same.

There was one more ball in Evans's over, and as Allen took guard he was not particularly afraid of it. Evans, more than any man, stood between him and Test-match honours, for he bowled, although rather faster, exactly the same ball as Allen – and Evans had experience of cricket against the Australians to back him. The ground was silent as it always was while a batsman was receiving his first ball, and Allen could hear the pounding of Evans's feet as he ran up to the wicket. There was a magnificent antagonism about his bowling, a feeling of concentrated effort and aggression which Allen respected, and in which he rejoiced. Whenever he and Evans met, he felt a faint approximation to the emotions of John Ridd as he faced Carver Doone.

He thought of this for a split fraction of a second, and wondered with amusement what John Ridd's comment would have been, and then all his mind and body was contracted into a small, intense entity which concentrated on Evans's right hand. As the ball left it he realized he had unconsciously expected the normal break-back, but he had plenty of time to realize the wrist had dropped a fraction and that the ball was going to run away from him. He put his left leg across, lifted his bat, and watched it into the wicket-keeper's hands. From the taking of his guard to the death of the ball had been a moment in time, but during it he had become familiar with, as it seemed to him, every blade of grass, the exact pattern cut into the turf by the footmarks of the bowlers – his own included – and for every tiny detail within a few yards of him his eyes were microscopes. He did not know whether other players underwent the same experience before they had received their first ball, but it was always the same with him, and now that the ordeal was over he was aware again of the background of the crowd and of the men he knew in the Northshire team.

Alf came up from square-leg and said he didn't know 'ow Ernest missed that ball. 'E was square with the wicket, of course, and couldn't see proper, but all the same 'e didn't see 'ow Ernest missed it. Allen noticed that Patmore walked back from his run as though he were a weary man, but he knew that Patmore, just when he looked as though he could not last another yard, had a way of producing a devastating ball. Richards played two balls and ran a single for the third, and so Allen had to face him. He was surprised to notice that he had not got a man deep out at square-leg, and he had a picture in his mind of the hook as a safe and profitable shot. He got his chance of playing it off the first ball Patmore sent him down. It was short, fast, and coming for his head, but Allen, with a fierce, subconscious exaltation, knew he would not fail, and his instinct saw the ball at the square-leg boundary before it was there in fact.

The shot loosened up his mental faculties, the pitch had more the look of his beloved net in the garden at home, and he felt Petzenheuffer watching him. He felt an absurd desire to wave his bat in reassurance, certain the gesture would be seen from that giant window in the 'Goat and Compasses', and he smiled at the acid comment one of the Northshire slips made in a stage whisper. There were no more fours in that over, but the last ball he jumped into and drove hard, and mid-off deserved the claps he received for stopping it.

The game was still at a crisis, but for some time things went well for Downshire. Allen and Richards got the bowling changed, and twice in the first over from a left-hand slow bowler who had not got his length Allen drove over-pitched balls to the pavilion rails. The clock hands stood at six, but no one in the silent, attentive crowd thought of going – the habit of leaving early is confined to southern grounds. Allen was living at the height of his mental and physical powers, his feet, his body, his bat, and his brain all seemed welded into one harmonious whole, moving with a disciplined instinct, incapable of error. The score flashed through the fifties and sixties, and Allen brought it up to the seventies with an on-drive, which was half a pull, for a six, the ball pitching below the score-board. There was no recklessness about the stroke – the ball was a bad one. He did not feel in the least reckless; his recklessness in his cricket as in his life was a product of defeatism and of detestation of himself, but now the mood of the conqueror was on him, and a distant, impersonal part of his mind sat back and approved of his accomplishments.

The ball was thrown back, the applause ceased, and Allen settled down to play the next ball from the slow left-hander, who was a shade faster than slow and a deadly bowler when the pitch was helping him. As the ball left his fingers and started on its curved flight Allen saw that there was no six this time – a controlled forward stroke was shot to play. His left foot and his bat went out and then, at that precise moment when it was too late to do anything, he realized, with a sickening sense of doom, that the flight had deceived him, and that the ball was shorter than he had anticipated. It was too late; he half-checked his shot, but that made matters worse, and Owen following up, brought off one of the simplest caught-and-bowled's in his destructive career. The catch was so simple and unexpected that the crowd for a moment was too stunned to be vocal. Then it broke into a full-throated Northshire roar, for it realized the importance of a wicket at that particular moment, and the roar had a touch of savage and gloating triumph in it.

Allen himself stayed in the attitude in which he had played his shot, and he was possessed by a passion of loyalty towards his side and a hatred towards Northshire. Images of Philip watching from the balcony, of Wield, of the worn handle of the beer-pull in the bar, each scratch and mark on it clear, of Joe's gold watch-chain and, monstrous and irrelevant intrusion, Miranda as she had looked up from her chair last night as he came into the room, filled him, and, stronger than them all, fury for those who had done this senseless thing and destroyed something which could never again be repeated.

His pause was so momentary that no one on all the ground noticed it. In a second he had pulled himself together and started his walk back to the pavilion. Alf said, as he passed, 'Well, to think of being taken in like that at your age, ought to be ashamed of yourself,' and he said to Owen, 'Well bowled, you old fox, blast you.' All his resentment had gone as though it had never been, but still there remained an intense desire in him that Downshire should win, and he could not bear the thought that Philip might fail.

The crowd had again become silent, but as he neared the pavilion the claps, loud and hearty, began. The fourth wicket had put on 38 runs in twenty minutes, of which Allen had made 32, and, although it was delighted to see the back of him, the crowd was determined to let him know how much it appreciated his batting. The pavilion was as enthusiastic as the rest of the ground, and the members stood up as he ran up the steps.

Philip was waiting for him at the entrance of the passage and he said, 'I'm sorry, skipper, I didn't know he could bowl that one so well.'

'It was a damned good innings, Allen.'

'There's nothing to worry about out there. You ought to get a packet. Good luck.' He went on up to the dressing-room and realized how hot and tired he was, and how marvellous a shower and a change would be. His flannels were sticking to him, and the sweat was pouring down his face. He felt all the exaltation of an athlete who has done his work well and the bitterness of that moment when he knew he had make the one mistake no batsman can afford to make was forgotten.

The dressing-room was sympathetic and congratulatory. As he stripped Ernest came up to him and said, 'We should both be out there now, Mr. Allen. It was bad luck for both of us.'

'It wasn't so much bad luck with me. I simply didn't realize Owen had it in him. His flight's usually so simple. I hope to God the skipper doesn't go tonight.'

'He won't go. We ought to have got four hundred, Mr. Allen. The wicket's perfect.' Ernest was grave and patriarchal. 'As for that there Sammy . . .'

'Oh, I know, but still . . .' Allen was strict in his rule of avoiding gossip about the other professionals. 'Cheer up, Ernest, there's no reason why we shouldn't get three hundred even now. Richards isn't playing half badly.'

Ernest was grudging. 'He hasn't got any strokes.'

'He *has* got strokes, but he won't use them. More brain, O Lord, more brain.' Ernest ignored the allusion, but stated emphatically, 'He's got none of that.' 'How many of them have?' Allen stepped under the shower, came out again, and felt he wanted to go on with the argument. 'You know it all boils down to that, brain and imagination.' He began to dry himself and went on, 'Cricket's all right in spite of the newspapers, but the trouble is that three-quarters of us don't know how to use our own gifts. Think of the pleasure you and people like' – he named five or six cricketers – 'give to thousands of people. The crowd knows they're going to play the proper stroke at the ball they receive, and that's all they want. I could take eleven men out of this pavilion who know far more about the game than seven out of the ten men who make a thousand runs in first-class cricket a year. Give them half our technical skill, and they would set the game on fire. That's the tragedy of it.'

'Last over,' said someone from the balcony, and then, a minute or two later, as Allen was halfway through the dressing, the day's play was over. The thought that it was finished filled him with a quick, irrational melancholy. He realized suddenly that he was quite alone, that he had nothing to do that evening, and that there was Sunday to be got through somehow, a long and forbidding day. The other pros had made their own plans and did not want him, and Philip was staying with the Draytons.

In the midst of the animation of the dressing-room he felt lonelier than he had ever felt in his little bedroom at the 'Goat and Compasses'. He finished dressing and walked out on to the balcony. The ground was already nearly empty, and sheets of newspaper on the grey stone of the terracing gave the whole place a sordid and dishevelled look. He left the dressing-room without saying goodnight, at once craving for and frightened of the society of other men.

from THE SON OF GRIEF
1936

TEDDY'S FIRST SEASON

by

Bruce Hamilton

Like The Son of Grief *Bruce Hamilton's* Pro *– which is subtitled 'An English Tragedy' – also concentrates on the world of the professional cricketer. Teddy Lamb, son of A. E. Lamb 'the great Midhampton all-rounder of the 1890s and the earlier years of the present century', is on the Midhamptonshire staff waiting for his chance to play for the county. First he is selected, then replaced at the eleventh hour by an amateur. Now it looks as though his moment may have come.*

There was a blank of three days after the Warfield Week, then came the south-eastern tour, with Sussex, Hampshire, and Kent to be met. The day before they started Teddy was told to pack up and go with the team. Cecil was to go too, reverting to his old position as twelfth man.

At Brighton the weather was glorious, and the town crowded with holidaymakers. Young men with straw hats and canes, girls in light summer dresses basked, and paraded, and paddled, and ogled. Donkeys trotted with children on their backs, bath-chairmen pushed invalids about, the little cars of Volk's Electric Railway bumped backwards and forwards between the Palace Pier and Black Rock. Potential cavaliers, vigilant but wary, passed and repassed between the Metropole and the Queen's, where the courtesans walked. A trace of aristocracy lingered round East Street and Castle Square, where an odd-looking Sussex squire in check tweeds could be glimpsed here and there;

but democracy ran riot in West Street with generous stenches from Harris's Pork Sausage Restaurant, three cinemas offering continuous programmes, and gross or sentimental picture postcards on sale every yard or two. Cecil and Teddy, strolling down to the front after arriving in the early afternoon, found the scene enormously stimulating. There was something exciting, boldly erotic about it, and Teddy began to imagine what he could do if he ever got a holiday in this place. But he was on the job now, no distractions that might impair physical effectiveness could be permitted. They went on to the West Pier, plied the Gipsy Fortune-Teller with pennies, discovered What the Butler Saw and How Bridget served the Salad Undressed (with some disappointment in each case), tried their strength, and manipulated odd little cricketers in voluminous sweaters but, apparently, no trousers. At half-past-ten they got back to their hotel and went to bed.

They found a very different town surrounding the County Ground at Hove – quiet, dignified, spacious. Teddy, a little self-conscious with his cricket-bag, was looked at rather hard by the gatekeeper at the Members' and Players' entrance, but not challenged. As he came down to the ground in his flannels he was beset by two or three small autograph hunters, very insistent that he should sign his name in the right place. At a quarter to twelve the first bell rang, the nets were taken down, and it was learned that Sussex had won the toss. At twelve Teddy came on the field for his first appearance as a county player.

Vine and Robert Relf came out to open for Sussex. Lemon bowled from the north end – strong, purposeful, really fast. His first ball was short, and Vine cut it to right of third man, whence Teddy, running at full speed, cut down a possible four and a likely two to a single. The little round of applause put him on terms with himself.

The score advanced: Vine, slow, somewhat fidgety, looking in greater difficulty than he was. Relf, very elegant and graceful, almost disdainful of the bowling. At 23, however, he played a careless stroke at Lemon, and was bowled. Vine and Killick now settled down to a very sober game. Lumley went on instead of Lemon, and a little later Mr Stokes, who had been bowling with his usual accuracy for nearly an hour, was replaced by Plant, whose slow right-hand deliveries, pitched well up and breaking from the leg, had Vine in trouble for an over or two. A sharp chance to Cumberbatch at short slip was dropped; then Killick got to Plant's end, and unexpectedly hit a six into the pavilion, scattering a few members.

At a quarter-past-one, when Sussex had made 70, Arthur Meadows beckoned Teddy up to the north wicket. Teddy had been kept fairly busy at third man, and fielding singles in the country, and had already made the discovery that first-class cricket feels less awe-inspiring from the middle than it looks from the ring. He was less anxious than he expected, as he arranged his field with Mr Meadows, but it was nevertheless an ordeal, with the certainty at the back of his mind that people all over the ground, as Number 11 went up on the board, were looking at their score cards and reading his name. There would be remarks, 'Lamb? Never heard of him.' 'He's been playing for Midhampton for years.' 'No – that's an old fellow; he's retired.' 'Dead, I believe.' 'Must be his son.' 'It's his nephew.'

'Don't try anything much the first over, Ted,' advised Arthur Meadows. 'Just a length.'

Teddy realised that the ball was too old for him to move it in the air to any extent. He concentrated on pitching just outside the off stump, allowing his body break to turn the ball on to the wicket. Vine played strictly defensive strokes until the last ball of the over, which was a little over-pitched and went for a single to extra cover.

Plant bowled a maiden over at the other end. Teddy now had to attack Killick, who, as a left-hander, found the ball going away from the bat instead of coming to it. He snicked the first ball rather dangerously through the slips to the boundary. Teddy was now bowling with more venom. The fourth was of the same sort, but it turned an extra inch or so. It just found the edge of the bat, and Buckley took it cleanly. Teddy yelled his appeal exultantly, and the umpire gave him his first wicket without hesitation.

Cartwright came in, another left-hander, with a pronounced crouch and a curious back-lift, in the three distinct stages – body straightened, bat raised to the level of the bails, finally to that of the shoulder. Teddy, over-excited, bowled the first ball too fast and short, and Cartwright cut it wide of third man for two. The last of the over was a yorker on the leg stump – a very good ball. Cartwight came down on it too late and not hard enough. The ball trickled on to the wicket.

The applause was the loudest of the morning. Arthur Meadows came over to pat Teddy on the shoulder; the whole team was delighted at his success.

He bowled one more over, a maiden, to Albert Relf, and then it was lunch-time. Sussex had made 81 for 3, Vine being not out 32.

It was warm work in the afternoon. Vine and Albert Relf got on top of the bowling and were not separated till nearly the two hundred, when Vine was brilliantly caught by Reville at backward point. After tea, Lemon took the new ball and got three quick wickets, but Vincett, driving hard, and Cox, cutting very cleanly, gave a lot of trouble. Teddy, who had kept the runs down quite successfully for a longish spell during the big stand, came in for severe punishment from Vincett before getting him with a ball that came straight through. The Sussex innings ended for 323. Teddy had taken 3 for 59.

He was a little over-elated that evening. He revealed his mood, not exactly by positive boastfulness, but by a lack of the unobtrusive modesty becoming to a very young player in the company of his elders. He talked, not indeed about himself, but too much. Four or five of the professionals were dining at the hotel, and when, in discussing some of the points of the day's play, Teddy put forward his view a little too didactically, Frank Buckley decided to put in a word. He took him aside after dinner.

'Now look here, Ted,' he said, 'you bowled very well today, and there's no reason why you shouldn't go on doing well if you don't get uppish. But you remember this – most of the Sussex men know our bowling inside and out, they've played against it a score of times. You're new to them, they don't know what's up your sleeve. It's not hard for a young bowler to get wickets before the word goes round about what he can do. You take it from me. You'll have to stomach a mort of hammering before you get anywhere near the top of the tree. You aren't so good a bowler yet as Mr Stokes or George Lemon or Joe Plant, not by a long chalk.' Teddy was rather dashed, but he recognised the wisdom and real kindess behind the warning. He did his best to bear it in mind next morning, which brought a letter asking for brief biographical particulars from a cricket periodical, a request to pose from a Brighton photographer who specialised in cricket, and a copy of the *Morning Post*, handed him by Mr Meadows, containing in the account of the game a reference to 'Lamb – it is good to see the name in the Midhampton ranks again. A medium-paced bowler with a beautiful action, he got and deserved the wickets of Killick and Mr Cartwright in his second over – not bad for a beginning.'

The rest of the match, however, brought him no particular success. After a second wicket stand between Revill and Shelly, Midhampton collapsed rather badly to Holloway's aggressive fast bowling. Teddy was bowled third ball. But he was given the honour of opening the bowling in the Sussex second innings, Stokes having hurt his hand while batting. He bowled Vine with an inswinger but got no further wickets. Sussex piled on runs at the expense of a weakened attack, Robert Relf getting a century, and eventually declared at half-past twelve on the third day, nearly 400 ahead. A brave fight to save the game ended in failure just before six. Teddy managed to stay with Plant for twenty minutes. He fluked a four off his first ball from Holloway and afterwards played some nice strokes before an indiscreet attempt to cut Albert Relf ended his innings and the match.

After the game was over he bought a score card with the final score (*see opposite*).

Teddy bought a scrap-book next day, and pasted in this card, together with the *Morning Post* clipping, others from the *Midhampton Courier* and the *Sussex Daily News*, and a proof of the photograph, in which he looked very awkward; his arm stretched above his head and his legs together in such a position that it would have been barely possible for him to project the ball twenty-two yards.

He played in the Hampshire and Kent matches and, although he had the satisfaction of getting the wickets of both Philip Mead

SUSSEX

	First innings		Second innings	
1	Relf (R.R.), b. Lemon	16	run out	135
2	Vine, c Revill b Lumley	79	b Lamb	4
3	Killick, c Buckley b Lamb	28	c Meadows b Plant	35
4	P. Cartwright, b Lamb	2	hit wkt, b Pearson-Phillips	47
5	Relf (A.E.), c Shelly b Lemon	56	not out	2
6	H.P. Chaplin (capt.), b Lemon	9		
7	P.G.H. Fender, b Lemon	2	st Buckley b Plant	29
8	Vincett, lbw b Lamb	63	b Plant	9
9	Cox, c and b Stokes	37		
10	N.J. Holloway, st Buckley b Plant	14		
11	Street, not out	6		
	B 7, lb 3, nb 1	11	B 11, nb 3, w1	15
	Total	323	(6 wkts decl'd)	276

BOWLING	O.	M.	R.	W.		O.	M.	R.	W.
Lemon	18	3	61	4		9	0	39	0
Stokes	32	12	59	1		—	—	—	—
Lumley	15	6	28	1		22	5	58	0
Plant	29.5	6	94	1		18	3	78	3
Lamb	21	5	59	3		15	4	49	1
Pearson-Phillips	2	0	11	0		6	0	32	1
					Cumberbatch	3	1	5	0

MIDHAMPTON

	First innings		Second innings	
1	Revill, b Vine	84	b Relf (A.E.)	17
2	Buckley, c Cox, b Relf (A.E.)	12	c Fender b Vincett	32
3	Shelly, c Street, b Holloway	64	c Relf (R.) b Vincett	40
4	Cumberbatch, lbw b Cox	4	b Fender	23
5	Lumley, b Holloway	7	c and b Cox	55
6	A.R. Meadows (capt.), c Relf (A.E.) b Holloway)	0	b Cox	9
7	Plant, c Relf (A.E.) b Holloway	2	not out	42
8	Lemon, c Vine b Vincett	28	b Vincett	1
9	F.G. Pearson-Phillips, b Holloway	4	b Relf (A.E.)	9
10	G.L. Stokes, not out	11	lbw b Holloway	1
11	Lamb (E.W.), b Holloway	0	c Street b Relf (A.E.)	12
	B 4, lb 1, nb 3	8	lb 5	5
	Total	224		246

BOWLING	O.	M.	R.	W.		O.	M.	R.	W.
Holloway	21.4	5	51	6		18	2	63	1
Relf (A.E.)	29	9	54	1		34.2	13	60	3
Relf (R.R.)	5	1	14	0		—	—	—	—
Cox	18	5	56	1		21	6	45	2
Vincett	10	2	22	1		23	5	54	3
Fender	3	0	11	0		6	1	19	1
Vine	5	1	9	1		—	—	—	—
					Killick	1	1	0	0

Umpires – Flowers and West.
Result – Sussex won by 129 runs.

and Woolley – his success against left-handers was curious and unexpected – his bowling figures were not impressive. He was less accurate than he had been at Brighton, and twenty minutes' furious punishment by E.M. Sprott of Portsmouth did something to impair his confidence. The last two matches of the season were at home, and he was not picked for them. Cecil got his place for the first, and Curtis, a very good club amateur, for the second. Seven wickets for 312, and a batting average of 6.25 was Teddy's not remarkable record for the three games which constituted his first season in big cricket.

from PRO: AN ENGLISH TRAGEDY
1926

MY HOUR ON THE STAGE

by
Christopher Hollis

Christopher Hollis (1902–77) was a writer and controversialist of wide interests and sympathies, a Roman Catholic convert, M.P. for Devizes from 1945–55 and Parliamentary writer for Punch. *He was always passionately interested in the fortunes of Somerset C.C.C.; published books on the game at Hollis and Carter; and wrote match reports for* The Times. *The extract which follows is taken from his novel* Death of a Gentleman *which came out in 1943 and is told mainly through letters written by its enthusiastic central character, Robert Fossett who, in contrast to the two previous extracts, is very much the Somerset amateur.*

To George Borthwick

BARSTON MANOR
July 20, 1924

MY DEAR GEORGE,

Unto this day it doth mine hertë boot
That I have had my world as in my time.

Does Fame penetrate to New Zealand? I have had my hour, and, since it never will come again, I think it best now to begin gracefully to slip out of county cricket, play a few more matches only this summer, and then only a few next, until, as will very soon happen, they say, 'Thank you very much, but, if you can't play regularly, we think it best that you should not play at all.'

Then I will give myself undivided to the village both for cricket and for other purposes.

I will tell you all about it. I was chosen to play for the Gentleman against the Players. Now that was not quite as grand as it sounds because it was only The Oval match, and, as you know, while for Lord's all the counties release their players and they get representative sides, for The Oval they just pick up whoever happens to be at a loose end. However, what of that? I was chosen to play for the Gentlemen against the Players. Is not that good enough?

Well, Ruth and I packed up like the country cousins coming to town. Martin, my son and heir, distinguished the occasion by being sick all over the counterpane, and, hastily mopping up the what-not, we dashed for the car and caught the train by the skin of our teeth. Arrived at The Oval, we found that Tony had given the slip to the House of Commons and ducked out, hastily pursued by a couple of Junior Whips, asking him where the hell he was going to. He was there to welcome me, but his ideas of a welcome were so unimaginatively alcoholic that he was really under the circumstances almost an embarrassment.

The Gentlemen won the toss. I was put in third wicket down. Two wickets fell pretty quickly, and I sat there in the pavilion, twiddling my gloves round and round and feeling as I had never felt since that day in the Middle Division when the Brown Man swept into the middle of the siege of Syracuse and we all shivered while Conundrum looked round to see who was next to be put on. Somewhere in the seventies the third wicket fell and I had to go in. It was worse going out to the pitch there than going over the top in France. I got there in the end after a walk of a hundred years and took guard. I looked round, pretending to take note of the field. A red-headed miner from Derbyshire, called Braithwaite, was bowling. As he ran up to bowl, I haunched myself back on to my right leg, and prayed like a lunatic, 'O God, may I hit it. O God, may I hit it.' Braithwaite came pounding down, and I played it, got to it all right, and it rolled innocuously along the ground to mid-off. The next ball was wide to the off and I left it alone. The third and the fourth I played harmlessly, and then it was over. In the third over I succeeded in breaking my duck. Braithwaite bowled one on my legs, and I pushed it out towards mid-wicket, where there was not a fielder, and got a single. Then I got a two, then a few more singles, and so on until the score had got to twelve. I was not yet comfortable and still had to resist the temptation to lash out wildly and end it all with a silly catch. But at twelve a little black-haired slow bowler from Kent over-pitched one to me. Before I knew what I was doing, I had come out to it, caught it on the half-volley and driven it all along the ground to the right of cover-point's hand to the ropes. Cover-point did not even try to stop it. The next ball was slightly further out, but I took such risk as there was, came out to it again and smacked it again to the ropes. It was not perhaps quite such a clean hit as the other, but it was a good four all the way. Suddenly and in a flash, you know, one gets set. After those two strokes I was in one moment the master of the world. I was, like Admiral Blake in Newbolt's poem, 'fulfilled with the glory of achievement'.

Then for a time nothing could go wrong. The ball became my courtier, flashing off to do my messages in every corner of the world. You know, 'superfluous kings shall be my messengers' – such a good line – *Antony and Cleopatra*, isn't it? And before I knew where I was, I was tottering on the verge of 50. I then slowed myself up a bit through over-caution and at 49 I missed a gorgeous gift to leg that I had only to touch in order to make sure of at least the one run that was necessary. However, I got it in the next over with a not very convincing chop of a stroke in the direction of mid-wicket. Then I relapsed again into my inspired poetry, and, by dint of it, had soon got it up to 74. There they put on Titler, the Yorkshire slow left-hander.

From Titler's first ball I knew that I was up against it. He is one of those bowlers of whom it is alleged that he could pitch a ball on a threepenny bit, and, although this is certainly untrue of him or of any other bowler, yet he is remarkably and inconveniently accurate. It is possible to play him, if you watch him like a cat and make no effort at all to do any more than play him, but it is suicide to attempt the smallest liberty with him. I knew at once what I was up against and accepted the challenge. Three overs – three maidens. Then in the fourth he sent one slightly over a length; I came out to it, caught it on the half-volley and sent it to the boundary. There was a ripple of applause from the crowd, which had got a bit bored at this slowing up of things. Then the next ball, which looked exactly like its predecessor. I came out to it again, but did not quite get hold of it, and it spun off through the air to Cobbleton at extra-cover. It was travelling fairly fast and hardly more than ankle-high. Still Cobbleton has one of the safest pair of hands in the country, and I had no reason to doubt at all that my number was up. Like a fool, I had done exactly what Titler plotted for me to do. Cobbleton got both hands to the ball, and then quite unaccountably dropped it. An 'Oh!' went up all around the ground.

So I was reprieved, but I knew that morally I was out, and I never got back into my previous form again. I slogged about a bit more, but they were going up in the air now, and it was certainly no surprise to me, and I imagine not to anyone else, when at 86 I got under a long-hop, did not get hold of it sufficiently to lift it for six, and was comfortably caught on the square-leg boundary. 'Bad luck, sir,' said Titler, who was by then fielding in the slips. Well, it was good fun. 'Close of Play – Fine Innings by Fossett,' I found on the posters when I left the ground, and inside the papers, 'The main feature of the Gentlemen's innings was an attractive eighty-six from the bat of Mr Fossett, the Somerset amateur. Mr Fossett, whose figures included twelve boundary strokes, gave only one chance – at seventy-four. He was eventually caught on the on-boundary while attempting a big hit.' Why 'eventually', I wonder.

Sorry to write such a boring and egotistical letter, but after all there is nothing to make you read it, if you don't want to, and half the joy of cricket is playing the innings over again in your mind afterwards – and half the joy of a friend that he is a person to whom you can from time to time boast about trivial things.

Yours ever,
BOBBY.

from DEATH OF A GENTLEMAN
1943

A LANCASHIRE TRIUMPH

by

Cyril Alington

'Harry Foster and Reggie Spooner . . . came down to Liverpool to see me. They want me to play at The Oval on Monday.' It seems amazing, in our days of ball-by-ball commentaries, that the plot of this 'cricketo-detective story' centres around the hero, Reginald Courthorpe's attempt to keep from his uncle – Mr Jasper Merivale, JP – the intelligence that he, one of his uncle's employees, is taking leave of absence to play cricket for England. Since the date of publication is 1922, we can take it that the romantic dream of beating Australia is not unconnected with the desperate events of 1920 and 1921.

The account of the match is given in 'Epilogue 1' of Mr Evans, *in the form of a quotation from the* Liverpool Guardian *with all its proper sense of regional pride.*

> Forbear to deem the chronicler unwise.
>
> WORDSWORTH.

A cutting from the *Liverpool Guardian* of Thursday:

CRICKET NOTES

The Test Match which ended yesterday has been universally – and rightly – hailed as a veritable triumph for English cricket. But Lancashire men will have no hesitation in going a step further and claiming the lion's share in the victory for the County Palatine. England won by one wicket – the narrowest possible margin. Where would that margin have been but for the runs and wickets contributed by the wearers of the Red Rose? Sixteen of the twenty Australian wickets fell to Birkin and Winterton, and when England's ninth wicket in the second innings fell with 18 runs still to make, it was upon Birkin and Winterton alone that English hopes rested. Any failure of nerve or skill on the part of either and the cloud which has overcast English cricket for the last three months would have had no silver lining. But Lancashire men do not fail in nerve or skill, and yet another doughty deed has to be inscribed on the galaxy where already shine the names of Gladstone and MacLaren, of John Bright, John Briggs, and Arthur Mold.

But while giving all possible credit to Birkin for his steady bowling and his plucky and spirited batting, Liverpudlians will note with especial gratification that it is to a fellow-citizen that the laurels of the match undoubtedly fall. Seldom indeed has a first appearance in representative cricket been crowned with such lustre as that of Mr 'Jack' Winterton. For the benefit of posterity we may here record his achievement in some detail. On Monday Mr Winterton's bowling was of a very high order, but met with excruciating luck. Time and again he missed the stumps by a hair's breadth, and three wickets were but a poor reward for his work. But on Tuesday evening and Wednesday morning there was a very different story to tell. The pitch was certainly favourable to a bowler, but was never a real 'glue pot.' Mr Winterton, however, was not to be denied. Rarely in these days has been seen such a combination of length and break and 'devil,' and before it our formidable opponents appeared as the merest tyros. In the striking words of the genial and burly skipper, 'We could do nothing with it.' We have no hesitation in saying that Mr Winterton's seven wickets for 34 runs will take rank with any of the most brilliant feats in the annals of Test cricket.

It was not, however, until the very last moments of the match that Mr Winterton produced his real 'surprise packet.' Few of his friends, we imagine, would claim for his batting even a tithe of the respect which is due to his proficiency in the sister art, and the hearty if sympathetic laughter which his somewhat rustic methods had elicited in the first innings showed some symptoms of breaking out afresh as Mr Winterton lifted the first ball – a very fast one – of his second innings high over the head of what in our grandfathers' time would have been long-stop. But there were 18 runs to be got, and although 4 runs accrued from this unorthodox audacity, it was hardly of the kind to rouse hopes of its successful repetition. A couple of byes followed and a sharp single, and Mr Winterton had to face an over from the fastest living bowler. And a most eventful over it was. The first ball produced four runs from a stroke which we believe used to be known among Etonians as the Harrow drive. Be that as it may, the ball reached the boundary at lightning speed just beyond long-leg's reach. The second one was a yorker which Mr Winterton missed, and itself missed the wicket; how, it is impossible to say. The third Mr Winterton swept from the off-stump first bounce over the ropes, a stroke that had to be seen to be believed, and the laughter and cheering sank into an agonised silence before the realisation that one more of these astonishing combinations of eye, courage, and luck, would achieve the impossible. The end indeed was near, and, as often in cricket, it was something of an anticlimax. The fourth ball struck Mr Winterton upon the foot with considerable violence, but the consequent appeal was answered in the batsman's favour. The fifth he stopped somehow. Then came the last ball of the match. The fast bowler hurled himself towards the crease, gathered himself for a superhuman effort, and – slipped. The ball trickled down the pitch harmless and inviting, slowed up, and stopped. Mr Winterton approached it, paused, looked round, and struck it with careful force to a vacant part of the boundary, and England had won.

Of the ensuing pandemonium no description is necessary, but it is safe to say that the rejoicings have found an echo, quieter but no less sincere, in every heart in Liverpool. Mr Winterton, we hear, is a clerk in the employ of Mr Jasper Merivale of 'The Beeches,' one of our most respected citizens. It is indeed gratifying to find in the world of business so lively an appreciation of the things which have made England what she is, and Mr Merivale may rest assured that from this moment his repute as a Maecenas of sport is secure for all time.

from MR EVANS
1922

GINGER STOTT'S GENIUS

by

J.D. Beresford

Beresford's book, published in 1911, is called The Hampdenshire Wonder, *but 'the Wonder' is not Ginger Stott himself, even though his career with that first-class county could be so described. When the Hampdenshire Wonder does come on the scene, his story proves to be quite different and to have nothing to do with cricket – except insofar as it came about through Ginger Stott's belief in his own peculiar skill as a bowler, and his ambition.*

There was a narrow strip of yard, or alley, at the back of Mrs Stott's paper-shop, a yard that, unfortunately, no longer exists. It has been partly built over, and another of England's memorials has thus been destroyed by the vandals of modern commerce . . .

This yard was fifty-three feet long, measuring from Mrs Stott's back door to the door of the coal-shed, which marked the alley's extreme limit. This measurement, an apparently negligible trifle, had an important effect upon Ginger Stott's career. For it was in this yard that he taught himself to bowl, and the shortness of the pitch precluded his taking any run. From those long studious hours of practice he emerged with a characteristic that was – and still remains – unique. Stott never took more than two steps before delivering the ball; frequently he bowled from a standing position, and batsmen have confessed that of all Stott's puzzling mannerisms, this was the one to which they never became accustomed. S.R.L. Maturin, the finest bat Australia ever sent to this country, has told me that to this peculiarity of delivery he attributed his failure ever to score freely against Stott. It completely upset one's habit of play, he said: one had no time to prepare for the flight of the ball; it came at one so suddenly. Other bowlers have since attempted some imitation of this method without success. They had not Stott's physical advantages.

Nevertheless, the shortness of that alley threw Stott back for two years. When he first emerged to try conclusions on the field, he found his length on the longer pitch utterly unreliable, and the effort necessary to throw the ball another six yards, at first upset his slowly acquired methods.

It was not until he was twenty years old that Ginger Stott played in his first Colts' match.

The three years that had intervened had not been prosperous years for Hampdenshire. Their team was a one-man team. Bobby Maisefield was developing into a fine bat (and other counties were throwing out inducements to him, trying to persuade him to qualify for first-class cricket), but he found no support, and Hampdenshire was never looked upon as a coming county. The best of the minor counties in those years were Staffordshire and Norfolk.

In the Colts' match Stott's analysis ran:

overs	maidens	runs	wickets
11.3	7	16	7

and reference to the score-sheet, which is still preserved among the records of the County Club, shows that six of the seven wickets were clean bowled. The Eleven had no second innings; the match was drawn, owing to rain. Stott has told me that the Eleven had to bat on a drying wicket, but after making all allowances, the performance was certainly phenomenal.

After this match Stott was, of course, played regularly. That year Hampdenshire rose once more to their old position at the head of the minor counties, and Maisefield, who had been seriously considering Surrey's offer of a place in their Eleven after two years' qualification by residence, decided to remain with the county which had given him his first chance.

During that season Stott did not record any performance so remarkable as his feat in the Colts' match, but his record for the year was eighty-seven wickets with an average of 9.31; and it is worthy of notice that Yorkshire made overtures to him, as he was qualified by birth to play for the northern county.

I think there must have been a wonderful *esprit de corps* among the members of that early Hampdenshire Eleven. There are other evidences beside this refusal of its two most prominent members to join the ranks of first-class cricket. Lord R—, the president of the H.C.C.C., has told me that this spirit was quite as marked as in the earlier case of Kent. He himself certainly did much to promote it, and his generosity in making good the deficits of the balance sheet, had a great influence on the acceleration of Hampdenshire's triumph.

In his second year, though Hampdenshire were again champions of the second-class counties, Stott had not such a fine average as in the preceding season. Sixty-one wickets for eight hundred and sixty-eight (average 14.23) seems to show a decline in his powers, but that was a wonderful year for batsmen (Maisefield scored seven hundred and forty-two runs, with an average of forty-two) and, moreover, that was the year in which Stott was privately practising his new theory.

It was in this year that three very promising recruits, all since become famous, joined the Eleven, viz.: P.H. Evans, St. John Townley, and Flower the fast bowler. With these five cricketers Hampdenshire fully deserved their elevation into the list of first-class counties. Curiously enough, they took the place of the old champions, Gloucestershire, who, with Somerset, fell back into the obscurity of the second-class that season.

I must turn aside for a moment at this point in order to explain the 'new theory' of Stott's, to which I have referred, a theory which became in practice one of the elements of his most astounding successes.

Ginger Stott was not a tall man. He stood only 5ft. 5¼in. in his socks, but he was tremendously solid; he had what is known as a 'stocky' figure, broad and deep-chested. That was where his muscular power lay, for his abnormally long arms were rather thin, though his huge hands were powerful enough.

Even without his 'new theory', Stott would have been an exceptional bowler. His thoroughness would have assured his success. He studied his art diligently, and practised regularly in a barn through the winter. His physique, too, was a magnificent instrument. That long, muscular body was superbly steady on the short, thick legs. It gave him a fulcrum, firm, apparently immovable. And those weirdly long, thin arms could move with lightning rapidity. He always stood with his hands behind him, and then – as often as not without even one preliminary step – the long arm would flash round and the ball be delivered, without giving the batsman any opportunity of watching his hand; you could never tell which way he was going to break. It was astonishing, too, the pace he could get without any run. Poor Wallis used to call him the 'human catapult'; Wallis was always trying to find new phrases.

The theory first came to Stott when he was practising at the nets. It was a windy morning, and he noticed that several times the balls he bowled swerved in the air. When those swerving balls came they were almost unplayable.

Stott made no remark to any one – he was bowling to the groundsman – but the ambition to bowl 'swerves', as they were afterwards called, took possession of him from that morning. It is true that he never mastered the theory completely; on a perfectly calm day he could never depend upon obtaining any swerve at all, but, within limits, he developed his theory until he had any batsman practically at his mercy.

He might have mastered the theory completely, had it not been for his accident – we must remember that he had only three seasons of first-class cricket – and, personally, I believe he would have achieved that complete mastery. But I do not believe, as Stott did, that he could have taught his method to another man. That belief became an obsession with him, and will be dealt with later.

My own reasons for doubting that Stott's 'swerve' could have been taught, is that it would have been necessary for the pupil to have had Stott's peculiarities, not only of method, but of physique. He used to spin the ball with a twist of his middle finger and thumb, just as you may see a billiard professional spin a billiard ball. To do this in his manner, it is absolutely necessary not only to have a very large and muscular hand, but to have very lithe and flexible arm muscles, for the arm is moving rapidly while the twist is given, and there must be no antagonistic muscular action. Further, I believe that part of the secret was due to the fact that Stott bowled from a standing position. Given these things, the rest is merely a question of long and assiduous practice. The human mechanism is marvellously adaptable. I have seen Stott throw a cricket ball half across the room with sufficient spin on the ball to make it shoot back to him along the carpet.

I have mentioned the wind as a factor in obtaining the swerve. It was a head-wind that Stott required. I have seen him, for sport, toss a cricket ball into the teeth of a gale, and make it describe the trajectory of a badly sliced golf-ball. This is why the big pavilion at Ailesworth is set at such a curious angle to the ground. It was built in the winter following Hampdenshire's second season of first-class cricket, and it was so placed that when the wickets were pitched in a line with it, they might lie south-west and north-east, or in the direction of the prevailing winds.

The first time I ever saw Ginger Stott, was on the occasion of the historic encounter with Surrey; Hampdenshire's second engagement in first-class cricket. The match with Notts, played at Trent Bridge a few days earlier, had not foreshadowed any startling results. The truth of the matter is that Stott had been kept, deliberately, in the background; and as matters turned out his services were only required to finish off Notts' second inings. Stott was even then a marked man, and the Hampdenshire captain did not wish to advertise his methods too freely before the Surrey match. Neither Archie Findlater, who was captaining the team that year, nor any other person, had the least conception of how unnecessary such a reservation was to prove. In his third year, when Stott had been studied by every English, Australian, and South African batsman of any note, he was still as unplayable as when he made his début in first-class cricket.

I was reporting the Surrey match for two papers, and in company with poor Wallis interviewed Stott before the first innings.

His appearance made a great impression on me. I have, of course, met him, and talked with him many times since then, but my most vivid memory of him is the picture recorded in the inadequate professional dressing-room of the old Ailesworth pavilion.

I have turned up the account of my interview in an old press-cutting book, and I do not know that I can do better than quote that part of it which describes Stott's personal appearance. I wrote the account on the off chance of being able to get it taken. It was one of my lucky hits. After that match, finished in a single day, my interview afforded copy that any paper would have paid heavily for, and gladly.

Here is the description:

'Stott – he is known to everyone in Ailesworth as "Ginger" Stott – is a short, thick-set young man, with abnormally long arms that are tanned a rich red up to the elbow. The tan does not, however, obliterate the golden freckles with which arm and face are richly speckled. There is no need to speculate as to the *raison d'être* of his nickname. The hair of his head, a close, short crop, is a pale russet, and the hair on his hands and arms is a yellower shade of the same colour. "Ginger" is, indeed, a perfectly apt description. He has a square chin and a thin-lipped, determined mouth. His eyes are a clear, but rather light blue, his forehead is good, broad, and high, and he has a well-proportioned head. One might have put him down as an engineer, essentially intelligent, purposeful, and reserved.'

The description is journalistic, but I do not know that I could improve upon the detail of it. I can see those queer, freckled, hairy arms of his as I write – the combination of colours in them produced an effect that was almost orange. It struck one as unusual . . .

Surrey had the choice of innings, and decided to bat, despite the fact that the wicket was drying after rain, under the influence of a steady south-west wind and occasional bursts of sunshine. Would any captain in Stott's second year have dared to take first innings under such conditions? The question is farcical now, but not a single member of the Hampdenshire Eleven had the least conception that the Surrey captain was deliberately throwing away his chances on that eventful day.

Wallis and I were sitting together in the reporters' box. There were only four of us: two specials – Wallis and myself – a news-agency reporter, and a local man.

'Stott takes first over,' remarked Wallis, sharpening his pencil and arranging his watch and scoresheet – he was very meticulous in his methods. 'They've put him to bowl against the wind. He's medium right, isn't he?'

'Haven't the least idea,' I said. 'He volunteered no information; Hampdenshire have been keeping him dark.'

Wallis sneered. 'Think they've got a find, eh?' he said. 'We'll wait and see what he can do against first-class batting.'

We did not have to wait long.

As usual, Thorpe and Harrison were first wicket for Surrey, and Thorpe took the first ball.

It bowled him. It made his wicket look as untidy as any wicket I have ever seen. The off stump was out of the ground, and the other two were markedly divergent.

'Damn it, I wasn't ready for him,' we heard Thorpe say in the professionals' room. Thorpe always had some excuse, but on this occasion it was justified.

C.V. Punshon was the next comer, and he got his first ball through the slips for four, but Wallis looked at me with a raised eyebrow.

'Punshon didn't know a lot about that,' he said, and then he added, 'I say, what a queer delivery the chap has. He stands and shoots 'em out. It's uncanny. He's a kind of human catapult.' He made a note of the phrase on his pad.

Punshon succeeded in hitting the next ball, also, but it simply ran up his bat into the hands of short slip.

'Well, that's a sitter, if you like,' said Wallis. 'What's the matter with 'em?'

I was beginning to grow enthusiastic.

'Look here, Wallis,' I said, 'this chap's going to break records.'
Wallis was still doubtful.

He was convinced before the innings was over.

There must be many who remember the startling poster that heralded the early editions of the evening papers:

SURREY
ALL OUT
FOR 13 RUNS

For once sub-editors did not hesitate to give the score on the contents bill. That was a proclamation which would sell. Inside, the headlines were rich and varied. I have an old paper by me, yellow now, and brittle, that may serve as a type for the rest. The headlines are as follows:

SURREY AND HAMPDENSHIRE

EXTRAORDINARY BOWLING
PERFORMANCE

DOUBLE HAT-TRICK

SURREY ALL OUT IN 35 MINUTES
FOR 13 RUNS

STOTT TAKES 10 WICKETS FOR 5

The 'double hat-trick' was six consecutive wickets, the last six, all clean bowled.

'Good God!' Wallis said, when the last wicket fell, and he looked at me with something like fear in his eyes. 'This man will have to be barred; it means the end of cricket.'

I need not detail the remainder of the match. Hampdenshire hit up ninety-three – P.H. Evans was top scorer with twenty-seven – and then got Surrey out a second time for forty-nine.

I believe Stott did not bowl his best in the second innings. He was quite clever enough to see that he must not overdo it. As Wallis had said, if he were too effective he might have to be barred. As it was, he took seven wickets for twenty-three.

That was Stott's finest performance. On eight subsequent occasions he took all ten wickets in a single innings, once he took nineteen wickets in one match (Hampdenshire *v.* Somerset at Taunton), twice he took five wickets with consecutive balls, and any number of times he did the 'hat-trick,' but he never afterwards achieved so amazing a performance as that of the celebrated Surrey match.

I am still of the opinion that Stott deliberately bowled carelessly in the second innings of that match, but, after watching him on many fields and after a careful analysis of his methods – and character – I am quite certain that his comparative failures in later matches were not due to any purpose on Stott's part.

Take, for instance, the match which Hampdenshire lost to Kent in Stott's second season – their first loss as a first-class county; their record up to that time was thirteen wins and six drawn games. It is incredible to me that Stott should have deliberately allowed Kent to make the necessary one hundred and eighty-seven runs required in the fourth innings. He took five wickets for sixty-three; if he could have done better, I am sure he would have made the effort. He would not have sacrificed his county. I have spoken of the *esprit de corps* which held the Hampdenshire Eleven together, and they were notably proud of their unbeaten record.

No; we must find another reason for Stott's comparative failures. I believe that I am the only person who knows that reason, and I say that Stott was the victim of an obsession. His 'swerve' theory dominated him, he was always experimenting with it, and when, as in the Kent match I have cited, the game was played in a flat calm, his failure to influence the trajectory of the ball in his own peculiar manner, puzzled and upset him. He would strive to make the ball swerve, and in the effort he lost his length and became playable. Moreover, when Stott was hit he lost his temper, and then he was useless. Findlater always took him off the moment he showed signs of temper. The usual sign was a fast full pitch at the batsman's ribs.

I have one more piece of evidence, the best possible, which upholds this explanation of mine, but it must follow the account of Stott's accident.

That accident came during the high flood of Hampdenshire success. For two years they had held undisputed place as champion county, a place which could not be upset by the most ingenious methods of calculating points. They had three times defeated Australia, and were playing four men in the test matches. As a team they were capable of beating any Eleven opposed to them. Not even the newspaper critics denied that.

In this third year of Hampdenshire's triumph, Australia had sent over the finest eleven that had ever represented the colony, but they had lost the first two test matches, and they had lost to Hampdenshire. Nevertheless, they won the rubber, and took back the 'ashes.' No one has ever denied, I believe, that this was due to Stott's accident. There is in this case no room for any one to argue that the argument is based on the fallacy of *post* and *propter*.

The accident appeared insignificant at the time. The match was against Notts on the Trent Bridge ground. I was reporting for three papers; Wallis was not there.

Stott had been taken off. Notts were a poor lot that year and I think Findlater did not wish to make their defeat appear too ignominious. Flower was bowling; it was a fast, true wicket, and Stott, who was a safe field, was at cover.

G. L. Mallinson was batting and making good use of his opportunity; he was, it will be remembered, a magnificent though erratic hitter. Flower bowled him a short-pitched, fast ball, rather wide of the off-stump. Many men might have left it alone, for the ball was rising, and the slips were crowded, but Mallinson timed the ball splendidly, and drove it with all his force. He could not keep it on the ground, however, and Stott had a possible chance. He leaped for it and just touched the ball with his right hand. The ball jumped the ring at its first bound, and Mallinson never even attempted to run. There was a big round of applause from the Trent Bridge ground.

I noticed that Stott had tied a handkerchief round his finger, but I forgot the incident until I saw Findlater beckon to his best bowler, a few overs later. Notts had made enough runs for decency; it was time to get them out.

I saw Stott walk up to Findlater and shake his head, and

through my glasses I saw him whip the handkerchief from his finger and display his hand. Findlater frowned, said something and looked towards the pavilion, but Stott shook his head. He evidently disagreed with Findlater's proposal. Then Mallinson came up, and the great bulk of his back hid the faces of the other two. The crowd was beginning to grow excited at the interruption. Everyone had guessed that something was wrong. All round the ring men were standing up, trying to make out what was going on.

I drew my inferences from Mallinson's face, for when he turned round and strolled back to his wicket, he was wearing a broad smile. Through my field glasses I could see that he was licking his lower lip with his tongue. His shoulders were humped and his whole expression one of barely controlled glee. (I always see that picture framed in a circle; a bioscopic presentation.) He could hardly refrain from dancing. Then little Beale, who was Mallinson's partner, came up and spoke to him, and I saw Mallinson hug himself with delight as he explained the situation.

When Stott unwillingly came into the pavilion, a low murmur ran round the ring, like the buzz of a great crowd of disturbed blue flies. In that murmur I could distinctly trace the signs of mixed feelings. No doubt the crowd had come there to witness the performances of the phenomenon – the abnormal of every kind has a wonderful attraction for us – but, on the other hand, the majority wanted to see their own county win. Moreover, Mallinson was giving them a taste of his abnormal powers of hitting, and the batsman appeals to the spectacular, more than the bowler.

I ran down hurriedly to meet Stott.

'Only a split finger, sir,' he said carelessly, in answer to my question; 'but Mr Findlater says I must see to it.'

I examined the finger, and it certainly did not seem to call for surgical aid. Evidently it had been caught by the seam of the new ball; there was a fairly clean cut about half an inch long on the fleshy underside of the second joint of the middle finger.

'Better have it seen to,' I said. 'We can't afford to lose you, you know, Stott.'

Stott gave a laugh that was more nearly a snarl. 'Ain't the first time I've 'ad a cut finger,' he said scornfully.

He had the finger bound up when I saw him again, but it had been done by an amateur. I learnt afterwards that no antiseptic had been used. That was at lunch time, and Notts had made a hundred and sixty-eight for one wicket; Mallinson was not out, a hundred and three. I saw that the Notts Eleven were in magnificent spirits.

But after lunch Stott came out and took the first over. I don't know what had passed between him and Findlater, but the captain had evidently been over-persuaded.

We must not blame Findlater. The cut certainly appeared trifling, it was not bad enough to prevent Stott from bowling, and Hampdenshire seemed powerless on that wicket without him. It is very easy to distribute blame after the event, but most people would have done what Findlater did in those circumstances.

The cut did not appear to inconvenience Stott in the least degree. He bowled Mallinson with his second ball, and the innings was finished up in another fifty-seven minutes for the addition of thirty-eight runs.

Hampdenshire made two hundred and thirty-seven for three wickets before the drawing of stumps, and that was the end of the match, for the weather changed during the night and rain prevented any further play.

I, of course, stayed on in Nottingham to await results. I saw Stott on the next day, Friday, and asked him about his finger. He made light of it, but that evening Findlater told me over the bridge-table that he was not happy about it. He had seen the finger, and thought it showed a tendency to inflammation. 'I shall take him to Gregory in the morning if it's not all right,' he said. Gregory was a well-known surgeon in Nottingham.

Again one sees, now, that the visit to Gregory should not have been postponed, but at the time one does not take extraordinary precautions in such a case as this. A split finger is such an everyday thing, and one is guided by the average of experience. After all, if one were constantly to make preparation for the abnormal, ordinary life could not go on . . .

I heard that Gregory pursed his lips over that finger when he had learned the name of his famous patient. 'You'll have to be very careful of this, young man,' was Findlater's report of Gregory's advice. It was not sufficient. I often wonder now whether Gregory might not have saved the finger. If he had performed some small operation at once, cut away the poison, it seems to me that the tragedy might have been averted. I am, I admit, a mere layman in these matters, but it seems to me that something might have been done.

I left Nottingham on Saturday after lunch – the weather was hopeless – and I did not make use of the information I had for the purposes of my paper. I was never a good journalist. But I went down to Ailesworth on Monday morning, and found that Findlater and Stott had already gone to Harley Street to see Graves, the King's surgeon.

I followed them, and arrived at Graves's house while Stott was in the consulting-room. I hocussed the butler and waited with the patients. Among the papers, I came upon the famous caricature of Stott in the current number of *Punch* – the 'Stand-and-Deliver' caricature, in which Stott is represented with an arm about ten feet long, and the batsman is looking wildly over his shoulder to square leg, bewildered, with no conception from what direction the ball is coming. Underneath is written 'Stott's New Theory – the Ricochet. Real Ginger.' While I was laughing over the cartoon, the butler came in and nodded to me. I followed him out of the room and met Findlater and Stott in the hall.

Findlater was in a state of profanity. I could not get a sensible word out of him. He was in a white heat of pure rage. The butler, who seemed as anxious as I to learn the verdict, was positively frightened.

'Well, for God's sake tell me what Graves said,' I protested.

Findlater's answer is unprintable, and told me nothing.

Stott, however, quite calm and self-possessed, volunteered the information. 'Finger's got to come off, sir,' he said quietly. 'Doctor says if it ain't off today or tomorrer, he won't answer for my 'and.'

This was the news I had to give to England. It was a great coup from the journalistic point of view, but I made up my three columns with a heavy heart, and the congratulations of my editor only sickened me. I had some luck, but I should never have become a good journalist.

The operation was performed successfully that evening, and Stott's career was closed.

I have already referred to the obsession which dominated Stott after his accident, and I must now deal with that overweening anxiety of his to teach his method to another man.

I did not see Stott again till August, and then I had a long talk with him on the Ailesworth County Ground, as together we watched the progress of Hampdenshire's defeat by Lancashire.

'Oh! I can't learn him *nothing*,' he broke out, as Flower was hit to the four corners of the ground, ' 'alf vollies and long 'ops and then a full pitch – 'e's a disgrace.'

'They've knocked him off his length,' I protested. 'On a wicket like this . . .'

Stott shook his head. 'I've been trying to learn 'im,' he said, 'but he can't never learn. 'E's got 'abits what you can't break 'im of.'

'I suppose it *is* difficult,' I said vaguely.

'Same with me,' went on Stott, 'I've been trying to learn myself to bowl without my finger' – he held up his mutilated hand – 'or left-'anded; but I can't. If I'd started that way . . . No! I'm always feeling for that finger as is gone. A second-class bowler I might be in time, not better nor that.'

'It's early days yet,' I ventured, intending encouragement, but Stott frowned and shook his head.

'I'm not going to kid myself,' he said, 'I know. But I'm going to find a youngster and learn 'im. On'y he must be young.'

'No 'abits, you know,' he explained.

The next time I met Stott was in November. I ran up against him, literally, one Friday afternoon in Ailesworth.

When he recognised me he asked me if I would care to walk out to Stoke-Underhill with him. 'I've took a cottage there,' he explained, 'I'm to be married in a fortnight's time.'

His circumstances certainly warranted such a venture. The proceeds of matinée and benefit, invested for him by the Committee of the County Club, produced an income of nearly two pounds a week, and in addition to this he had his salary as groundsman. I tendered my congratulations.

'Oh! well, as to that, better wait a bit,' said Stott.

He walked with his hands in his pockets and his eyes on the ground. He had the air of a man brooding over some project.

'It *is* a lottery, of course . . .' I began, but he interrupted me.

'Oh that!' he said, and kicked a stone into the ditch; 'take my chances on that. It's the kid I'm thinking on.'

'The kid?' I repeated, doubtful whether he spoke of his fiancée, or whether his nuptials pointed an act of reparation.

'What else 'ud I tie myself up for?' asked Stott. 'I must 'ave a kid of my own and learn 'im from his cradle. It's come to that.'

'Oh! I understand,' I said; 'teach him to bowl.'

'Ah!' replied Stott as an affirmative. 'Learn 'im to bowl from his cradle; before 'e's got 'abits. When I started I'd never bowled a ball in my life, and by good luck I started right. But I can't find another kid over seven years old in England as ain't never bowled a ball o' some sort and started 'abits. I've tried . . .'

'And you hope with your own boys . . .?' I said.

'Not 'ope, it's a cert;' said Stott. 'I'll see no boy of mine touches a ball afore he's fourteen, and then 'e'll learn from me; and learn right. From the first go off.' He was silent for a few seconds, and then he broke out in a kind of ecstasy. 'My Gawd, 'e'll be a bowler such as 'as never been, never in this world. He'll start where I left orf. He'll . . .' Words failed him, he fell back on the expletive he had used, repeating it with an awed fervour. 'My Gawd!'

I had never seen Stott in this mood before. It was a revelation to me of the latent potentialities of the man, the remarkable depth and quality of his ambitions . . .

from THE HAMPDENSHIRE WONDER
1911

WE WANT JESSOP!

by

A.A. Thomson

Before he became primarily a cricket writer in the 1950s, A.A. Thomson (born in 1894) was a novelist and playwright as well as a journalist. His eloquent and mellow writing in such books as Cricket My Pleasure *and* Cricket My Happiness *– as well as his natural hero-worship in* The Great Cricketer *and* Hirst and Rhodes, *for example – are charmingly foreshadowed in this boy's-eye-view of one unforgettable day out.*

The most completely satisfying day of Philip's life was a certain Wednesday towards the end of the summer term. Yorkshire were playing Gloucestershire on the Nidvale county ground and on the third day the Grammar School was given a whole holiday. Dusty Millar was no cricketer, but Mr Freeth, his head assistant, was an old Cambridge Blue and it was freely rumoured that he had talked old Dusty round, persuading him that no boy's education was complete unless he had seen the county of the Graces in action. The unique W.G. no longer played for Gloucestershire, but his halo lingered. Besides, the Gloucestershire eleven contained one name which meant more to Philip's generation than the great W.G. could ever have meant. W.G., with his bulk and his beard, was an authentic god, but his very greatness caused him to be shrouded in Olympian mists. To the schoolboy, a Titan is nearer than a god. Grace was Zeus, but Jessop was Prometheus, a being, heroic but human, whom all could see and worship. Every boy in England thought his own county the best, but every boy outside Gloucestershire thought Gloucestershire the second best. And the reason for this second preference was one name. Gilbert Leese Jessop.

Philip did not dare to admit at home that the school had holiday and that masters and boys had abandoned themselves to an orgy of laking. If he had made such a confession, Aunt Annie would have kept him at home to chop sticks and do extra piano-practice. Fancy chopping orange-goxes or playing Czerny's Exercises while G.L. Jessop was in the town! Uncle Roger could be told, of course. Boot-brushing that morning had all the thrill of a Jacobite conspiracy.

'Ay, tha mun see Jessop,' said Uncle Roger. He said it eagerly but with a shade of wistfulness. 'It'll be summat to tell thy children and thy children's children. Do you know, Philip, as true as I'm standin' beside this copper, I once saw Jessop hit a six through the slips. And off George Hirst, too, may the Lord forgive him.'

'But what shall I do at dinner-time?' asked Philip agitatedly. 'The lunch-hour isn't till half-past one and I don't want to miss a minute.'

Uncle Roger pondered this problem.

'Don't thee worrit,' he said at last. 'I'll fix it wi' thy Aunt Polly to give thee a bit o' summat in a paper-bag. Tell thy Aunt Annie t'schoolmaster said all t'lads had to take their dinners with 'em today. That wouldn't be tellin' a walloper, would it?'

'No,' agreed Philip, feeling that this statement, though disingenuous, was not technically a falsehood.

'And hasta got thy tanner for t'gate?'

'Yes, Uncle, I've been saving for – for a long time.'

'Well, good luck, lad, and I hope tha sees Jessop make ninety-nine.'

(Sportsman as he was, Uncle Roger could not quite bring himself to suggest that even Jessop should make a century against Yorkshire.)

'Only think on and don't be late home for tea, or t'band'll play.'

Philip left home in the usual way at twenty-minutes to nine, as though he were going to morning school. In his satchel was a package containing bread and cheese and two slices of cold fried spotted dick. He had made the confession about not coming home to dinner to Aunt Polly, while Aunt Annie was upstairs, and Aunt Polly's insistence on packing him a bulky parcel, had almost sent him into a high fever, lest Aunt Annie should come downstairs before he could get away. Why did Aunt Polly think food so important? He would have gone without dinner for a week, rather than miss a minute of this match.

But now he was safely out of the house and the sun was shining in benison upon Jessop's day. He walked past the school and then making a wide circuit, walked up the long avenue at the west end of the town that led to the cricket ground. The high white boarding that surrounded the field gleamed in the morning sun. Sometimes on Saturday afternoons he had peeped through cracks in this fencing, but he was no peeping Peri today. His hand clutched a sixpence and four hot pennies in his trousers-pocket. It was still only a few minutes after nine and the big gates were shut, but presently he saw a man in a bowler hat open a little side-door. Philip walked in and planked down his sixpence royally.

'Nay, lad,' said the man at the pay-box, 'tha'll have t'County Ground all to thysen.'

Philip walked inside, moving on air. Nidvale cricket twenty-seven years ago was the leisured game of a leisured town. There was no press-whipped scurry or rush for seats, and the ground at nine o'clock was deserted. The fear of Aunt Annie, which had driven him out so early, had its compensations, for now he had a whole county ground to himself. The rows of benches and the two big stands were empty. A little knot of groundsmen were pushing a heavy roller towards the pitch, but no one else was in sight. He drank in the scene, drawing in deep breaths of satisfaction. The Nidvale ground was a small one, but to Philip the expanse of green turf seemed vast. There was the pavilion opposite, gay with flags. There, on the left, was the refreshment-tavern where you bought the regulation cricket-match lunch – a pork-pie and a bottle of stone-ginger. People were beginning to come in now and, to Philip's shocked surprise, he discovered that they were not walking humbly round the boundary railing, as he himself was doing. They were actually walking on the sacred turf. A small holy of holies round the pitch was roped off, but apart from this, it seemed, you could go about the field just as you liked. Scarcely able to believe his eyes, Philip slid under the boundary railing and walked along inside it. Then, as more and more people began to stroll on to the field, he grew bolder and walked out into the middle, where a small number of Nidvale's citizens stood, portentously inspecting the pitch and solemnly shaking their heads over the state of the game. The first innings total had been approximately equal, but Yorkshire had done wretchedly at the second attempt. The overnight total still stood on the scoring-boards. 137 for 7, last man 0. There was a general disposition round the ropes to consider that it was a bad do. Yorkshire should have framed better than that.

'They'll lose by seven wickets,' Philip heard a pessimistic pundit growl. 'Just lakin' at it, like a lot o' lads. They'll set Gloucester nobbut about a hundred and fifty to win, and what's a hundred and fifty to Jessop?'

'Nay,' said his friend, 'they're not beat yet, not while David Denton's still in.'

'Who's Denton?' sneered the pessimist. 'Lucky Denton, I call him. They'll lose by seven wickets, I tell thee, or happen eight.'

It was most alarming to hear this gloomy forecast of Yorkshire's fate, but Philip felt the drama and the thrill of it. Even if the dreadful tragedy of a Yorkshire defeat was to occur, at least he was in the centre of it, on the very stage itself.

The growing crowd began to move slowly towards the pavilion, in front of which a row of nets had been set up, just like the First Eleven nets at school. And now flannelled figures were emerging from the pavilion, strolling carelessly down the steps towards the little wicket gate. Philip did not need his cigarette cards to recognise those heroes with the white rose on their dark caps: Rhodes, lean, lithe and youthful; Hirst, round and jovial, and Tunnicliffe with those amazing long arms that could shoot out like lightning in the slips. The men of Gloucestershire were not so familiar, but there were one or two who stood out. There was Jack Board the stumper and C.L. Townsend, gracefullest of left-handers – gallock-handers or cuddy-wifters, Nidvale called them – and one other. Could it be? Philip knew the features and the cap, but surely the great Jessop should have been bigger. Why, this was what you might almost have called a little man. The players were splitting up into little groups at each net and the crowd was standing respectfully at the side. But Philip had no intention of standing cravenly behind the shelter of a net. He would have entered a lion's cage to catch a glimpse of Jessop. Yes, it was Jessop. As soon as he took his stance at the wicket, you knew. There was only one man in England who crouched like that. He crouched lower than you would have believed possible and as the ball pitched, his body unbent like a steel spring. The ball went flying as though impelled by primaeval fury. In a dream Philip edged nearer and nearer, until he was standing only a yard behind the bowler. Then suddenly, in his dream he heard a voice speaking to him.

'There's an extra ball, sonny.'

Jessop had spoken to him. G.L. Jessop. Nay, more, Jessop was inviting him to bowl at the nets. Almost shuddering with excitement, he picked up the ball. No time to explain that he was not a bowler; had never bowled, even in a Lower School practice match. The ball he delivered was a slow long-hop which scarcely reached the pitch. The steep spring unbent. The ball soared and crashed against the sight-screen at the opposite side of the ground. For ten minutes Philip bowled, solemnly, desperately . . . A bell rang. The spectators began to make for their seats round the boundary. In leisurely fashion the players, laughing and chatting among themselves, started to move back to the pavilion. As G.L. Jessop passed Philip he smiled and said 'Thanks.' It was the perfect romantic episode. ('Tha'll be able to tell thy children and thy children's children.') He smiled and said 'Thanks.' That was all, but Philip knew that he would remember it all his life.

And now he must find his place on the boundary.

Still panting with excitement, he scrambled in with a crowd of Grammar School juniors, squatting on the grass's edge, with feet inside the railings. Another bell rang. He revelled in the ritual of it. The subdued hum of the crowd, the shouts of the boys going round selling Hirst's toffee, the piercing voice of the man selling score-cards, with his fascinating formula: 'I have all on for one penny and the orders of bowlers and batters.' The umpires with their slow deliberate tread, walking as though fully conscious that the fate of worlds lay in their fingers. The fielding team, tossing the ball from hand to hand. A polite cheer for them. Denton and Schofield Haigh, the not-out batsmen. A slightly louder cheer for these two, but still not, on the whole, an enthusiastic cheer. The position is too serious. And then, as Haigh takes centre, dead silence. Yorkshire backs are against the wall.

The slow bowler trots up to the crease. Innocuous-looking stuff. Atkinson, the boy who knows everything, is sitting next to Philip. He is just telling the little crowd of Grammar School boys, huddled near him, that this chap Dennett can't bowl for toffee, when this chap's fifth delivery spread-eagles Haigh's stumps. A reproachful sigh goes round the ground. A thousand voices, blent as one, murmur:

'Na . . . ay, Schofield.'

Eight wickets down. The outlook is grim indeed. There is a loyal cheer for the next batsman, Lord Hawke, but underneath the applause lies the suggestion that responsibilities heavier than rank and wealth lie on his lordship's shoulders. The rank is but the guinea-stamp; fifty runs at this juncture would be the gold for 'a that. Lord Hawke makes two slashing hits and is caught at square-leg. Nine wickets down. The crowd is in the Slough of Despond. Now comes the last man, old David Hunter, the grizzled Yorkshire stumper. Can he stay in while Denton hits a few? Grimmer and grimmer . . . Hunter plays out the over. Atkinson informs the world that Hunter lives at Scarborough and keeps canaries in private life. Denton, at the other end, hits a four and two. The thrills of that brave last-wicket stand. The two Davids . . . Hunter at one end, resolute as an old soldier, solid as a brick wall; Denton, at the other, merry and light-hearted as though he were playing in a Saturday-afternoon game, driving, pulling, cutting with a crispness only to be matched by one of aunt Polly's Yorkshire puddings. Lucky Denton? Happy-hearted, gaily adventurous Denton. Slowly the crowd's tension relaxed. Yorkshire's grip was coming back. The Tyke had got his teeth into the foe again. There was no wild applause for Denton. He was a batsman. That was what he was there for. No Yorkshireman ever praised another Yorkshireman for doing his plain duty. But Hunter, who had no pretentions to batting skill, was doing more than his duty. Every time he blocked a shooter or smothered an evil-looking spinner, he had his meed of praise.

'Stick it, lad! Good owd David!'

The score mounted steadily – 170, 180, 190 – until, just as it seemed that Hunter might reach double figures, he was out. 'Stepping in front of a straight one,' wrote Old Ebor, 'the veteran failed to connect and paid the inevitable penalty.'

During the lunch-hour the ground buzzed with anxious questioning. Gloucester had been left with a mere two hundred to get to win. Was it enough? Could they be dismissed for less? It was all too doubtful.

'They'll do it easy as tumblin' off a house,' said the pessimists.

'You wait till Rhodes has a go at 'em,' said the optimists, but they said it with hope rather than with conviction.

The Gloucestershire innings was no affair for people with weak hearts. From the first ball sent down it surged with a dramatic intensity that even Yorkshire phlegm could scarcely withstand. The first wicket fell at seven and the second at fifteen and the optimists looked at one another meaningly. They were not going to say anything yet, but they were all registering the same cautious determination. If things should be going equally well in an hour's time, they would mutter: 'What did I tell thee?'

Then followed a long, stonewalling stand in which bat fought in desperate defence against ball. Hirst was bowling with dynamic energy, the embodiment of fierce aggression. At the other end was Rhodes, graceful in action, immaculate in length, matchless in cunning. Could any batsman face this combination and live? The two men of Gloucester, harassed by this deadly attack and beset by fieldsmen ringed on tiptoe round the bat's edge, looked as if they might succumb at any moment, but by some miracle they survived. Play was dead slow but never for an instant dull. The attack was too keen for that. Philip sat spellbound, arms clasped tight about his knees, eyes glued to the pitch. He was witnessing, not a game, but a spectacle of high art and mortal combat. By ones and twos the score crept along. For a full hour the batsmen defended their wickets with a kind of forlorn heroism, fighting against overwhelming odds. It had to end at last. A snick. A yell. The giant Tunnicliffe in the slips shot out an arm, long as the arm of coincidence. Thirty-five for three. ('What did I tell thee?') And then Jessop came in, running the last ten yards to the wickets. There were white marks on Philip's brown knees where his hands so fiercely clasped them.

If you should visit the pretty little Nidvale cricket ground today, beware of sitting next to any man over forty years of age. It is ten to one that he saw that innings of Jessop's. If he did, it is a thousand to one that he will describe it to you, ball by ball, for it lives ineradicably in the mind of every man or boy who saw it, a St. Crispin's day of cricket, freshly remembered at nearly thirty years' distance. Vainly will you stuff your fingers in your ears. You will be in the presence of one who has looked on glory and seen a great light.

That innings of Jessop's . . . It was not an innings. It was a glamour; it was witchery; it was thunder and lightning. The Croucher bent almost double. The steel spring snapped viciously. The ball sped, as though hurled to everlasting punishment. It was not Ajax defying the lightning. It was Ajax catching the lightning and insolently flinging it back in the face of heaven. Fieldsmen who, a moment before, had been practically leaning against the bat's face, went scurrying back to the boundary-edge. They were at the mercy of elemental force. For thirty-three minutes the might of Yorkshire was impotent. Rhodes was a schoolboy. Hirst a village-green trundler.

Old men will show you the marks on the face of the pavilion clock which Jessop's second sixer shattered. They will point out the exact spot in Copperbeech Avenue where the hansom cab was standing at the moment when Jessop's third stupendous sixer fell through its roof. That crowded half-hour was hardly cricket; it was divine madness. The telegraph-board moved like a cinema-film till even the ranks of Tuscany – and there is nothing quite as Tuscan in the world as a Yorkshire cricket crowd – could scarce forbear to cheer. In those thirty-three minutes Jessop's partner made four runs. Jessop made eighty-nine. Then, in the height of his glory, Haigh clean bowled him. After the bails flew, there was for at least five seconds, a silence, dazed and palpable. Then a hysterical roar rent the sky. Jessop was out. Lucifer had fallen. Rhodes took the remaining six wickets for nineteen, in the manner of a lion-hunter rather reluctantly potting rabbits, and at the end of this tame anti-climax, Yorkshire had won by fifty-two.

The crowd would not go home. They surged round the pavilion gate, gaping at the smashed clock and yelling: 'We want Jessop!' Pushed and jostled, Philip was carried along with the others. He was in a trance of pure delight. Vaguely he heard his own voice, strange and cracked, shouting with the others, 'We want Jess . . . op, we want Jess . . .op!'

When he came back to earth, he was aimlessly wandering down Copperbeech Avenue. For the last three hours time and space had not existed, but now they were returning swiftly, remorselessly. Time . . . Joshua had commanded the sun and moon to stand still in the valley of Ajalon. Jessop had smashed the clock. But time did not stand still. What time was it?

With sinking heart he fired the agitated question at a passing postman.

'Please can you tell me the right time?'

'Half-past six, lad, or rather better.'

Half-past six. And tea was at half-past five. He was already an hour late and a good twenty minutes from home. Dully he remembered Uncle Roger's words: 'Only think on, don't be late for tea, or t'band'll play.'

from THE EXQUISITE BURDEN
1935

‘I TOOK UP RHODES’ BAT’

by

Stanley Shaw

On the third morning of The Oval Test, 13 August 1902, Sherlock Holmes is called in by no less a person than Lord Hawke, accompanied by Mr Alcock, the Surrey secretary, to investigate the disappearance of Wilfred Rhodes. Rhodes has been reported missing by George Hirst (‘not out’ overnight) who was staying at the same hotel.

Sherlock Holmes has with him John Fairhurst (who tells the story) whom he met accidentally the night before. Since the kidnapper must surely be on the ground Holmes’ plan is to reveal his identity by making it appear that Rhodes is in truth batting. How fortunate it is that Fairhurst so closely resembles Rhodes, even though he is an Australian.

I took up Rhodes’ bat. It was a Crawford’s – a popular make – and it looked as if it had been well looked after, despite having seen a great deal of use. I was glad it was not a fearfully heavy bat, such as the blacksmiths and stonemasons back home used to wield.

As I made a few airy practice shots with it I recalled the knobstick I had fooled about with in Holmes’ sitting-room at Baker Street, indulging a whimsical fancy that I was Australia’s No. 11, arriving at the crease with only four runs needed for a famous victory in a Test Match against England. I recalled my arrogant driving of the first ball to the boundary. Fantasy now trembled on the brink of being translated into reality. The trouble was that, in the process, something had got terribly distorted.

It could, surely, not be right that I should score the winning run for England.

Ten minutes later, with great suddenness, the door burst open. Lord Hawke entered, followed by Sherlock Holmes.

'Lilley's out. Played like a hero. Fifteen runs to win. Are you ready?' He stared at my changed appearance. 'By George, you could be his twin brother. By the way, are you a right-hander?'

I nodded, and opened my mouth to say that I was also an Australian, but I was not quick enough.

'Thank the Lord for that! Rhodes bowls with his left and bats with his right. Listen, young man! I've managed to get a message to George Hirst. The message says: 'Lord Hawke says Play On.' Now if he says anything to you when you get there, just repeat the message. Don't linger. Hirst is a great talker, given half a chance. Get straight to the crease and take guard. Middle and leg. Put your gloves on as you walk to the wicket. Where's your cap? Put your cap on. Right! Come along!'

And so I went along. I went out to bat for England.

With bat and batting gloves in hand, I, the puppet, followed the two puppet-masters down the corridor and round and about until we had to force a way through the throng of high-spirited Members at the top of the stairs. It was a rowdy reception, with salutations and shouts of encouragement bombarding my ears from all sides, and it was startling to hear 'Good old Rhodes!' chorused at me. The masquerade had met its first challenge and was holding up well.

Suddenly I noticed that I was alone, the puppet-masters having halted. I had felt a pat on the shoulder and that was all. Trembling in the legs I went down the few remaining steps and stepped on to the green turf of the Kennington Oval. It was close-cropped and yielded excitingly to my tread. The atmosphere crackled with high-tension electricity, and the hubbub was frightening. Twenty thousand pairs of eyes were fixed upon me and it made me feel distinctly uneasy. The applause was for the real Wilfred Rhodes who, although he had not been among the wickets in this, the Fifth Test, had performed very creditably in the other four Tests. In the First Test he and George Hirst had shot out Australia for 36 runs on a rain-affected pitch.

When I had my gloves firmly fitted on I tried to get my bearings. I saw that all but one or two of the fielding side were looking straight at me as I approached. It made me drop my head, but I jerked it back up defiantly. I tried to locate Saunders and Trumble, who were to bowl to me. I had seen them at Melbourne the year before and could recognize them well enough. I saw Trumble, who was nearly a foot taller than me, standing beside one of the umpires. He it was who was to bowl to me when I got to the crease.

My legs wobbled when I saw the thickset, padded-up figure of George Hirst, my batting partner, sauntering over to intercept me and I realised that it was he, not Hugh Trumble, who was to be the first bogeyman I had to overcome. He came right up to me so that we stood face to face, only a foot apart. His expression was one of amazement. 'Who the hell are *you*!' he said.

I leapt in at once and hissed at him, in an undertone: 'Lord Hawke says Play On!' With that I left him, strode to the wicket and busied myself taking guard. A legend grew up that the words spoken at this brief, but historic confrontation had been: 'We'll get 'em in singles!'

I stood in my ground, bat pointing to the heavens, and casually glanced round, taking note of the fielding positions – for all the world as if I had been doing it, season after season, in front of many thousands of people, ever since my voice had broken. I heard the umpire call out 'One to come!' and was profoundly thankful. The close-in field crouched menacingly, and there was an abatement of the deep humming from the encircling crowd of spectators.

The gaunt figure of Trumble loped up to the wicket and bowled a well-pitched-up ball. I reached forward, met it in the meaty middle of a correctly angled bat and it dropped safely in front of me. A feeling of wild relief and well-being swept over me. Perhaps I would not be called upon to face another ball. George Hirst could knock off the fifteen runs and he could shield me from the bowling – White Beard had said that he was a pastmaster at shielding a less experienced partner from hostile bowling, and I had seen him do just that when batting with

Lockwood. However, I knew that if I did have to face a few more balls – say, one or two – it would be necessary for me to make a good showing, in case Doctor Redthorn entertained any suspicions that I was an impostor.

The field changed over. I glanced at George Hirst and was disconcerted to see that he was staring hard at me. Poor devil, I thought – he must be in the same state of bewilderment that I had been in for the past forty-five minutes – ever since I had walked into the Club Secretary's office and found all eyes scrutinizing me. At least I now knew what was happening. Hirst didn't have the remotest idea. He must be thinking the world had gone mad.

It was not Saunders, but Noble who was to bowl the next over to Hirst, and, while he was pacing out his run-up, I lectured myself about backing up. I must concentrate and listen for my partner's calls. I had had some dire experiences at home in Bairnsdale, running myself out and, what was far worse – almost a hanging offence – running my partner out. I grounded my bat behind the crease, flexed my legs and was keyed up to go.

It was as well I was ready because Noble's first ball was pushed wide of close-in cover and Hirst called sharply – 'ONE!' – and I bolted down the wicket.

As I pulled up I was surprised to hear a great roar from the crowd; it was only when I saw my partner give a modest wave of the bat in the approved fashion that it dawned on me that he had reached his fifty. An emotional wave of admiration rolled over me. I might be a renegade Australian but I could appreciate a gritty, fighting, rearguard innings, so I stuck my bat under my arm and banged my gloved hands together in company with the Aussie fielders. It was what Wilfred Rhodes would have done, unless he were an awfully cold fish. It struck me that had I foozled that solitary ball I had received from Trumble, George Hirst would not be standing there, enjoying the ovation.

The noise subsided. Now I was at the batting end and had to forget about ovations, concentrate my mind and face the bowling of Noble, classified as a medium-pacer. Yes, a medium-pacer in first-class cricket but, to me, a club cricketer, that ball he had just bowled to Hirst had seemed like a rocket. I must keep bat and pad together – three slips and gulley were crouched, breathing down my neck.

Noble ran up with swift, smooth strides. The ball scorched down at me and hardly had I raised my bat than I felt it nick the outside edge. I jerked my head back over my right shoulder and glimpsed the slips in disarray, all lunging. It took a second or two for me to realise that the ball had flown past second slip's cap to the boundary. I had scored four runs – wonder of wonders! No credit to me, but no matter.

The four remaining balls of the over were all nightmares in their own way. The first was a yorker that struck my left boot. I felt a searing pain in my big toe and hopped about and stamped my foot on the ground. I nearly swore an Australian oath. I had no idea where the ball had gone and whether a run had gone begging. I saw Hirst – when the ball was dead – take a few steps up the pitch to me, so rather than run the risk of another confrontation with him I took up my stance at the crease, defied the painful toe and that prompted everyone to go back to their positions.

I was still wincing when I got the second ball. I tried to get my bat out of the way but I got an edge – a thin one this time. I looked back in time to see it drop out of Warwick Armstrong's left hand. It had bisected Armstrong and the 'keeper, and it had to be judged an awfully difficult chance. I breathed again.

The third ball reared up and terrified the life out of me. I got my bat up but the ball hit me on the back of the wrist, dropped and fell between my leg and the flap of my pad. As I fished it out and tossed it to the 'keeper, did I actually grin? I should have liked an adjournment for a few minutes so that I might have alternately stamped my foot and rubbed my sore wrist, but it was not an option – Noble was moving smoothly in for the kill. My character was about to be searched again.

The last ball of that torrid over I played forward to but failed to connect – it went clean through and must have shaved the leg-stump. The crowd gasped, fearing that a bail might have been dislodged. 'AAAaaaaah!' It was uncanny. They were living every moment of it alongside me. The whole drama of life was compressed into that seething area, and only the six grey gas-holders that brooded over the ground were indifferent. I glanced back and there was my right toe securely anchored behind the crease. I may not have connected with the ball, but I had gone through the motions of playing it correctly. Could a young, highly-trained amateur do more?

The field briskly changed over and Trumble bowled to Hirst. He dabbed at the ball – I heard him call 'ONE!' and catapulted forward. Now I was angry. What had happened to the pastmaster of the art of shielding the bowling from the more inexperienced player? Talk about 'farming' the bowling. He simply didn't believe in it. I had to face another five deliveries while he leaned on his bat.

I thumped my bat into the mark I had made. Six or seven thumps relieved my feelings. I settled down. Trumble loped up and bowled. It was a straight and well-pitched-up ball and, although I felt afterwards I could have driven it, I played limply forward and it came to rest a few feet in front of me, swooped on by a fielder. I made up my mind that if I got an identical delivery I would drive it; Trumble, being so tall, might not be able to get down quickly enough to stop it shooting past him to the long-off boundary. (What a fool I was to think that the great Hugh Trumble would bowl two consecutive balls alike.)

What I thought was an identical delivery came down and I went to drive. I failed to connect properly and it cocked up dangerously. Trumble jack-knifed, strained forward to reach it and missed it by inches. 'AAAaaaah!' Twenty thousand hearts stopped beating for an instant.

The next ball was a yorker. I stabbed down on it and mercifully kept it out. The next two were short, breaking away sharply to leg, but I wouldn't be tempted to go for any kind of pull shot. I knew I was at that stage in my duels with the two bowlers when they were setting out to tempt me and, if that failed, to intimidate me. It crossed my mind, as the field crossed, that the Aussie captain might bring Saunders back into the attack. A shudder ran through me at the thought. He was the fast-bowling spearhead of the attack. He had been savaged and demoralised by Jessop, and had been taken off and replaced by Monty Noble. I did not want to see him back, gunning for me.

In the next over, to my amazement, Hirst, for the third successive time, took a scurried single off the first delivery, leaving me to face the rest. If it hadn't been for the gravity of the situation I should have thought it funny, and I should have made an ironic bow in Hirst's direction. I certainly faced Noble with trepidation, remembering the last ball I had had from him, the one that had gone straight through me. I had to watch for the ball that swung into me, aiming to go through the gate.

I played the first two in classic style and, perhaps, played them so well that the bowler got annoyed and tried a couple of bouncers, but my wicket stayed intact. Provided the lightning ducking of my head was not going to rick my neck, I would stay intact as well. Had the bowler known that I have an aversion to playing the hook shot he would not have wasted two missiles from his armoury. I will say again that Noble was a medium-pacer, but he was undoubtedly bowling flat out, and it must be borne in mind that I was only a useful club cricketer who had not touched a bat for six months, batting in a poorish light on a wearing pitch – to say nothing of being encircled by a frenzied crowd. I was batting to hold my end up. As I saw it, it was my partner's responsibility to advance the score.

In the next over – Trumble bowling to Hirst – he took his single *again* – but this time off the second ball of the over. So I faced the third ball and it was a shooter, at which I played and inevitably made no contact. The crowd gasped. It was my second stump-shaver, but I believe Hirst would not have fared any better with such a treacherous delivery. Unexpectedly, I got a single off the next ball, poking at and touching one that veered away to leg. When I got to the other end I saw that Hirst had put a firm hand up. I had thought there might have been two in it but my vastly experienced partner was taking no risks of a run-out. His vetoing a second run was the first thing he had done that I approved of.

The next ball Hirst met so sweetly in the middle that mid-on failed to gather it – it really sped from the bat. We started to run and I made my ground easily. Fortuitously, there were two in it. The fielder had thrown wildly to the 'keeper but it never reached him, deflecting off Hirst's shoulder and running twenty yards or so behind the slips. I was surprised to see a grin – almost a laugh – on my partner's face as we crossed. The last ball of the over was neatly dabbed away for a quick single and I was not unhappy about that. It was the first time Hirst had deliberately shielded me from the bowling. It was a luxury.

Before Noble was permitted to run up, however, Hirst embarked upon a series of preparatory acts. Perhaps he wanted to break the bowler's rhythm. He took a new guard. He surveyed the field placings, standing and pointing his bat heavenwards as if he had just arrived at the crease. He stared at the scoreboard, after which he made a signal to me, showing three fingers. I had not troubled with the scoreboard because I had never been sure what total we were aiming for, and I had not been keeping a tally of the runs we had scored since I had come in. His signal I interpreted as meaning that we were within three runs of victory. The crowd knew it well enough and their excitement was at fever-pitch.

Lastly, Hirst stared at the sky and, at that moment, I felt a few spots of rain on my cheek. The clouds were low and leaden in colour, and I guessed it might be raining in earnest in five or ten minutes. Looking at it realistically, however, I could not see play being abandoned at this stage of the game, with three runs wanted for victory, unless a downpour of monsoon proportions descended upon the ground. The crowd would never have stood for it. There would have been a riot.

Hirst indicated that he was ready. Four balls were bowled in a pretty negative way, outside the leg stump. The batsman was not having any. His method was strictly defensive and there was no daylight to be seen between his bat and his body. He was waiting, with true Yorkshire patience, for the ball that could be struck safely. The fifth was a faster ball, wide outside the off. Hirst stared challengingly at the umpire, but no wide was signalled. Before the last ball was bowled Noble and his skipper stood, hugger-mugger, for a time; after which a wave of the skipper's arm brought fielders closer in.

Noble bowled a well-pitched-up ball and Hirst went to drive with his minimal back-lift. He played at it a shade too early. Noble leapt up, his fingers straining, but failed to reach it. At the same time, mid-on tore across, dived and got it into his hands *at first bounce*. I did not have a clear view of the escape, as Hirst and I were scampering a single. The crowd, not unnaturally, thought it was a clean catch and that awful groan chilled the air – followed by an ecstatic roar of relief when they saw that the umpire's hands remained clasped behind his back. Three runs for victory had been cut to two runs for victory. I stood, vastly contented, at the non-striker's end once again. That was the end for me.

It was now raining, but not heavily. My view of the matter now was that it was all up to my partner. It rested with him. Surely, with the fielders pressing in so closely, it would be a simple matter for him to pierce the field and we could run an easy two for victory? I saw, out of the corner of my eye, that the crowd, wild with excitement, were encroaching upon the arena. Figures of small boys were darting forward and darting back.

With the rain falling Hirst dispensed with elaborate precautions. Now, the very last thing I wanted him to do was to push at the first ball and call for a single. He pushed. I heard him call 'ONE!' *I could not believe it!* He had done precisely what I had dreaded. As I set off to run I felt the strength drain out of my legs. The crowd noise battered my ear-drums.

As I pulled up, after gaining the crease, I saw the figure of a spectator hurtling towards the middle. He came to within twenty yards of the wicket and then he was headed off by a couple of fielders who grabbed him round the waist. To my amazement I saw that he sported a dog-collar. It was a clergyman! Of course, I thought – that single had drawn us level. He thinks the winning hit has been made.

Drawn us level. *Us? Us?* What am I saying? The old, nagging uncertainty about my identity, and the ethics of my playing for England against my native land, returned to plague me. I had to accept, now that we had run that single, Hirst and I – that the drama had been so contrived that the knife had found its way into my hand, and it was I who was called upon to strike with it. I had to strike at my own blood-brothers.

Suddenly there was George Hirst, right at my elbow. He had walked up the pitch while I had been watching the clergyman being led away. 'What's going on then?'

A surge of irritation swept over me. What a time to choose for explanations. 'Lord Hawke says Play On!' I hissed at him, as before – and added: 'Don't breathe a *word*!'

I saw his eyes blinking at me. I gazed all around me, trying to convey that we had to get on with the game. Perhaps, with rainwater trickling down my cheek like tears, I presented a pathetic spectacle. Mercifully, he at last turned and shuffled his way back to his end.

Now, in my view, Hirst, batting at No. 8 – having made 43 in the first innings and standing unbeaten with 58 to his credit in the second – ought to have chanced his arm with a drive or a pull. (I did not know then that chancing one's arm was not the Yorkshire way of meeting a crisis.) He had left me, yet again, with five balls to deal with. Hang it all! I had done everything Holmes had wanted. I had suffered my chin to be shaved. I had donned shirt, sweater, pads and gloves and walked, with as much *sang-froid* as I could muster, to the very rim of the volcano and faced five overs of Test-class bowling. Holmes had said not a word about going out to win the game for England. He was only concerned with the success of his stratagem.

I took up my guard. The gaunt, remorseless figure of Trumble ran up to bowl. It was a full toss that came so quickly to me I was content to see it right on to my bat, left wrist limp. The fielders uncoiled, vastly disappointed.

The next ball broke a huge distance and went harmlessly to the 'keeper on the leg side.

The next I looked at too long and came down very late on. It occurred to me I was in danger of making the same mistake Lockwood had made – allowing himself to be forced back on the right foot, seeking the advantage of being able to look for the turn of the ball. I gritted my teeth. It had to be forward play when in doubt. I dreaded the thump of the ball on the left pad and the screamed appeals for leg before.

A fleet-footed twelfth man had run on to the field and deposited a double handful of sawdust just where Trumble started his run up. Trumble took half a minute to attempt to dry the ball. Not to be outdone I rubbed and dried my glove-palms on my trousers. Inside my gloves my hands were sweating but that mattered little.

Trumble was ready to bowl. He pitched one well up to me. I was leaning forward like the prow of a ship, resolved to play forward whatever happened. *This was the ball for it.* I drove it in the direction of mid-on, but a touch wide of his right hand. He would not reach it. I started running.

As Hirst and I crossed he shouted to me but the words were lost in the inferno of noise from all round the ground. As I reached the crease the umpire put his hand on my back and urged me forward. It took me a second or two to realise he was urging me to run for the pavilion so as to escape being engulfed by the spectators, now flooding all over the playing area.

from SHERLOCK HOLMES AT THE 1902 FIFTH TEST
1985

VERSUS AUSTRALIA

by

B. and C.B. Fry

'If A Mother's Son *had been a simple collaboration between Charles and Beatrice Fry (his wife),' writes Clive Ellis in his biography of Fry, 'it would certainly have been a more satisfying book than it turned out to be, unbalanced by distinctly unhelpful editorial intervention.' Nonetheless it contains vibrant accounts of hunting and especially of Mark Lovell's Test début.*

Mark's selection comes as something of a surprise. But his excellent performance in the field and as a bowler in Australia's first innings of 377 is followed by his shaping better than most of his seniors when England collapse for 151. As a result his distinguished captain . . .

Mark was taking off his pads when his veteran captain came to him, and said, 'Don't take 'em off, Lovell,' and lumbered off on his nailed boots without other comment. A minute or two more and Mark was telling his mother that the thing he'd never dreamed of had come to pass – he was going in first with the greatest cricketer in the world.

As those two, the veteran giant, and the lithe, slim youth appeared on the green, there were some who appreciated in a degree greater than ever before, the magic and poetry of cricket. The veteran, they knew, felt no alarm at the large score against him; and the young man, they thought, looked as if he meant to hit-off the runs within the hour. No more confident pair ever came through the wicket-gate at Lord's than the two amateurs, the veteran and the youth, who led the follow-on for England.

'Well played; I forgot you'd won the Matechley steeplechase,' said the veteran, smoothing his grizzled beard and twinkling at Mark; 'you don't mind stiff going, eh?'

'It's all right with a good start,' answered Mark.

'Well, don't run 'em too short,' said the veteran cheerily, as if he had no idea of getting out otherwise. 'I'm not quite your class on the cinder-path, you know. But play your own game again.'

The sun had come out during the luncheon hour; the clouds had fallen away from the central heaven; and Mark noticed with delight that the wicket looked firm and true now the heavy roller had been over it.

From the first moment of that follow-on, the confidence and the luck were with England. The veteran made six in the first over; and Mark retorted with eight. The third over added six again to the veteran's score; and Mark hit three swinging boundaries in the fourth. Thirty-two runs in less than fifteen minutes!

After this, excitement and cheerfulness reigned supreme. The crowd could see the bristling confidence in the long square face of the veteran, and the alert determination in the ever-quick athletic movement of the capless Oxonian. There was a feeling all round the green of hope, confidence, and good-humour.

Mark played the more vigorous game of the two. His mind had not yet learned the restrained enterprise of a long-experienced batsman; he had no thought of wearing down the bowlers. His one thought was to watch each ball with all his might and then to hit it – hard. He had reached his fifty, when the captain stood at twenty-eight. He hit with the most consummate and unerring truth; only once did he lift the ball, all his strokes were in front of the wicket and along the ground; timing perfection; his wrists seemed to manage his bat at the last fraction of a second as if his bat itself had eyes. The man who had been chosen for his slow bowling was proving himself one of the fastest scorers that had ever faced Australian bowlers. Mark had struck one of those wonderful days when the bat can do no wrong, when the ball is so plain to see, and hand and eye are in electric sympathy.

Then the captain, having settled down, and getting the larger share of the bowling, began to gain on Mark's score. The crowd almost forgot Mark in its joy of witnessing one of the veteran's best innings. He played with all his old mastery, his consummate assurance, his unruffled calm. Only those perhaps who have actually bowled to him, know the masterful strength of his cricket, the breadth of his bat. Spectators see the result of his stroke, they can hardly see the stroke itself. With what force, with what frowning certainty, he did the unexpected!

'I puts the ball where I chooses,' quoted an old man, sitting near the far screen, 'and he puts it where he chooses.' And he laughed long and chucked his chin at such wonderful cricket.

Beautiful solid drives; amazing pulls to square leg; sudden and heavy late cuts, from a guiding pressure of the bat; straight balls dragged to leg, perfectly intended – all these master strokes followed each other in quick succession. The crowd could see the ruddy face glowing ruddier, the dark eyes shining darker under the bushy eyebrows, and they laughed to see him laughing with the wicket-keeper as he balanced his bat towards point, waiting for the return of the ball from the boundary.

And how firmly he settled himself on his right foot, left toe cocked, before he turned his frowning eyes full-square to the bowler again.

One hundred and twenty-six for no wicket. The veteran sixty-four, and Mark sixty-two. Mark added now a three, and now a single to his score; the veteran crept on with fours, twos and singles, forging ahead till his score was ninety-eight.

Mark began an over with his score at eighty-four. Would they both reach the century? asked the delighted crowd.

Mark had no idea what was his score, or what was the veteran's; he never looked at the board, and he had no thought of rivalry. The first ball of that over, a good-length on the leg stump, he stepped out at, and lifted it clean and skimming first bounce over the ropes. A roar of delight went up from the crowd. The second ball he drove to the 'on' for four, the third ball he turned to leg for another four, and was equal with his captain's score, the fourth ball he let alone. The fifth he ran out at and hit clean over the bowler's head. It struck the pavilion rails, thud! and bounded back on to the ground.

You should have seen Long Crawford at the end of that

wonderful over. His hat was off his head, his face was transfigured, and he was shouting the most amazing congratulations at the top of his voice. Other people were shouting, cheering, laughing, crying – at least Madeleine had tears in her eyes – but Crawford's shout was louder than them all. What it was he said no one exactly remembered. But Mr Westcott said that once he distinctly heard him say through the roar of cheers, 'Hit 'em! HIT 'em! HIT 'em, by . . .!'

The enthusiasm was extraordinary; and was redoubled when a few minutes later the captain cunningly placed a ball to the 'on' and landed his century with the fastest second run he ran that day. Without wishing in the least to detract from Lovell's performance, which was admirable in every way, it must be said that he was playing with things in his favour. Not only was the Australian bowling somewhat tired by the follow-on, and not only was the wicket playing perfectly, but he had the most comfortable and happy assurance in his heart that his captain wanted him to hit, that the game did not depend in the least on his playing carefully, and that the object of his going in first was that by hard and almost reckless hitting he should restore confidence to his side.

It was a bold stroke in tactics, putting the hard-hitting and nerve-hardened boy in first. It was brilliant because it was successful. Instead of seeing two first-rate and dependable bats playing themselves in and scoring only judiciously, conscious of the huge score against them, the spirits of England and the very atmosphere of the ground were absolutely transformed by the confidence and splendid hitting of the slow bowler.

There was the knowledge, too, that the only chance of victory lay in getting runs at a tremendous pace. If a draw were necessary there were those who could play their deadliest for it later on. Mark with his splendid boy's heart – his wholesome young body, fit in all its fibres, and those hard crystal eyes of his, perfectly clear and true – knew that his business was to help his side by getting runs as quickly as possible. They could not come too quickly. So, with confidence, he played his innings – that quality which is always half the victory in a game of skill – and succeeded where a far greater batsman, with more depending on him, might have failed.

He was the first to go, but not until England had wiped off the runs without the loss of a wicket. He was caught low down in the slips for a hundred and thirty-six runs, finely made in two hours and five minutes; and when he went to bed that night he had the happy knowledge that England, with five wickets in hand, was one hundred and eighty-eight runs on.

The third and last day brought the greatest crowd of all to the headquarters of cricket. It was a Saturday, and a line of cabs wound unceasing like a huge serpent all the morning from the City to St. John's Wood. The pavements were thronged by a mass of black-coated men, among whom a red-coated soldier here and there relieved monotony, and in the gutter a line of tattered urchins shouted their newspaper and pictoral wares. The sky was cloudless, the sun was scorching hot, and a glare beat up from the road and pavement. English summer weather, but not the weather England wanted.

Seventy runs were added quickly before England were all out. So the Australians had two hundred and fifty-nine to get in just over five hours, and the real business of the day began.

For nearly an hour the two English fast bowlers commanded the game. Thirty-two runs only had been made, but no wicket had fallen. Ball after ball, till the unthinking spectators murmured, was left alone by the batsman. The first change quickened the scoring, and after eighty minutes' play got a wicket. One for fifty-two. Ten runs came in the next ten minutes. At luncheon time the score stood at one for sixty-two, and the Australians had all the afternoon to make their score. The match was still in the balance.

Afterwards runs came more freely. Without further loss the score was taken to ninety-six. At this point Mark was put on to bowl. He was played cautiously for the two first overs, both maidens, till the high-tossed, easy-looking slows tempted one batsman, and another wicket fell with the score at one hundred and eight – a good catch at cover-point.

Steadily ten after ten went up on the big scoreboard. Mark was taken off and the score stood at four wickets for one hundred and fifty-six. Then the Australian batsmen began to hit. The score went to two hundred.

Fifty-nine runs to get and six wickets to fall.

The veteran held a conference with three of his most trusty players, tossing the ball from hand to hand as he talked. Then Mark was put on again.

His first ball got a wicket. It was the ball that broke from the 'off' though the fingers said 'from leg.' The batsman jumping out, hit outside the ball and was stumped by the best of all English wicket-keepers. The second ball was hit for a single. His third ball clean bowled a man who scraped forward at a leg-break. His fourth was played. His fifth got a man caught in the country. In one over the whole complexion of the game had been changed. Instead of two hundred for four, the score stood at two hundred and one for seven. There was plenty of time to finish the game. Three wickets to fall and fifty-eight runs to get.The crowd realised that they were in for a sensational finish, how sensational they did not guess.

In the following over twelve runs were made. Two hundred and thirteen for seven. Mark's over got no wicket, and a couple of runs were scored. Two hundred and fifteen for seven. The next over, three boundaries. Two hundred and twenty-seven for seven. Thirty-two to get and three wickets in hand. Mark's first ball was hit for four. Twenty-eight to get. The second for four; twenty-four to get. His third for four. The crowd sent up a dismal 'Oh!' Twenty to get and still three wickets in hand. Then a roar of delight. His fourth ball got the batsman caught by slip standing very close in.

Twenty to get and two wickets to fall.

You could have heard a bird sing as Mark delivered the last ball of that over. It was one of his slowest, hanging in the air, and utterly deceptive in its flight, the batsman, sternly coached before he left the pavilion, waited for it with his bat raised, stepped forward, drew back sharply, fumbled with his bat, tottered with his legs – and – 'How's that?' cried the clear sharp voice of Mark, and he was out, l.b.w. Twenty to get and only one wicket to fall.

The crowd was now on the best of terms with itself. As Mark ran to his place on the boundary (he asked to go there though he was bowling), people called hysterical compliments to him from the ropes, and at least a dozen ladies felt that they would like to kiss him. England would win. This last wicket would go in ten minutes. People were putting away their glasses, folding their newspapers, putting on their gloves – preparing for the rush.

What excitement all round that ground! Thousands of people waiting there for English bowlers to beat Australian batsmen before twenty runs were made. Thousands of people to whom life and the universe just then hung upon the fall of a wicket! Outside racing there is perhaps no excitement comparable with the sensational finish of a great England *versus* Australia cricket match.

The batsman at the other end knew that he could not depend greatly on his partner; to play for a draw was out of the question. He hit the first ball of the over hard and clean, and sent the hopes of the crowd down to zero with a boundary. Sixteen to get The second ball he hit, but could not run for. The third he left alone. The fourth he got away for two. The fifth brought him a single. Thirteen to get.

He was now opposed to Mark. The third ball he placed for two, the fifth he drove for three.

Eight runs to get.

Then England, gathered round the ropes, tasted the extreme of bitterness. Jumping out at the first ball of the next over, the great batsman, one of the best that ever came from Australia, hit it clean over the far screen for six.

Two runs to get.

The second and the third ball he failed to score from: the fourth he pushed away towards third-man, and the other called him for a run.

They were equal!

The bowler, the fielders, and the spectators all seemed to abandon hope at the next ball.

'And there!' cried the wrathful public, 'goes the winning scoop!'

It was a shocking mis-hit by the Australian fast bowler, a wild, half-humorous swipe, that went high and slow over the bowler's head. The bowler turned quickly and ran in vague hope. A shout like the cry of a tiger's rage stopped him. 'Mine!' It was Mark running for dear life, with his cupped hands shooting out in front of him, low to the ground.

The multitude rose to their feet, as though a trumpet had called them, the players watched with their limbs stiffened. The batsmen walked their run, watching that swift young figure and that slow dropping ball. Would he reach it? would he hold it?

That cry of 'Mine!' had frozen the blood in Mary Lovell's veins. All her calm and repose were gone; she leaned forward with the rest of them, and Madeleine heard her whisper, 'Oh, Mark, hold it!' She had seen him start to run almost before the batsman had hit. She knew that watchful eye had judged where the ball would fall; she knew that he would not misjudge his speed. 'Mine!' – like an angry snarl, bidding the bowler not balk him, and she cried between her parted lips, 'Oh, Mark, hold it!'

The excited multitude watched that wonderful race of the Oxford Quarter-miler against the falling ball, the race from deep long-off to midway between the wicket and the pavilion rails, and prayed with all the tense energy of their enthusiasm that the man would win. There was only one man who abandoned hope: it was the English captain, with one of his great hairy hands picking at a button on his flannel shirt. He abandoned hope. Not that Mark would fail to reach the ball, but that he would overreach it at that pace.

The crowd saw him with his outstretched arms and low hanging hands flash between their vision and the ball – his body was almost level with the ground: they saw his legs go up behind him, they saw him pitch forward, they saw the ball again, shooting up and forward an inch or two from his hands, they saw one hand thrust out to catch it again, and then they saw the man fall and the ball fall.

Mark had missed that catch, and England was beaten by one wicket.

Long Crawford swore by all his gods that the catch was impossible. He protested that no one on earth could have caught it. This, he said, jumping the rail of the stand, and running forward to Mark. He found the boy with moisture in his eyes. 'Magnificent try!' he cried; 'impossible catch; finest thing I ever saw!' but Mark, panting hard, shook his head, and said nothing.

He was just as grim and taciturn when he met the gaze of Mary Lovell. 'I am so sorry, mother,' he said quietly.

Then, when he saw the smile come to her eyes, he smiled too. 'It was rather a teazer,' he said, and slipped his arm through hers.

That night Long Crawford read in the *Globe* that Mr Lovell most unfortunately failed to bring off a difficult catch, and the match ended with a victory for Australia by one wicket. Our friend immediately took pen and paper – he rather prided himself on the Macaulay richness of his composition – and wrote two whole sheets to the Editor of the *Globe*, proving that the catch was not merely a difficult one, but an impossible one. He stated exactly where Mr Lovell was standing at long-off, and calculated precisely the distance he had to run and the time the ball was in the air: as an old cricketer of nearly thirty years' experience, he gave it as his conviction that no one on earth could possibly have caught the ball.

This letter he signed, after much deliberation on the point, *Nullius addictus jurare in verba magistri*. It was painful to him waiting all through Sunday without seeing Mark's honour cleared, and when on Monday his order of six copies was delivered, the letter did not appear.

He had forgotten to enclose his card.

from A MOTHER'S SON
1907

RUGBY v. KENT

by

George Macdonald Fraser

In the late summer of 1842 Flashman has come home from Afghanistan a popular hero, winning, as he says himself, 'undeserved but undying fame in the siege of Jallalabad', and being received by the Queen. Then one day, promenading down Regent Street, he finds himself outside 'The Green Man'.

In those days 'The Green Man' was a famous haunt of cricketers, and it was the sight of bats and stumps and other paraphernalia of the game in the window that suddenly brought back memories, and awoke a strange hunger – not to play, you understand, but just to smell the atmosphere again, and hear the talk of batters and bowlers, and the jargon and gossip. So I turned in, ordered a plate of tripe and a quart of home-brewed, exchanged a word or two with the jolly pipe-smokers in the tap, and was soon so carried away by the homely fare, the cheery talk and laughter, and the clean hearty air of the place, that I found myself wishing I'd gone to the Haymarket and got myself a dish of hot spiced trollop instead. Still, there was time before supper, and I was just calling the waiter to settle up when I noticed a fellow staring at me across the room. He met my eye, shoved his chair back, and came over.

'I say,' says he, 'aren't you Flashman?' He said it almost warily, as though he didn't wish quite to believe it. I was used to this sort of thing by now, and having fellows fawn and admire the hero of Jallalabad, but this chap didn't look like a toad-eater. He was as tall as I was, brown-faced and square-chinned, with a keen look about him, as though he couldn't wait to have a cold tub and a ten-mile walk. A Christian, I shouldn't wonder, and no smoking the day before a match.

So I said, fairly cool, that I was Flashman, and what was it to him.

'You haven't changed,' says he, grinning. 'You don't remember me, though, do you?'

'Any good reason why I should try?' says I. 'Here, waiter!'

'No, thank'ee,' says this fellow. 'I've had my pint for the day. Never take more during the season.' And he sat himself down, cool as be-d----d, at my table.

'Well, I'm relieved to hear it,' says I, rising. 'You'll forgive me, but –'

'Hold on,' says he, laughing. 'I'm Brown. Tom Brown – of Rugby. Don't say you've forgotten!'

Well, in fact, I had. Nowadays his name is emblazoned on my memory, and has been ever since Hughes published his infernal book in the 'fifties, but that was still in the future, and for the life of me I couldn't place him. Didn't want to, either; he had that manly, open-air reek about him that I can't stomach, what with his tweed jacket (I'll bet he'd rubbed down his horse with it) and sporting cap; not my style at all.

'You roasted me over the common-room fire once,' says he, amiably, and then I knew him fast enough, and measured the distance to the door. That's the trouble with these snivelling little sneaks one knocks about at school; they grow up into hulking louts who box, and are always in prime trim. Fortunately this one appeared to be Christian as well as muscular, having swallowed Arnold's lunatic doctrine of love-thine-enemy, for as I hastily muttered that I hoped it hadn't done him any lasting injury, he laughed heartily and clapped me on the shoulder.

'Why, that's ancient history,' cries he. 'Boys will be boys, what? Besides, d'ye know – I feel almost that *I* owe *you* an apology. Yes,' and he scratched his head and looked sheepish. 'Tell the truth,' went on this amazing oaf, 'when we were youngsters I didn't care for you above half, Flashman. Well, you treated us fags pretty raw, you know – of course, I guess it was just thoughtlessness, but, well, we thought you no end of a cad, and – and . . . a coward, too.' He stirred uncomfortably, and I wondered was he going to fart. 'Well, you caught us out here, didn't you?' says he, meeting my eye again. 'I mean, all this business in Afghanistan . . . the way you defended the old flag . . . that sort of thing. By George,' and he absolutely had tears in his eyes, 'it was the most splendid thing . . . and to think that you . . . well, *I* never heard of anything so heroic in my life, and I just wanted to apologize, old fellow, for thinking ill of you – 'cos I'll own that I did, once – and ask to shake your hand, if you'll let me.'

He sat there, with his great paw stuck out, looking misty and noble, virtue just oozing out of him, while I marvelled. The strange thing is, his precious pal Scud East, whom I'd hammered just as generously at school, said almost the same thing to me years later, when we met as prisoners in Russia – confessed how he'd loathed me, but how my heroic conduct had wiped away all old scores, and so forth. I wonder still if they believed that it did, or if they were being hypocrites for form's sake, or if they truly felt guilty for once having harboured evil thoughts of me? D----d if I know; the Victorian conscience is beyond me, thank G-d. I know that if anyone who'd done *me* a bad turn later turned out to be the Archangel Gabriel, I'd *still* hate the b-----d; but then, I'm a scoundrel, you see, with no proper feelings. However, I was so relieved to find that this stalwart lout was prepared to let bygones be bygones that I turned on all my Flashy charms, pumped his fin heartily, and insisted that he break his rule for once, and have a glass with me.

'Well, I will, thank'ee,' says he, and when the beer had come and we'd drunk to dear old Rugby (sincerely, no doubt, on his part) he puts down his mug and says:

'There's another thing – matter of fact it was the first thought that popped into my head when I saw you just now – I don't know how you'd feel about it, though – I mean, perhaps your wounds ain't better yet?'

He hesitated. 'Fire away,' says I, thinking perhaps he wanted to introduce me to his sister.

'Well, you won't have heard, but my last half at school, when I was captain, we had no end of a match against the Marylebone men – lost on first innings, but only nine runs in it, and we'd have beat 'em, given one more over. Anyway, old Aislabie – you remember him? – was so taken with our play that he has asked me if I'd like to get up a side, Rugby past and present, for a match against Kent. Well, I've got some useful hands – you know young Brooke, and Raggles – and I remembered you were a famous bowler, so . . . What d'ye say to turning out for us – if you're fit, of course?'

It took me clean aback, and my tongue being what it is, I found myself saying: 'Why, d'you think you'll draw a bigger gate with the hero of Afghanistan playing?'

'Eh? Good lord, no!' He coloured and then laughed. 'What a cynic you are, Flashy! D'ye know,' says he, looking knowing, 'I'm beginning to understand you, I think. Even at school, you always said the smart, cutting things that got under people's skins – almost as though you were going out of your way to have 'em think ill of you. It's a contrary thing – all at odds with the truth, isn't it? Oh, aye,' says he, smiling owlishly, 'Afghanistan proved that, all right. The German doctors are doing a lot of work on it – the perversity of human nature, excellence bent on destroying itself, the heroic soul fearing its own fall from grace, and trying to anticipate it. Interesting.' He shook his fat head solemnly. 'I'm thinking of reading philosophy at Oxford this term, you know. However, I mustn't prose. What about it, old fellow?' And d--n his impudence, he slapped me on the knee. 'Will you bowl your expresses for us – at Lord's?'

I'd been about to tell him to take his offer along with his rotten foreign sermonizing and drop 'em both in the Serpentine, but that last word stopped me. Lord's – I'd never played there, but what cricketer who ever breathed wouldn't jump at the chance? You may think it small enough beer compared with the games I'd been playing lately, but I'll confess it made my heart leap. I was still young and impressionable then and I almost knocked his hand off, accepting. He gave me another of his thunderous shoulder-claps (they pawed each other something d--nable, those hearty young champions of my youth) and said, capital, it was settled then . . . .

If I close my eyes I can see Lord's as it was then, and I know that when the memories of bed and battle have lost their colours and faded to misty grey, that at least will be as bright as ever. The coaches and carriages packed in the road outside the gate, the fashionable crowd streaming in by Jimmy Dark's house under the trees, the girls like so many gaudy butterflies in their summer dresses and hats, shaded by parasols, and the men guiding 'em to chairs, some in tall hats and coats, others in striped weskits and caps, the gentry uncomfortably buttoned up and the roughs and townies in shirt-sleeves and billycocks with their watch-chains and cutties; the bookies with their stands outside the pavilion, calling the odds, the flash chaps in their mighty whiskers and ornamented vests, the touts and runners and swell mobsmen slipping through the press like ferrets, the pot-boys from the Lord's pub thrusting along with trays loaded with beer and lemonade, crying 'Way, order, gents! Way, order!'; old John Gully, the retired pug, standing like a great oak tree, feet planted wide, smiling his gentle smile as he talked to Alfred Mynn, whose scarlet waist-scarf and straw boater were a magnet for the eyes of the hero-worshipping youngsters, jostling at a respectful distance from these giants of the sporting world; the grooms pushing a way for some doddering old Duke, passing through nodding and tipping his tile, with his poule-of-the-moment arm-in-arm, she painted and bold-eyed and defiant as the ladies turned the other way with a rustle of skirts; the bowling green and archery range going full swing, with the thunk of the shafts mingling with the distant pomping of the artillery band, the chatter and yelling of the vendors, the grind of coach-wheels and the warm hum of summer ebbing across the great green field where Stevie Slatter's boys were herding away the sheep and warning off the bob-a-game players; the crowd ten-deep at the nets to see Pilch at batting practice, or Felix, agile as his animal namesake, bowling those slow lobs that seemed to hang forever in the air.

Or I see it in the late evening sun, the players in their white top-hats trooping in from the field, with the ripple of applause running round the ropes, and the urchins streaming across to worship, while the old buffers outside the pavilion clap and cry 'Played, well played!' and raise their tankards, and the Captain tosses the ball to some round-eyed small boy who'll guard it as a relic for life, and the scorer climbs stiffly down from his eyrie and the shadows lengthen across the idyllic scene, the very picture of merry, sporting old England, with the umpires bundling up the stumps, the birds calling in the tall trees, the gentle even-fall stealing over the ground and the pavilion, and the empty benches, and the willow wood-pile behind the sheep pen where Flashy is plunging away on top of the landlord's daughter in the long grass. Aye, cricket was cricket then.

Barring the last bit, which took place on another joyous occasion, that's absolutely what it was like on the afternoon when the Gentlemen of Rugby, including your humble servant, went out to play the cracks of Kent (twenty to one on, and no takers). At first I thought it was going to be a frost, for while most of my team-mates were pretty civil – as you'd expect, to the Hector of Afghanistan – the egregious Brown was decidedly cool, and so was Brooke, who'd been head of the school in my time and was the apple of Arnold's eye – that tells you all you need to know about him; he was clean-limbed and handsome and went to church and had no impure thoughts and was kind to animals and old ladies and was a midshipman in the Navy; what happened to him I've no idea, but I hope he absconded with the ship's funds and the admiral's wife and set up a knocking-shop in Valparaiso. He and Brown talked in low voices in the pavilion, and glanced towards me; rejoicing, no doubt, over the sinner who hadn't repented.

Then it was time to play, and Brown won the toss and elected to bat, which meant that I spent the next hour beside Elspeth's chair, trying to hush her imbecile observations on the game, and waiting for my turn to go in. It was a while coming, because either Kent were going easy to make a game of it, or Brooke and Brown were better than you'd think, for they survived the opening whirlwind of Mynn's attack, and when the twisters came on, began to push the score along quite handsomely. I'll say that for Brown, he could play a deuced straight bat, and Brooke was a hitter. They put on thirty for the first wicket, and our other batters were game, so that we had seventy up before the tail was reached, and I took my leave of my fair one, who embarrassed me d--nably by assuring her neighbours that I was sure to make a score, because I was so strong and clever. I hastened to the pavilion, collared a pint of ale from the pot-boy, and hadn't had time to do more than blow off the froth when there were two more wickets down, and Brown says: 'In you go, Flashman.'

So I picked up a bat from beside the flagstaff, threaded my way through the crowd who turned to look curiously at the next man in, and stepped out on to the turf – you must have done it yourselves often enough, and remember the silence as you walk out to the wicket, so far away, and perhaps there's a stray handclap, or a cry of 'Go it, old fellow!', and no more than a few spectators loafing round the ropes, and the fielding side sit or lounge about, stretching in the sun, barely glancing at you as you come in. I knew it well enough, but as I stepped over the ropes I happened to glance up – and Lord's truly smote me for the first time. Round the great emerald field, smooth as a pool table, there was this mighty mass of people, ten deep at the boundary, and behind them the coaches were banked solid, wheel to wheel, crowded with ladies and gentlemen, the whole huge multitude hushed and expectant while the sun caught the glittering eyes of thousands of opera-glasses and binocles glaring at me – it was d----d unnerving, with that vast space to be walked across, and my bladder suddenly holding a bushel, and I wished I could scurry back into the friendly warm throng behind me.

You may think it odd that nervous funk should grip me just then; after all, my native cowardice has been whetted on some real worthwhile horrors – Zulu impis and Cossack cavalry and Sioux riders, all intent on rearranging my circulatory and nervous systems in their various ways, but there were others to share the limelight with me then, and it's a different kind of fear, anyway. The minor ordeals can be d----d scaring simply because you know you're going to survive them.

It didn't last above a second, while I gulped and hesitated and strode on, and then the most astounding thing happened. A murmur passed along the banks of people, and then it grew to a roar, and suddenly it exploded in the most deafening cheering you ever heard; you could feel the shock of it rolling across the ground, and ladies were standing up and fluttering their handkerchieves and parasols, and the men were roaring hurrah and waving their hats, and jumping up on the carriages, and in the middle of it all the brass band began to thump out 'Rule, Britannia', and I realized they weren't cheering the next man in, but saluting the hero of Jallalabad, and I was fairly knocked sideways by the surprise of it all. However, I fancy I played it pretty well, raising my white topper right and left while the music and cheering pounded on, and hurrying to get to the wicket as a modest hero should. And here was slim little Felix, in his classroom whiskers and charity boy's cap, smiling shyly and holding out his hand – Felix, the greatest gentleman bat in the world, mark you, leading me to the wicket and calling for three cheers from the Kent team. And then the silence fell, and my bat thumped uncommon loud as I hit it into the blockhole, and the fields crouched, and I thought, oh G-d, this is the serious business, and I'm bound to lay an egg on the scorer, I know I am, and after such a welcome, too, and with my bowels quailing I looked up the wicket at Alfred Mynn.

He was a huge man at the best of times, six feet odd and close on twenty stone, with a face like fried ham garnished with a double helping of black whisker, but now he looked like Goliath, and if you think a man can't tower above you from twenty-five yards off, you ain't seen young Alfie. He was smiling, idly tossing up the ball which looked no bigger than a cherry in his massive fist, working one foot on the turf – pawing it, bigod. Old Aislabie gave me guard, quavered 'Play!' I gripped my bat, and Mynn took six quick steps and swung his arm.

I saw the ball in his hand, at shoulder height, and then something fizzed beside my right knee, I prepared to lift my bat – and the wicket-keeper was tossing the ball to Felix at point. I swallowed in horror, for I swear I never saw the d----d thing go, and someone in the crowd cries, 'Well let alone, sir!' There was a little puff of dust settling about four feet in front of me; that's where he pitches, thinks I, oh J---s, don't let him hit me! Felix, crouching facing me, barely ten feet away, edged just a little closer, his eyes fixed on my feet; Mynn had the ball again, and again came the six little steps, and I was lunging forward, eyes tight shut, to get my bat down where the dust had jumped last time. I grounded it, my bat leaped as something hit it a hammer blow, numbing my wrists, and I opened my eyes to see the ball scuttling off to leg behind the wicket. Brooke yells 'Come on!' and the lord knows I wanted to, but my legs didn't answer, and Brooke had to turn back, shaking his head.

This has got to stop, thinks I, for I'll be maimed for life if I stay here. And panic, mingled with hate and rage, gripped me as Mynn turned again; he strode up to the wicket, arm swinging back, and I came out of my ground in a huge despairing leap, swinging my bat for dear life – there was a sickening crack and in an instant of elation I knew I'd caught it low down on the outside edge, full swipe, the b----y thing must be in Wiltshire by now, five runs for certain, and I was about to tear up the pitch when I saw Brooke was standing his ground, and Felix, who'd been fielding almost in my pocket, was idly tossing the ball up in his left hand, shaking his head and smiling at me.

How he'd caught it only he and Satan know; it must have been like snatching a bullet from the muzzle. But he hadn't turned a hair, and I could only trudge back to the pavilion, while the mob groaned in sympathy, and I waved my bat to them and tipped my tile – after all I was a bowler, and at least I'd taken a swing at it. And I'd faced three balls from Alfred Mynn.

We closed our hand at 91, Flashy caught Felix, nought, and it was held to be a very fair score, although Kent were sure to pass it easily, and since it was a single-hand match that would be that. In spite of my blank score – how I wished I had gone for that single off the second ball! – I was well received round the pavilion, for it was known who I was by now, and several gentlemen came to shake my hand, while the ladies eyed my stalwart frame and simpered to each other behind their parasols; Elspeth was glowing at the splendid figure I had cut in her eyes, but indignant that I had been out when my wicket hadn't been knocked down, because wasn't that the object of the game? I explained that I had been caught out, and she said it was a most unfair advantage, and that little man in the cap must be a great sneak, at which the gentlemen around roared with laughter and ogled her, calling for soda punch for the lady and swearing she must be taken on to the committee to amend the rules.

I contented myself with a glass of beer before we went out to field, for I wanted to be fit to bowl, but d---e if Brown didn't leave me loafing in the outfield, no doubt to remind me that I was a whoremonger and therefore not fit to take an over. I didn't mind, but lounged about pretty nonchalant, chatting with the townies near the ropes, and shrugging my shoulders eloquently when Felix or his partner made a good hit, which they did every other ball. They fairly knocked our fellows all over the wicket, and had fifty up well within the hour; I observed to the townies that what we wanted was a bit of ginger, and limbered my arm, and they cheered and began to cry: 'Bring on the Flash chap! Huzza for Afghanistan!' and so forth, which was very gratifying.

I'd been getting my share of attention from the ladies in the carriages near my look-out, and indeed had been so intent on winking and swaggering that I'd missed a long hit, at which Brown called pretty sharply to me to mind out; now one or two of the more spirited ladybirds began to echo the townies, who egged them on, so that 'Bring on the Flash chap!' began to echo round the ground, in gruff bass and piping soprano. Finally Brown could stand it no longer, and waved me in, and the mob cheered like anything, and Felix smiled his quiet smile and took fresh guard.

On the whole he treated my first three with respect, for he took only eleven off it, which was better than I deserved. For of course I flung my deliveries down with terrific energy, the first one full pitch at his head, and the next three horribly short, in sheer nervous excitement. The crowd loved it, and so did Felix, curse him; he didn't reach the first one, but he drew the second beautifully for four, cut the third on tip-toe, and swept the last right off his upper lip and into the coaches near the pavilion.

How the crowd laughed and cheered, while Brown bit his lip with vexation, and Brooke frowned with disgust. But they couldn't take me off after only one turn; I saw Felix say something to his partner, and the other laughed – and as I walked back to my look-out a thought crept into my head, and I scowled horribly and clapped my hands in disgust, at which the spectators yelled louder than ever. 'Give 'em the Afghan pepper, Flashy!' cries one, and 'Run out the guns!' hollers another; I waved my fist and stuck my hat on the back of my head, and they cheered and laughed again.

They gave a huge shout when Brown called me up for my second turn, and settled themselves to enjoy more fun and fury. You'll get it, my boys, thinks I, as I thundered up to the wicket, with the mob counting each step, and my first ball smote about half-way down the pitch, flew high over the batsman's head, and they ran three byes. That brought Felix to face me again, and I walked back, closing my ears to the shouting and to Brown's muttered rebuke. I turned, and just from the lift of Felix's shoulders I could see he was getting set to knock me into the trees; I fixed my eye on the spot dead in line with his off stump – he was a left-hander, which left the wicket wide as a barn door to my round delivery – and ran up determined to bowl the finest, fastest ball of my life.

And so I did. Very well, I told you I was a good bowler, and that was the best ball I ever delivered, which is to say it was unplayable. I had dropped the first one short on purpose, just to confirm what everyone supposed from the first over – that I was a wild chucker, with no more head than flat beer. But the second had every fibre directed at that spot, and from the moment it left my hand Felix was gone. Granted I was lucky, for the spot must have been bald; it was a shooter, skidding in past his toes when he expected it round his ears, and before he could smother it his stump was cart-wheeling away.

The yell that went up split the heaven, and he walked past me shaking his head and shooting me a quizzy look while the fellows slapped my back, and even Brooke condescended to cry 'Well bowled!' I took it very offhand, but inside I was thinking: 'Felix! Felix, by G-d!' – I'd not have swapped that wicket for a peerage. Then I was brought back to earth, for the crowd were cheering the new man in, and I picked up the ball and turned to face the tall, angular figure with the long-reaching arms and the short-handled bat.

I'd seen Fuller Pilch play at Norwich when I was a young shaver, when he beat Marsden of Yorkshire for the single-wicket championship of England; so far as I ever had a boyhood hero, it was Pilch, the best professional of his day – some say of any day, although it's my belief this new boy Rhodes may be as good. Well, Flash, thinks I, you've nothing to lose, so here goes at him.

Now, what I'd done to Felix was head bowling, but what came next was luck, and nothing else. I can't account for it yet, but it happened, and this is how it was. I did my d----dest to repeat my great effort, but even faster this time, and in consequence I was just short of a length; whether Pilch was surprised by the speed, or the fact that the ball kicked higher than it had any right to do, I don't know, but he was an instant slow in reaching forward, which was his great shot. He didn't ground his bat in time, the ball came high off the blade, and I fairly hurled myself down the pitch, all arms and legs, grabbing at a catch I could have held in my mouth. I nearly muffed it, too, but it stuck between finger and thumb, and the next I knew they were pounding me on the back, and the townies were in full voice, while Pilch turned away slapping his bat in vexation. 'B----y grave!' cries he. 'Hasn't Dark got any brooms, then?' He may have been right, for all I know.

By now, as you may imagine, I was past caring. Felix – and Pilch. There was nothing more left in the world just then, or so I thought; what could excel those twin glorious strokes? My grandchildren will never believe this, thinks I, supposing I have any – by George, I'll buy every copy of the sporting press for the next month, and paper old Morrison's bedroom with 'em. And yet the best was still to come.

Mynn was striding to the crease; I can see him now, and it brings back to me a line that Macaulay wrote in that very year: 'And now the cry is "Aster!" and lo, the ranks divide, as the great Lord of Luna comes on with stately stride.' That was Alfred the Great to a 't', stately and magnificent, with his broad crimson sash and the bat like a kid's paddle in his hand; he gave me a great grin as he walked by, took guard, glanced leisurely round the field, tipped his straw hat back on his head, and nodded to the umpire, old Aislabie, who was shaking with excitement as he called 'Play!'

Well, I had no hope at all of improving on what I'd done, you may be sure, but I was determined to bowl my best, and it was only as I turned that it crossed my mind – old Aislabie's a Rugby man, and it was out of pride in the old school that he arranged this fixture; honest to God, to be sure, but like all enthusiasts he'll see what he wants to see, won't he? – and Mynn's so tarnation big you can't help hitting him somewhere if you put your mind to it, and bowl your fastest. It was all taking shape even as I ran up to the wicket: I'd got Felix by skill, Pilch by luck, and I'd get Mynn by knavery or perish in the attempt. I fairly flung myself up to the crease, and let go a perfect snorter, dead on a length but a good foot wide of the leg stump. It bucked, Mynn stepped quickly across to let it go by, it flicked his calf, and by that time I was bounding across Aislabie's line of sight, three feet off the ground, turning as I sprang and yelling at the top of my voice: 'How was he there, sir?'

Now, a bowler who's also a Gentleman of Rugby don't appeal unless he believes it; that gooseberry-eyed old fool Aislabie hadn't seen a d----d thing with me capering between him and the scene of the crime, but he concluded there must be something in it, as I knew he would, and by the time he had fixed his watery gaze, Mynn, who had stepped across, was plumb before the stumps. And Aislabie would have been more than human if he had resisted the temptation to give the word that everyone in that ground except Alfie wanted to hear. 'Out!' cries he. 'Yes, out, absolutely! Out! Out!'

It was bedlam after that; the spectators went wild, and my team-mates simply seized me and rolled me on the ground; the cheering was deafening, and even Brown pumped me by the hand and slapped me on the shoulder, yelling 'Bowled, oh, well bowled, Flashy!' (You see the moral: cover every strumpet in London if you've a mind to, it don't signify so long as you can take wickets.) Mynn went walking by, shaking his head and cocking an eyebrow in Aislabie's direction – he knew it was a crab decision, but he beamed all over his big red face like the sporting ass he was, and then did something which has passed into the langugage: he took off his boater, presented it to me with a bow, and says:

'That trick's worth a new hat any day, youngster.'

(I'm d----d if I know *which* trick he meant, and I don't much care; I just know the leg-before-wicket rule is a perfectly

splendid one, if they'll only let it alone.)

After that, of course, there was only one thing left to do. I told Brown that I'd sprained my arm with my exertions – brought back the rheumatism contracted from exposure in Afghanistan, very likely . . . horrid shame . . . just when I was finding a length . . . too bad . . . worst of luck . . . field all right, though . . . (I wasn't going to run the risk of having the other Kent men paste me all over the ground, not for anything.) So I went back to the deep field, to a tumultuous ovation from the gallery, which I acknowledged modestly with a tip of Mynn's hat, and basked in my glory for the rest of the match, which we lost by four wickets. (If only that splendid chap Flashman had been able to go on bowling, eh? Kent would have been knocked all to smash in no time. They do say he has a jezzail bullet in his right arm still – no it ain't, it was a spear thrust – I tell you I read it in the papers, etc., etc.)

It was beer all round in the pavilion afterwards, with all manner of congratulations – Felix shook my hand again, ducking his head in that shy way of his, and Mynn asked was I to be home next year, for if the Army didn't find a use for me, he could, in the casual side which he would get together for the Grand Cricket Week at Canterbury. This was flattery on the grand scale, but I'm not sure that the sincerest tribute I got wasn't Fuller Pilch's knitted brows and steady glare as he sat on a bench with his tankard, looking me up and down for a full two minutes and never saying a word.

from FLASHMAN'S LADY
1977

PART TWO

WILLINGLY TO SCHOOL

COMIN' THRO' THE RYE

by

Helen Mathers

Helen Adair has been sent off to school at Charteris – where she is enthusiastic over her opportunity at last to wear 'trousers – and enjoy the exquisite satisfaction of not only feeling a boy, but looking *one' – and over her first experience of cricket. Mr Russell's 'fast round-arm bowling' reminds us that 'over-arm' was only legalised in 1864, eleven years before this novel was published. Also the closing paragraph is a reminder too that, in those days, boundaries had to be run out.*

We are all at work in the schoolroom, toiling at 'seam, gusset, and band,' and envying heartily the blackbird who is free as air, and knows it, singing at his ease as he swings on the apple bough that looks in at the tall narrow window! The sunbeams dance and flicker on the dull school-books impudently, saying, as plain as they can speak, 'We can play hide-and-seek all day if we please; we are not answerable to any one, and we have no lessons to learn, or work to do.'

Steps come down the corridor! no mincing feminine ones this time, but a man's bold decided tread. I lay down my stitching to listen. The door opens, a head is popped in. 'Cricket!' says a loud clear voice, the door is shut again, and down go work and thimbles, a Babel of delighted cries burst forth, and in thirty seconds the room is cleared, and we are all upstairs, pulling off ribbons, gowns, crinolines, all our feminine belongings, and putting on knickerbockers and blouses! Yes, *knickerbockers!* Let no one blush or look shocked, for they are long and ample, and tied modestly in at the ankle; and as to the blouse, which descends below the knee, and is trimly belted in at the waist, it is as decent and uncompromising as that worn by Dr Mary Walker; our costume being, in short, nothing more or less than that which is designated by the somewhat opprobrious title of 'Bloomer.' The knickerbockers bring comfort, the tunic confers respectability. It is a lovely thought that I can kick up my heels to my heart's content, and yet preserve decorum. As to what manner of female I look, I care nothing; my sensations are all I think about, and they are blissful. I feel as light as a feather, and equal to Jack at running, vaulting or hurdle jumping.

On my way downstairs I fall in with the girls – shrunken, insignificant creatures, measured by the standard of half an hour ago, when they boasted a circumference of from four to five yards of petticoat. They even look meek; for it is a fact that a large portion of a woman's assurance lies in her tail. Shear her of that, and she is no way superior to man. Out on the cricket field I scan the assembly critically, and nothing but the consciousness of looking a greater guy than any one present, prevents me from going off into a fit of convulsive laughter. If only Charles Lovelace, George Tempest, or Jack could see us!

We have roly-poly girls, and bean-stalk girls, little girls, big girls, long girls, short girls; girls whose plump proportions fit their garments as closely as a kernel fits a shell; girls whose garments hang upon them loose, as did the armour on Don Quixote's gaunt form; girls who waddle, amble, jig, trot, hurry, and stride – their action plainly shown in the narrow, straight costume. Can an English girl walk? I trow not. It is a pity the time spent in needlework is not used in drilling. Conspicuous, even among this remarkable throng, is the German governess, short, square, stout, not over-young, with a large flat face, enormous feet and hands, and that general look of a Dutch doll that marks her stolid race. She wears the regulation trousers and blouse; but whether under an impression that she is not sufficiently clad, or because she wishes to give a full dress air to a somewhat severe costume, I know not; at any rate, she has over and above arrayed herself in a very large, ample, white muslin jacket, profusely frilled and starched, and tightly belted in at the waist, and these frills set straight out from her sturdy form in a fashion that would bring a smile to the face of a crocodile.

The wickets are pitched; the ball is flying from hand to hand; we are all waiting for Mr Russell, the man who introduced the game of cricket at Charteris, or rather, made it an institution, for it had flourished many years, and many a pretty young mother now makes an excellent long-stop, or field to her sons, thanks to the training she received at this school. To Mr Russell, therefore, be our eternal thanks due, in that he has, for a time at least, emancipated us from the slavish thraldom of our petticoats, and enabled us to stretch our limbs and use them. He is coming over the grass from the school with Miss Tyburn now; tall, erect, a little grey, his dress showing but little of the clergyman about it (he is one of the committee, and owns 'The Charteris', the only big house in the place. He is married, and has olive branches). How my heart leaps as I look at him. Why did he not come home sooner? His daughter is with him. And now sides are being chosen, the game begins, and as my side is in, I have no opportunity for making myself look ridiculous, as yet, I merely look on.

It is a droll sight to see a girl walk up to the wicket, and send her ball in, if not as powerfully as a man, well nigh as straight; and to see another standing, bat in hand, with body slightly bent forward, awaiting it. Mr Russell is against us, and in the next over, his fast, round-arm bowling gives me an uneasy sense of fear, the ball hurtles along so swiftly that surely a slender ankle or arm might snap like sealing-wax at its onslaught; and something of that Frenchman's astonishment comes into my mind, who could not conceive the reason of Englishmen being so fond of cricket, for where was the pleasure of standing up in a hot sun for a man to shy a hard ball at you, while a lot of other fellows stood round, and looked on? If I do come to grief, I hope that any amount of arms and legs will be broken, but not my *teeth*. I could never stand false ones, and I could not do without any, so it would be awkward.

How hot it is! We are all sitting and lying about under the trees; a little farther off is Miss Tyburn, with Mr Frere, who has just come over from the parsonage. In common mercy to our numbers he ought to play, and allow us to enjoy the distinction of having a man on each side; but apparently he is more careful of his shins than ambitious of honour, so sits in the shade at his ease, looking on. All too soon comes that terrible moment when 'Helen Adair!' is called, and bat in hand, I walk forth to my fate. I begin my illustrious career by hit-wicket, but in consideration of my extreme greenness and inexperience, am permitted to take my innings, that is to say, if I can get it. The ground flies up into my face, the sky lies at my feet, as I stand awaiting my first ball, holding with stiff, nervous fingers my bat, in what may be called the 'first position' of cricketers – bolt upright, with my person carefully curved out, and away from it, like Cupid's bow. In comes the ball, and I swipe wildly at it. Have I hit it, or the wickets, or the wicket-keeper, or myself? I am still in doubt, and undecided as to whether I ought to walk off to the shade of the friendly tree, when another ball comes creeping in, very insidiously this time, and somehow I give it a neat little tip that sends it straight into Fräulein's face; and while I am looking all about, and marvelling where it has got to, she is led away, weeping bitterly, with a bleeding nose. Quite overpowered by this proof of my skill, I send the next ball, which somehow seems to run of its own accord against my bat, a tolerable distance; and being pleased at the circumstances, and engaged in looking round with a modest smirk for admiration, am amazed at being violently hustled by my fellow batswoman, who wildly exhorts me to *run*. Ah! I had forgotten all about the runs, I was too much taken up in congratulating myself, but I set out with a will, and am considerably taken aback on arriving at my bourne to find that I am ignominiously run out.

Moral: stick to business. Back to the tree I go, as crestfallen, miserable, and ashamed a lass as the world contains. As I am seating myself disconsolately, Miss Tyburn calls me, and I jump up to obey her bidding . . . .

By-and-by, I am able to do my side some small service. Mr Russell is in, and batting away with a determination and vigour that strike consternation to our feminine souls, and presently he sends a mighty ball straight over my head (who am standing long field on) straight across the cricket-field, and into the next. 'Six!'

cry the Russellites; but six it shall not be, if I can help it. Laying my legs to the ground with a will, I have cleared the field, and leaped the hedge beyond, before he has got *one*. I go plump into the midst of a stinging-nettle bed – but that is nothing, I espy the ball, and send it home with all my might. And after all he only gets two. He casts an approving glance on me as I return, evidently he is not used to sceing girls jump; if he only knew how thoroughly Jack has grounded me in that doubtful accomplishment!

from COMIN' THRO' THE RYE
1875

SIXTH v. SCHOOL

by

Talbot Baines Reed

Talbot Baines Reed was the writer of the first piece printed in the first issue of the Boy's Own Paper *in 1879. He published* The Fifth Form at St Dominic's *as a serial there in 1881–2, five years before it came out as a book. Reed was not in fact a professional author – he not only gave his royalties to the Religious Tract Society but worked as an active partner in his family's successful printing business and, for ten years, researched his* History of the Old English Letter Foundries. *He died in 1893, aged only forty-one.*

Professional writer or otherwise, Reed created in The Fifth Form at St Dominic's, *a pattern and a fashion for books about boys' schools that was still current when P.G. Wodehouse published* Mike *in 1909, and even into the 1920s. And that pattern includes an almost mandatory cricket match.*

Never had a Sixth *v.* School Match been looked forward to with more excitement at St Dominic's than the present one. Party feeling had been running high all the term, intensified on the one hand by the unpopularity of some of the monitors, and on the other by the defiant attitude of the Fifth and the tone of their organ, the *Dominican*.

The lower school naturally looked on with interest at this rivalry between the two head forms, the result of which, as might have been expected, was the reverse of beneficial for the discipline of the school generally. If the big boys set a bad example and disregard rules, what can one expect of the little ones?

So far, anything like conflict had been avoided. The Fifth had 'cheeked' the Sixth, and the Sixth had snubbed the Fifth; but with the exception of Loman's assault on Oliver, which had not led to a fight, the war had been strictly one of words. Now, however, the opposing forces were to be ranged face to face at cricket; and to the junior school the opportunity seemed a grand one for a display of partisanship one side or the other.

The School Eleven, on this occasion, moreover, consisted exclusively of Fifth Form boys – a most unusual circumstance, and one which seemed to be the result quite as much of management as of accident. At least so said the disappointed heroes of the Fourth.

The match was, in fact – whatever it was formally styled – a match between the Sixth and the Fifth, and the partisans of either side looked upon it as a decisive event in the respective glories of the two top forms.

And now the day had come. All St Dominic's trooped out to the meadows, and there was a rush of small boys as usual for the front benches. Stephen found himself along with his trusty ally, Paul, and his equally trusty enemy, Bramble, and some ten other Guinea-pigs and Tadpoles, wedged like sardines upon a form that would comfortably hold six, eagerly canvassing the prospects of the struggle.

'The Sixth are going to win in a single innings, if you fellows want to know,' announced Bramble, with all the authority of one who knows.

'Not a bit of it,' replied Paul. 'The Fifth are safe to win, I tell you.'

'But they've got no decent bowlers,' said Raddleston.

'Never mind,' said Stephen. 'Loman's not going to play for the Sixth. He's sprained his wrist.'

'Hip, hip, hurrah!' yelled Paul, 'that *is* jolly! They are sure to be licked now. Are you sure he's out of it?'

'Yes. Look at him there with his arm in a sling.'

And Stephen pointed to where Loman stood in his ordinary clothes talking to some of his fellows.

'Well that *is* a piece of luck,' said Paul. 'Who's to take his place?'

'Baynes, they say. He's no use, though.'

'Don't you be too cock-sure, you two,' growled Bramble. 'I say we shall beat you even if Loman don't play. Got any brandy-balls left, Greenfield?'

Similar speculations and hopes were being exchanged all round the field, and when at last the Fifth went out to field, and Callonby and Wren went in to bat for the Sixth, you might have heard a cat sneeze, so breathless was the excitement.

Amid solemn silence the first few balls were bowled. The third ball of the first over came straight on to Wren's bat, who played it neatly back to the bowler. It was not a run, only a simple block; but it was the first play of the match, and so quite enough to loosen the tongues of all the small boys, who yelled, and howled, and cheered as frantically as if a six had been run or a wicket taken. And the ice once broken, every ball and every hit were marked and applauded as if empires depended on them . . .

The two Sixth men went quickly to work, and at the end of the second over had scored eight. Then Callonby, in stepping back to 'draw' one of Wraysford's balls, knocked down his wicket.*

How the small boys yelled at this!

But the sight of Raleigh going in second soon silenced them.

'They mean hard work by sending in the captain now,' said Paul. 'I don't like that.'

'No more do I,' said Stephen. 'He always knocks Oliver's bowling about.'

'Oh, bother; is your brother bowling?' said Master Paul, quite unconscious of wounding anyone's feelings. 'It's a pity they've got no one better.'

Stephen coloured up at this, and wondered what made Paul such a horrid boy.

**Editor's footnote.* The draw was a popular stroke, particularly against under-arm or spin bowling. One of G.F. Watts's illustrations for *Felix on the Bat* (1845) shows how it was played, but essentially it was a late tapping or 'drawing' of the ball from off to leg between the batsman's body and the stumps. If deftly played – as I once saw P.G.H. Fender do it – it went just backward of square-leg and avoided the forward short-legs. Sadly, now that bowling is generally quicker, one rarely sees it in action.

'Better look out for your eyes,' said Bramble, cheerily. 'The captain always knocks up this way, over square-leg's head.'

There was a general buzz of youngsters round the field, as the hero of the school walked up to the wicket, and coolly turned to face Oliver's bowling.

The scorer in the tent hurriedly sharpened his pencil. The big fellows who had been standing up to watch the opening overs, sat down on the grass and made themselves comfortable. Something was going to happen, evidently. The captain was in, and meant business.

Oliver gripped the ball hard in his hand, and walked back to the end of his run. Then, turning sharply, and running up to the wicket, he delivered the ball amid dead silence.

Next moment there rose a shout loud enough to deafen all St Dominic's. The ball was flying fifty feet up in the air, and Raleigh was slowly walking, bat in hand, back to the tent he had only a moment ago quitted!

The captain had been clean bowled, first ball!

Who shall describe the excitement, the yelling, the cheering, the consternation that followed? Paul got up and danced a hornpipe on the bench; Bramble kicked the boy nearest to him. 'Well bowled, sir!' shouted some. 'Hard lines!' screamed others. 'Hurrah for the Fifth!' 'You'll beat them yet, Sixth!' such were a few of the shouts audible above the general clamour.

As for Stephen, he was wild with joy. He was a staunch partisan of the Fifth in any case, but that was nothing to the fact that it was *his* brother, his own brother and nobody else's, who had bowled that eventful ball, and who was at that moment the hero of St Dominic's. Stephen felt as proud and elated as if he had bowled the ball himself, and could afford to be absolutely patronizing to those around him, on the head of this achievement.

'That wasn't a bad ball of Oliver's,' he said to Paul. 'He can bowl very well when he tries.'

'It was a beastly fluke!' roared Bramble, determined to see no merit in the exploit.

'Shut up and don't make a row,' said Stephen, with a bland smile of forgiveness.

Bramble promised his adversary to shut *him* up, and after a little more discussion and altercation and jubilation, the excitement subsided, and another man went in.

All this while the Fifth were in ecstasies. They controlled their feelings, however, contented themselves with clapping Oliver on the back till he was nearly dead, and speculating on the chances of beating their adversaries in a single innings.

But they had not won the match yet.

Winter was next man in, and he and Wren fell to work very speedily in a decidedly business-like way. No big hits were made, but the score crawled up by ones and twos steadily, and the longer they were at it the steadier they played. Loud cheers announced the posting of thirty on the signal-board, but still the score went on. Now it was a slip, now a bye, now a quiet cut.

'Bravo! well played!' cried Raleigh and his men frequently. The captain, by the way, was in excellent spirits, despite his misfortune.

Thirty-five, forty! The Fifth began to look hot and puzzled. The batsmen were evidently far too much at home with the bowling. A change must be made, even though it be to put on only a second-rate bowler.

Tom Senior was put on. He was nothing like as good a bowler as either Wraysford, or Oliver, or Ricketts. He bowled a very ordinary slow lob, without either twist or shoot, and was usually knocked about plentifully; and this appeared likely to be his fate now, for Wren got hold of his first ball, and knocked it right over into the scorer's tent for five. The Fifth groaned, and could have torn the wretched Tom to pieces. But the next ball was more lucky; Winter hit it, indeed, but he hit it up, sky-high, over the bowler's head, and before it reached the ground Bullinger was safe underneath it. It was with a sigh of relief that the Fifth saw this awkward partnership broken up. The score was at forty-eight for three wickets; quite enough too!

After this the innings progressed more evenly. Men came in and went out more as usual, each contributing his three or four, and one or two their ten or twelve. Among the latter was Baynes, who, at the last moment, it will be remembered, had been put into the eleven to replace Loman. By careful play he managed to put together ten, greatly to his own delight, and not a little to the surprise of his friends.

In due time the last wicket of the Sixth fell, to a total of eighty-four runs.

The small boys on the bench had had leisure to abate their ardour by this time. Bramble had recovered his spirits, and Paul and Stephen looked a little blue as they saw the total signalled.

'Eighty-four's a lot,' said Stephen.

Paul nodded glumly.

'Ya, ha! How do you like it, Guinea-pigs?' jeered Bramble. 'I hope *you'll* get half as much. *I* knew how it would be.'

The two friends listened to these taunts in silent sorrow, and wished the next innings would begin.

It did presently, and not very brilliantly either. The Fifth only managed to score fifty-one, and to this total Wraysford was the only player who made anything like good scoring. Oliver got out for six, Ricketts for nine, and Tom Senior and Braddy both for a 'duck's-egg'. Altogether it was a meagre performance, and things looked very gloomy for the Fifth when, for a second time, their adversaries took the wickets.

Things never turn out at cricket as one expects, however, and the second innings of the Sixth was no exception to the rule. They only made thirty-six runs. Stephen and Paul were hoarse with yelling, as first one wicket, then another, went down for scarcely a run. Raleigh and Baynes seemed the only two who could stand up at all to the bowling of Oliver and Wraysford, but even their efforts could not keep the wickets up for long.

Everyone saw now that the final innings would be a desperate struggle. The Fifth wanted sixty nine to be equal and seventy to win, and the question was: Would they do it in time?

Stephen and his confederate felt the weight of this question so oppressive that they left the irritating company of Mr Bramble, and walked off and joined themselves to a group of Fourth Form fellows, who were watching the match with sulky interest, evidently sore that they had none of their men in the School Eleven.

'They'll never do it, and serve them right!' said one. 'Why didn't they put Mansfield in the eleven, or Banks? They're far more use than Fisher or Braddy.'

'For all that, it'll be a sell if the Sixth lick,' said another.

'I wouldn't much care. If we are going to be sat upon by those Fifth snobs every time an eleven is made up, it's quite time we did go in with the Sixth.'

'Jolly for the Sixth!' retorted the other; whereupon Stephen laughed, and had his ears boxed for being cheeky. The Fourth Senior could not stand 'cheek'.

But St Dominic's generally was 'sweet' on the Fifth, and hoped they would win. When, therefore, Tom Senior and Bullinger went in first and began to score there was great rejoicing.

But the Fourth Form fellows, among whom Stephen now was, refused to cheer for anyone; criticism was more in their line.

'Did you ever see a fellow hit across wickets more horribly than Senior?' said one.

'Just look at that!' cried another. 'That Bullinger's a downright muff not to get that last ball to leg! I could have got it easily.'

'Well, with that bowling, it's a disgrace if they *don't* score; that's all I can say,' remarked a third.

And so these Fourth Form grandees went on, much to Stephen's wrath, who, when Oliver went in, removed somewhere else, so as to be out of ear-shot of any offensive remarks.

Oliver, however, played so well that even the Fourth Form critics could hardly run him down. He survived all the other wickets of his side, and, though not making a brilliant score, did what was almost as useful – played steadily, and gradually demoralized the bowling of the enemy.

As the game went on the excitement increased rapidly; and when at length the ninth wicket went down for sixty-one, and the last man in appeared, with nine to win, the eagerness on both sides scarcely knew bounds. Every ball, every piece of fielding, was cheered by one side, and every hit and every piece of play was as vehemently cheered by the other. If Raleigh and Wren had been nervous bowlers, they would undoubtedly have been disconcerted by the dead silence, followed by terrific applause, amid which every ball – even a wide – was delivered. But happily they were not.

It was at this critical juncture that Loman reappeared on the scene, much consoled to have the interview with Mr Cripps over, and quite ready now to hear every one lament his absence from the match.

The last man in was Webster, a small Fifth boy, who in the last innings had signalized himself by making a duck's-egg. The Fifth scarcely dared hope he would stay in long enough for the nine runs required to be made, and looked on now almost pale with anxiety.

'Now,' said Pembury, near whom Loman, as well as our two Guinea-pigs, found themselves, 'it all depends on Oliver, and I back Oliver to do it, don't you, Loamy?'

Loman, who since the last *Dominican* had not been on speaking terms with Pembury, did not vouchsafe a reply.

'I do!' said Stephen, boldly.

'Do you, really?' replied Pembury, looking round at the boy. 'Perhaps you back yourself to talk when you're not spoken to, eh, Mr Greenhorn?'

'Bravo! bravo! Well run, sir! Bravo, Fifth!' was the cry as Oliver, following up the first ball of the over, pilfered a bye from a long-stop.

'Didn't I tell you!' exclaimed Pembury, delighted; 'he'll save us; he's got down to that end on purpose to take the bowling. Do you twig, Loamy? And he'll stick to that end till the last ball of the over and then he'll run an odd number, and get up to the other end. Do you comprehend?'

'You seem to know all about it,' growled Loman, who saw the force of Pembury's observations, but greatly disliked it all the same.

'Do I, really?' replied the lame boy; 'how odd that is,now – particularly without a crib!'

Loman was fast losing patience – a fact which seemed to have anything but a damping effect on the editor of the *Dominican*. But another hit for two by Oliver created a momentary diversion. It was quite clear that Pembury's version of Oliver's tactics was a correct one. He could easily have run three, but preferred to sacrifice a run rather than leave the imcompetent and flurried Webster to face the bowling.

'Six to win!' cried Stephen; 'I'm *certain* Oliver will do it!'

'Yes, Oliver was always a plodding old blockhead!' drily observed Pembury, who seemed to enjoy the small boy's indignation whenever anyone spoke disrespectfully of his big brother.

'He's not a blockhead!' retorted Stephen, fiercely.

'Go it! Come and kick my legs, young 'un; there's no one near but Loamy, and he can't hurt.'

'Look here, you lame little wretch!' exclaimed Loman in a passion; 'If I have any more of your impudence I'll box your ears!'

'I thought your wrist was sprained?' artlessly observed Pembury. 'Here, young Paul, let's get behind you, there's a good fellow, I *am* in such a funk!'

Whether Loman would have carried out his threat or not is doubtful, but at that moment a terrific shout greeted another hit by Oliver – the best he had made during the match – for which he ran four. One to tie, two to win! Will they do it?

It was a critical moment for St Dominic's. Had the two batsmen been playing for their lives they could not have been more anxiously watched; even Pembury became silent.

And now the last ball of the over is bowled in dead silence. Onlookers can even hear the whizz with which it leaves Wren's hand.

It is almost wide, but Oliver steps out to it and just touches it. Webster is half across the wickets already – ready for a bye. Oliver calls to him to come on, and runs. It is a desperate shave – too desperate for good play. But who cares for that when Oliver has got up to the proper end for the next over?

Equal! What a shout greets the announcement! But it dies away suddenly, and a new anxious silence ensues. The game is saved, but not won; another run is wanted.

No one says a word, but the Fifth everywhere look on with a confidence which is far more eloquent than words.

Raleigh is the bowler from the lower end, and the Sixth send out their hearts to him. He may save them yet!

He runs, in his usual unconcerned manner, up to the wicket and delivers the ball. It is one which there is but one way of playing – among the slips.

Oliver understands it evidently, and, to the joy of the Fifth, plays it. But why does their cheer drop suddenly, and why in a moment is it drowned, over and over and over again, by the cheers of the Sixth and their partisans, as the crowd suddenly breaks into the field, and the ball shoots high up in the air?

A catch! Baynes, the odd man, had missed a chance a few overs back from standing too deep. This time he had kept in close, and saved the Sixth by one of the neatest low-catches that had ever been seen in a Dominican match.

from THE FIFTH FORM AT ST DOMINIC'S
1887

Originally published in the BOY'S OWN PAPER
1881–2

MIKE AT THE NETS

by

P.G. Wodehouse

A strong admirer of Wodehouse's writing was George Orwell. In Paris in 1944 Malcolm Muggeridge arranged for Orwell to meet Wodehouse and he describes the outcome in his second volume of autobiography The Infernal Grove. *'The two of them got on very well, though afterwards Wodehouse said to me that Orwell seemed a gloomy sort of chap. Orwell did give this impression at first, but, on closer acquaintance it became clear that he was really, in his own odd way, quite a happy man; as I am sure Don Quixote was, even though known as the Knight of the Woeful Countenance. He and I talked a lot about Wodehouse, and I mentioned, as an example of how little writers can judge their own work, that Wodehouse had told me he considered his best book to be* Mike *– an early, and, I think, immature, school story, which first appeared in my childhood days as a serial in* The Captain. *Of it Wodehouse said in all seriousness that it recaptured 'the ring of a ball on a cricket bat, the green of a pitch, the white of flannels and the sound of schoolboy cheers' – or words to that effect. Orwell to my surprise, said that Wodehouse was perfectly right.* Mike, *he insisted,* was *his best book.*

Malcolm Muggeridge's opinion of Mike *may have arisen because he felt it did not differ markedly from other 'school' writing of the period such as, for example,* The Fifth Form at St Dominic's *from which the previous extract was taken. Yet Wodehouse, a fast bowler during his time at Dulwich, was surely justified in his opinion.*

There are few better things in life than a public school summer term. The winter term is good, especially towards the end, and there are points, though not many, about the Easter term: but it is in the summer that one really appreciates public school life. The freedom of it, after the restrictions of even the most easy-going private school, is intoxicating. The change is almost as great as that from public school to 'Varsity.

For Mike Jackson the path was made particularly easy. The only drawback to going to a big school for the first time is the fact that one is made to feel so very small and inconspicuous. New boys who have been leading lights at their private schools feel it acutely for the first week. At one time it was the custom, if we may believe writers of a generation or so back, for boys to take quite an embarrassing interest in the newcomer. He was asked a rain of questions, and was, generally, in the very centre of the stage. Nowadays an absolute lack of interest is the fashion. A new boy arrives, and there he is, one of a crowd.

Mike was saved this salutary treatment to a large extent, at first by virtue of the greatness of his family, and, later, by his own performances on the cricket field. His three elder brothers were objects of veneration to most Wrykynians, and Mike got a certain amount of reflected glory from them. The brother of first-class cricketers has a dignity of his own. Then Bob was a help. He was on the verge of the cricket team and had been the school full-back for two seasons. Mike found that people came up and spoke to him, anxious to know if he were Jackson's brother; and became friendly when he replied in the affirmative. Influential relations are a help in every stage of life.

It was Wyatt who gave him his first chance at cricket. There were nets on the first afternoon of term for all old colours of the three teams and a dozen or so of those most likely to fill the vacant places. Wyatt was there, of course. He had got his first eleven cap in the previous season as a mighty hitter and a fair slow bowler. Mike met him crossing the field with his cricket bag.

'Hullo, where are you off to?' asked Wyatt. 'Coming to watch the nets?'

Mike had no particular programme for the afternoon. Junior

cricket had not begun, and it was a little difficult to know how to fill in the time.

'I tell you what,' said Wyatt, 'nip into the house and shove on some things, and I'll try and get Burgess to let you have a knock later on.'

This suited Mike admirably. A quarter of an hour later he was sitting at the back of the first eleven net, watching the practice.

Burgess, the captain of the Wrykyn team, made no pretence of being a bat. He was the school fast bowler and concentrated his energies on that department of the game. He sometimes took ten minutes at the wicket after everybody else had had an innings, but it was to bowl that he came to the nets.

He was bowling now to one of the old colours whose name Mike did not know. Wyatt and one of the professionals were the other two bowlers. Two nets away Firby-Smith, who had changed his pince-nez for a pair of huge spectacles, was performing rather ineffectively against some very bad bowling. Mike fixed his attention on the first eleven man.

He was evidently a good bat. There was style and power in his batting. He had a way of gliding Burgess's fastest to leg which Mike admired greatly. He was succeeded at the end of a quarter of an hour by another eleven man, and then Bob appeared.

It was soon made evident that this was not Bob's day. Nobody is at his best on the first day of term; but Bob was worse than he had any right to be. He scratched forward at nearly everything, and when Burgess, who had been resting, took up the ball again, he had each stump uprooted in a regular series in seven balls. Once he skied one of Wyatt's slows over the net behind the wicket; and Mike, jumping up, caught him neatly.

'Thanks,' said Bob austerely, as Mike returned the ball to him. He seemed depressed.

Towards the end of the afternoon, Wyatt went up to Burgess.

'Burgess,' he said, 'see that kid sitting behind the net?'

'With the naked eye,' said Burgess. 'Why?'

'He's just come to Wain's. He's Bob Jackson's brother, and I've a sort of idea that he's a bit of a bat. I told him I'd ask you if he could have a knock. Why not send him in at the end net? There's nobody there now.'

Burgess's amiability off the field equalled his ruthlessness when bowling.

'All right,' he said. 'Only if you think that I'm to sweat to bowl to him, you're making a fatal error.'

'You needn't do a thing. Just sit and watch. I rather fancy this kid's something special.'

Mike put on Wyatt's pads and gloves, borrowed his bat, and walked round into the net.

'Not in a funk, are you?' asked Wyatt, as he passed.

Mike grinned. The fact was that he had far too good an opinion of himself to be nervous. An entirely modest person seldom makes a good batsman. Batting is one of those things which demand first and foremost a thorough belief in oneself. It need not be aggressive, but it must be there.

Wyatt and the professional were the bowlers. Mike had seen enough of Wyatt's bowling to know that it was merely ordinary 'slow tosh', and the professional did not look as difficult as Saunders. The first half-dozen balls he played carefully. He was on trial, and he meant to take no risks. Then the professional over-pitched one slightly on the off. Mike jumped out, and got the full face of the bat on to it. The ball hit one of the ropes of the net, and nearly broke it.

'How's that?' said Wyatt, with a smile of an impresario on the first night of a successful piece.

'Not bad,' admitted Burgess.

A few moments later he was still more complimentary. He got up and took a ball himself.

Mike braced himself up as Burgess began his run. This time he was more than a trifle nervous. The bowling he had had so far had been tame. This would be the real ordeal.

As the ball left Burgess's hand he began instinctively to shape for a forward stroke. Then suddenly he realised that the thing was going to be a yorker, and banged his bat down in the block just as the ball arrived. An unpleasant sensation as of having been struck by a thunderbolt was succeeded by a feeling of relief that he had kept the ball out of his wicket. There are easier things in the world than stopping a fast yorker.

'Well played,' said Burgess.

Mike felt like a successful general receiving the thanks of the nation.

The fact that Burgess's next ball knocked middle and off stumps out of the ground saddened him somewhat; but this was the last tragedy that occurred. He could not do much with the bowling beyond stopping it and feeling repetitions of the thunderbolt experience, but he kept up his end; and a short conversation which he had with Burgess at the end of his innings was full of encouragement to one skilled in reading between the lines.

'Thanks awfully,' said Mike, referring to the square manner in which the captain had behaved in letting him bat.

'What school were you at before you came here?' asked Burgess.

'A private school in Hampshire,' said Mike. 'King-Hall's. At a place called Emsworth.'

'Get much cricket there?'

'Yes, a good lot. One of the masters, a chap called Westbrook, was an awfully good slow bowler.'

Burgess nodded.

'You don't run away, which is something,' he said.

Mike turned purple with pleasure at this stately compliment. Then, having waited for further remarks, but gathering from the captain's silence that the audience was at an end, he proceeded to unbuckle his pads. Wyatt overtook him on his way to the house.

'Well played,' he said. 'I'd no idea you were such hot stuff. You're a regular pro.'

'I say,' said Mike gratefully, 'it was most awfully decent of you getting Burgess to let me go in. It was simply ripping of you.'

'Oh, that's all right. If you don't get pushed a bit here you stay for ages in the hundredth game with the cripples and the kids. Now you've shown them what you can do you ought to get into the Under Sixteen team straight away. Probably into the third, too.'

'By Jove, that would be all right.'

'I asked Burgess afterward what he thought of your batting,

and he said, "Not bad." But he says that about everything. It's his highest form of praise. He says it when he wants to let himself go and simply butter up a thing. If you took him to see N.A. Knox bowl, he'd say he wasn't bad. What he meant was that he was jolly struck with your batting, and is going to play you for the Under Sixteen.'

'I hope so,' said Mike.

The prophecy was fulfilled. On the following Wednesday there was a match between the Under Sixteen and a scratch side. Mike's name was among the Under Sixteen. And on the Saturday he was playing for the third eleven in a trial game.

'This place is ripping,' he said to himself, as he saw his name on the list. 'Thought I should like it.'

And that night he wrote a letter to his father, notifying him of the fact.

from MIKE: A Public School Story
1909

FATHERS OF MEN

by

E.W. Hornung

Although Hornung (who died in 1923 at the age of fifty-four) is best known for his Raffles *stories, at least one of his admirers, his brother-in-law Sir Arthur Conan Doyle, while praising their vividness and style, said: 'But in a way they harmed Hornung, for they got between the public and his better work'.*

He went on: 'Fathers of Men *is one of the very best school tales in the language, taking in the masters as well as the boys, and thereby perhaps marring the book for the latter. But it was a remarkable achievement . . . Hornung was the best-read man in cricket lore that I have ever met, and would I am sure have excelled in the game itself if he had not been hampered by short sight and a villainous asthma. To see him stand up behind the sticks with his big pebble glasses to a fast bowler was an object lesson in pluck if not in wicket-keeping.'*

In Fathers of Men *the match between the Old Boys and the School covers three separate chapters. In the second innings against the Old Boys Jan Rutter, captain of the School XI, has bowled brilliantly to take nine wickets for 26 runs. The School has now to make 215 to win but Rutter, who bats low down the order, has decided to help his friend Evan Devereux by going to meet on his behalf in Yardley Wood the man who has been supplying him with illicit champagne. But he is discovered by one of the masters, Haigh . . .*

'There's nothing to be said, Rutter, as between you and me, except on one small point that doesn't matter to anybody else. I gathered just now that you were not particularly surprised at being caught by *me*– that it's what you would have expected of me – playing the spy! Well, I have played it during the last hour; but I never should have dreamt of doing so if your own rashness had not thrust the part upon me.'

'I suppose you saw me get into the fly?' said Jan, with a certain curiosity in the incidence of his frustration.

'I couldn't help seeing you. I had called for this myself, and was in the act of bringing it to you for your – splitting head!'

Haigh had produced an obvious medicine bottle sealed up in white paper. Jan could not resent his sneer.

'I'm sorry you had the trouble, sir. There was nothing the matter with my head.'

'And you can stand there —'

Haigh did not finish his sentence, except by dashing the medicine bottle to the ground in his disgust, so that it broke even in that rank grass, and its contents soaked the smooth white paper. This was the old Adam, but only for a moment. Jan could almost have done with more of him.

'I know what you must think of me, sir,' he said. 'I had to meet a blackmailer at his own time and place. But that's no excuse for me.'

'I'm glad you don't make it one, I must say! I was going on to tell you that I followed the fly, only naturally, as I think you'll agree. But it wasn't my fault you didn't hear me in the wood before you saw me, Rutter. I made noise enough, but you were so taken up with your – boon companion!'

Jan resented that; but he had made up his mind not even to start the dangerous game of self-defence.

'He exaggerated that part of it,' was all that Jan said, dryly.

'So I should hope. It's not my business to ask for explanations —'

'And I've none to give, sir.'

'It's only for me to report the whole matter, Rutter, as of course I must at once.'

Jan looked alarmed.

'Do you mean before the match is over? Must the Eleven and all those Old Boys —'

'Hear all about it? Not necessarily, I should say, but it won't be in my hands. The facts are usually kept quiet in – in the worst cases – as you know. But I shan't have anything to say to that.'

'You would if it were a fellow in your house!' Jan could not help rejoining. 'You'd take jolly good care to have as little known as possible – if you don't mind my saying so.'

Haigh did mind; he was a man to mind the slightest word, and yet he took this from Jan without a word of reply. The fact was that, much to his annoyance and embarrassment, he was beginning to respect the youth more in his downfall than at the height of his cricketing fame. Indeed, while he had grudged a great and unforeseen school success to as surly a young numskull as ever impeded the work of the Middle Remove (and the only one who ever, ever scored off Mr Haigh), he could not but recognise the manhood of the same boy's bearing in adversity – and such adversity at such a stage in his career! There had been nothing abject about it for a moment, and now there was neither impertinence nor bravado, but rather an unsuspected sensibility, rather a redeeming spirit altogether. Yet it was an aggravated case, if ever there had been one in the whole history of schools; a more deliberate and daring piece of trickery could not be imagined. In that respect it was typical of the drinking row of Haigh's experience. And yet he found himself making jaunty remarks to Jan about the weather, and even bringing off his raucous laugh about nothing, for the flyman's benefit, as they came up to where that vehicle was waiting in the lane.

Haigh, of all masters, and Jan Rutter of all the boys who had ever been through his hands!

That was the feeling that preyed upon the man, the weight he tried to get off his chest when they had dismissed the fly outside the town, and had walked in together as far as Heriot's quad.

'Well, Rutter, there never was much love lost between us, was there? And yet – I don't mind telling you – I wish any other man in the place had the job you've given me!'

The quad was still deserted, but Jan had scarcely reached his study when a hurried but uncertain step sounded in the passage, and a small fag from another house appeared at his open door.

'Oh, please, Rutter, I was sent to fetch you if you're well enough to bat.'

'Who sent you?'

'Goose.'

'How many of them are out?'

'Seven when I left.'

'How many runs?'

'Hundred and sixty just gone up.'

'It hadn't! Who's been getting them?'

'Devereux, principally.'

The fag from another house always said that Rutter lit up at this as though the runs were already made, and then that he gave the most extraordinary laugh, but suddenly asked if Devereux was out.

'And when I told him he wasn't,' said the fag, 'he simply sent me flying out of his way, and by the time I got into the street he was almost out of sight at the other end!'

Certainly they were the only two creatures connected with the school who were to be seen about the town at half-past-four that Saturday afternoon; and half the town itself seemed glued to those palings affected by Jan's flyman; and on the ground every available boy in the school, every master except Haigh, and every single master's lady, watched the game without a word about any other topic under the sun. Even the tea-tent, a great feature of the festival, under the auspices of Miss Heriot and other ladies, was deserted alike by all parties to its usually popular entertainment.

Evan was still in, said to have made over 70, and to be playing the innings of his life, the innings of the season for the school. But another wicket must have fallen soon after the small fag fled for Jan, and Chilton who had gone in was not shaping with conspicuous confidence. Evan looked, however, as though he had enough for two, from the one glimpse Jan had of his heated but collected face, and the one stroke he saw him make, before diving into the dressing-room to clap on his pads. To think that Evan was still in, and on the high road to a century if anybody could stop with him! To think he should have chosen this very afternoon!

It was at this point that the hard Fates softened, for a time only, yet a time worth the worst they could do to Jan now. They might not have given him pause to put his pads on properly; they might not have suffered him to get his breath. When he had done both, and even had a wash, and pulled his cap well over his wet hair, they might have kept him waiting till the full flavour of their late misdeeds turned his heart sick and faint within him. Instead of all or any of this, they propped up Chilton for another 15 runs, and then sent Jan in with 33 to get and Evan not out 84.

But they might have spared the doomed wretch the tremendous cheering that greeted his supposed resurrection from the sick-room to which – obviously – his heroic efforts of the morning had brought him. It took Evan to counteract the irony of that reception with a little dose on his own account.

'Keep your end up,' whispered Evan, coming out to meet the captain a few yards from the pitch, 'and I can get them. Swallow's off the spot and the rest are pifflers. Keep up your end and leave the runs to me.'

It was the tone of pure injunction, from the one who might have been captain to his last hope. But that refinement was lost on Jan; he could only stare at the cool yet heated face, all eagerness and confidence, as though nothing whatever had been happening off the ground. And his stare did draw a change of look – a swift unspoken question – the least little cloud, that vanished at Jan's reply.

'It's all right,' said Jan, oracularly. 'You won't be bothered any more.'

'Good man!' said Evan. 'Then only keep your end up, and we'll have the fun of a lifetime between us!'

Jan nodded as he went to the crease; really the fellow had done him good. And in yet another little thing the Fates were kind; he had not to take the next ball, and Evan took care to make a single off the last one of the over, which gave the newcomer a good look at both bowlers before being called upon to play a ball.

But then it was A.G. Swallow whom he had to face; and, in spite of Evan's expert testimony to the contrary, that great cricketer certainly looked as full of wisdom, wiles, and genial malice as an egg is full of meat.

A.G. Swallow took his rhythmical little ball-room amble of a run, threw his left shoulder down, heaved his right arm up, and flicked finger and thumb together as though the departing ball were a pinch of snuff. I.T. Rutter – one of the many left-hand bowlers who bat right, it is now worth while to state – watched its high trajectory with terror tempered by a bowler's knowledge of the kind of break put on. He thought it was never going to pitch, but when it did – well to the off – he scrambled in front of his wicket and played the thing somehow with bat and pads combined. But A.G. Swallow awaited the ball's return with a smile of settled sweetness, and E. Devereux had frowned.

The next ball flew higher, with even more spin, but broke so much from leg as to beat everything except Stratten's hands behind the sticks. But Jan had not moved out of his ground; he had simply stood there and been shot at, yet already he was beginning to perspire. Two balls and two such escapes were enough to upset anybody's nerve; and now, of course, Jan knew enough about batting to know what a bad bat he was, and the knowledge often made him worse still. He had just one point: as a bowler he would put himself in the bowler's place and consider what he himself would try next if he were bowling.

Now perhaps the finest feature of Swallow's slow bowling was the fast one that he could send down, when he liked, without perceptible change of action; but the other good bowler rightly guessed that this fast ball was coming now, was more than ready for it, let go early with all his might, and happened to time it to perfection. It went off his bat like a lawn-tennis ball from a tight racket, flew high and square (though really intended for an on drive), and came down on the pavilion roof with a heavenly crash.

The school made music, too; but Evan Devereux looked distinctly disturbed, and indeed it was a good thing there was not another ball in the over. A.G. Swallow did not like being hit; it was his only foible; but to hit him half by accident was to expose one's wicket to all the knavish tricks that could possibly be combined and concentrated in the very next delivery.

Now, however, Evan had his turn again, and picked five more runs off three very moderate balls from the vigorous Whitfield; the fourth did not defeat Jan, and Evan had Swallow's next over. He played it like a professional, but ran rather a sharp single off the last ball, and in short proceeded to 'nurse' the bowling as though his partner had not made 25 in the first innings and already hit a sixer in his second.

Jan did not resent this in the least. The height of his own momentary ambition was simply to stay there until the runs were made; the next essential was for Evan to achieve his century, but the larger hope involved that consummation, and at this rate he would not be very long about it. To Jan his performance was a composite revelation of character and capacity. Surely it was not Evan Devereux batting at all, but a higher order of cricketer in Evan's image, an altogether stronger soul in his skin! Even that looked different, so fiery red and yet so free from the nervous perspiration welling from Jan's pores; surely some sheer enchantment had quickened hand and foot, and sharpened an eye that looked abnormally bright at twenty yards!

So thought Jan at the other end; and he wondered if the original stimulus could have been the very weight of an anxiety greater than any connected with the game; but he entertained these searching speculations almost unawares, and alongside all manner of impressions, visions and reminiscences, of a still more intimate character. The truth was that Jan himself was in a rarefied atmosphere, out there on the pitch, seeing and doing things for the last time, and somehow more vividly and with greater zest than he had ever seen or done such things before.

Though he had played upon it literally hundreds of times, never until today had he seen what a beautiful ground the Upper really was. On three sides a smiling land fell away in fine slopes from the very boundary, as though a hill-top had been sliced off to make the field; on those three sides you could see for miles, and they were miles of grazing country checkered with hedges, and of blue distance blotted with trees. But even as a cricket-field Jan felt that he had never before appreciated his dear Upper as he ought. It lay so high that at one end the batsman stood in position against the sky from the pads upwards, and the empyrean was the screen behind the bowler's arm.

Of course these fresh features of a familiar scene were due more to mental exaltation than to the first perfect day of the term; but they owed little or nothing to the conscientious sentimentality of a farewell appearance. Jan was a great deal too excited to think of anything but the ball while the ball was in play. But between the overs the spectres of the early afternoon were at his elbow, and in one such pause he espied Haigh in the flesh watching from the ring.

Yes! There was Haigh freshly groomed, in a clean collar and another suit of clothes, the grey hair brushed back from his pink temples, but his mouth inexorably shut on the tidings it was soon to utter. Decent of Haigh to wait until the match was lost or won; but then Haigh resembled the Upper inasmuch as Jan already liked everything about him better than he had ever done before. In front of the pavilion, in tall hat, frock-coat and white cravat, sat splendid little old Jerry himself, that flogging judge of other days, soon to assume the black cap at last, but still ignorant of the capital offence committed, still beaming with delight and pride in a glorious finish. Elsewhere a triangle of familiar faces made themselves seen and heard; its apex was gaunt old Heriot, who in his innocence had bawled a salvo for the sixer; and the gay old dog on his right was his friend Major Mangles, while Oxford had already turned the austere Crabtree into the gay young dog on his left.

Jan wondered what Crabtree would think – and then what the Major was saying as he poked Bob Heriot in the ribs. He soon saw what they were saying; all that Cambridge and Lord's had left of the original Charles Cave was going on to bowl instead of Swallow, and those three tense faces on the boundary had relaxed in esoteric laughter. But it was Jan who had to play Cave's over and it was almost worthy of the Cantab's youth three years ago. Jan, however, was almost at home by this time; all four balls found the middle of his bat; and then the public-spirited policy of A.G. Swallow dictated an audacious move.

Of course he must know what he was doing, for he had led a first-class county in his day, and had never been the captain to take himself off without reason. No doubt he understood the value of a double change; but was it really wise to put on Swiller Wilman at Whitfield's end with lobs when only 15 runs were wanted to win the match. Pavilion critics had their oracular doubts about it; old judges on the rugs had none at all, but gave

Devereux a couple of covers for the winning hit; and only Evan himself betrayed a certain apprehension as he crossed beckoning to Jan before the lobs began.

'Have you any idea how many I've got?' he asked below his breath. The second hundred had just gone up to loud applause.

'I can tell you to a run if you want to know.'

'I'm asking you.'

'You've made 94.'

'Rot!'

'You have. You'd made 84 when I came in. I've counted your runs since then.'

'I'd no idea it was nearly so many!'

'And I didn't mean to tell you.'

There Jan had been quite right, but it was not so tactful to remind the batsman of every batsman's anxiety on nearing the century. Evan, to be sure, repudiated the faint suggestion with some asperity; but his very lips looked redder than before.

'Well, don't you get out off him,' said Evan, consequentially.

'I'll try not to. Let's both follow the rule, eh?'

'What rule?'

'Dudley Relton's for lobs: a single off every ball, never more and never less, and nothing whatever on the half-volley.'

'Oh, be blowed!' said Evan. 'We've been going far too slow these last few overs as it is.'

Accordingly he hit the first lob just over mid-on's head for three, and Jan got his single off the next, but off both of the next two balls Evan was very nearly out for 97 and the match lost by 10 runs.

On the second occasion even George Grimwood gratuitously conceded that off a lob a fraction faster Mr Devereux would indeed have been stumped; as it was he had only just got back in time. This explanation was not acknowledged by Mr Stratten, whose vain appeal had been echoed by half the field. The nice fellow seemed to have lost all his looks as he crossed to the other end.

The next incident was a full-pitch to leg from Charles Cave and a fourer to Jan Rutter. That made 6 to tie and 7 to win, but only about another hit to Jan if Evan was to get his century. Jan thought of that as he played hard forward to the next ball but one, and felt it leap and heard it hiss through the covers; for even his old bat was driving as it had never done before; but a delightful deep-field sprinter just saved the boundary, and Jan would not risk the more than possible third run.

If this had been a modern match at Lord's, the revolving figures would now have stood at:

97 210 14

In less technical terms 5 runs were wanted to win the match. And Evan Devereux, within 3 of every cricketer's ambition, again faced the merry underhand bowler against whom he had shaped so precariously the over before last.

George Grimwood might have been seen shifting from foot to foot, and jingling pence in his accomplished palm. Another of these near things was not wanted this over, with the whole match hanging to it, and Mr Stratten still looking like that . . .

A bit better, was that! A nice two for Mr Devereux to the unprotected off – no! – blessed if they aren't running again! They must be daft; one of them'll be out, one of 'em must be! No – a bad return – but Mr Cave has it now. How beautifully this gentleman always throws! You wouldn't think it of him, to see him crossing over, or even batting or bowling; he's got a return like a young cannon, and here it comes!

No umpire will be able to give this in; there's Mr Rutter a good two yards down the pitch, legging it for dear life; and here comes the ball like a bullet. He's out if it doesn't miss the wicket after all; but it does miss it, by a coat of varnish, and ricochets to the boundary for another four, that wins the match for the school, the ultimate honour of three figures for Evan Devereux, and peace beyond this racket for George Grimwood.

Over the ground swarm the whole school like a small Surrey crowd, but Evan and Jan have been too quick for them; they break through the swift outer fringe; and it is not Lord's or the Oval after all. Nobody cares so much who wins this match, it's the magnificent finish that matters and will matter while the school exists.

So the dense mass before the pavilion parts in two, and the smiling Old Boys march through the lane; but it does not close up again until Rutter has come out and given Devereux his colours in the dear old way, by taking the blue sash from his own waist and tying it round that of his friend.

Did somebody say that Devereux was blubbing from excitement? It was not the case; but nobody was watching Jan.

from FATHERS OF MEN
1912

TEN TO MAKE ...

by

E.F. Benson

E.F. Benson (1867–1940) was born at Wellington College where his father E.W. Benson – later Archbishop of Canterbury – was Master. E.F. himself was educated at Marlborough and Cambridge – his elder brother, A.C., and his younger, R.H., both going to Eton. School, indeed, was in his blood, as was writing. E.F. became the prolific popular novelist of Dodo *(1893) and* Queen Lucia *(1920), both of which produced several sequels. He also published two lively volumes of reminiscence –* As We Were *(1930) and* As We Are *(1932).*

David Blaize *was published in 1915 and had reached its fourth edition by the following year. It is well characterised by its stirring, if somewhat sententious House cricket match (chapter XII). And* David Blaize *too had its sequel (*David at King's*).*

David Blaize was sitting on the steps in front of the cricket-pavilion in school-field, with a pad on each leg and a glove on each hand, and an icy lump of nervous fear inside his canvas shirt to take the place of a heart. But nobody paid the least attention to him, or gave him a single word of encouragement, or cared at all for his panic-stricken condition, because everybody was utterly absorbed in what was going on at the wickets. The whole school and the whole staff were there watching the end of the final tie in house-matches in absolute tense silence, except when a run was scored, or a smart piece of fielding prevented one being scored. Then a roar went up from all round the ground, cut off again suddenly, as if a hand had been placed over all the mouths of some many-throated beast, as the bowler received the ball again. During the pause between overs a buzz of talk rose as if the cork had been taken out of a bottle where sonorous bees were confined; this talk was silenced as the next over began.

Probably such a final as this had been seen before, but that did not detract from the tenseness of the excitement. The present position, arrived at through many delightful adventures, was that Adams's wanted twenty more runs to win, with two wickets to fall. Maddox, luckily, was in still, and Cruikshank (a miserable performer with the bat) was in with him. If either of them got out, the forlorn and trembling David had to take his place, last wicket, to totter down the steps and walk apparently about twenty miles to the wicket, in the full light of day, with the eyes of the world on him. Maddox, of course, was the only hope of salvation; neither David nor Cruikshank could, even by their most optimistic friends, be considered as capable of doing anything but getting out against such strength of bowling as they had against them. And, in order to make David quite happy and comfortable about it all, there was indelibly written on the tablets of his memory the fact that he had got out second ball in the first innings 'without,' as the school paper would record on Saturday, 'having troubled the scorer . . .' What if the paper added that in the second innings he proved himself as independent of the scorer again? So, while the groups of boys round him, regaling themselves the while on bags of cherries and baskets of strawberries, seethed with pleasant, irresponsible excitement, David was merely perfectly miserable, as he waited for the roar that would go up round the field, to show another wicket had fallen that would not be abruptly cut off like the tumult that succeeded a run or a piece of fielding: the Toveyites would go on screaming 'Well bowled' or 'Well caught' until he marched out across the field. All that he could think of in this hour of waiting was the fact that he had been completely bowled by the second ball he received in the first innings after having been completely beaten by the first. Tomlin, who had kindly sent down that fatal delivery, was bowling now, and no doubt he would be bowling still when he went in.

The match had been full of entrancing and agonizing vicissitudes. Adams's had batted first, piling up a respectable total of 182, which gave no cause for complaint. Then Tovey's had gone in and had been ignominously dismissed by Cruikshank and Mellor for 81, and the sages were inclined to think that the match was as good as over. They had followed on, but, instead of being dismissed for 81 again, they had amassed the huge total of 329. Cruikshank, the demon of the first innings, had been hit completely off his length, and David had been put on as first change, not having bowled at all in the first innings. But the glorious personal result of that afternoon's work gave him no encouragement now, for his mind was filled to the exclusion of all else with the fact that in his previous appearance with the bat, and not the ball, Tomlin had beaten him twice and bowled him once. But yesterday, when he was bowling, Tovey's could do nothing with him; he bowled their captain, Anstruther, in his first over (after being hit twice to the boundary by him) and had proved himself altogether too much for the rest of the side. The wicket was fast and true, and there was no reason for their not being able to play him, except the excellent one that he bowled extremely well. He was left-handed, with very high action, and had (as an accessory) cultivated a terrifying prance up to the wickets, with a crooked run and a change of feet in the middle of it, like a stumbling horse. After this he delivered a slow high ball, while every now and then (but not too often) he laced one in as hard as ever he could with precisely the same delivery. In the end he had taken seven wickets for 90 runs, while the rest of the 329 had been scored off the other bowlers of the side, who had captured two wickets (one being run out) between them.

There came a roar from the ring of spectators round the field, and shouts of derisive laughter from a group of Adams's boys standing near, and David, forgetting everything else for the moment, added a piercing catcall whistle to the general hubbub. Tomlin had changed his field with the obvious intention of getting Maddox caught in the slips, sending mid-on there, making the fourth of them. Then he proceeded to bowl a little wide of the off-stump. Maddox had let three balls go by, but the fourth he pulled round to exactly where mid-on had been, and scored four for it. Oh, a great stroke, and no one could tell, perhaps not even Maddox, how it was done.

There was one more ball of this over, and it was wonderfully important that Maddox should score one or three or five off it, so as to get the bowling again. But it was no use attempting to do anything with such a ball, it was all he could do to play it. So Cruikshank got the bowling. Well, it was better that Cruikshank should face Crawley than Tomlin. If only Tomlin could receive a telegram saying that his father and mother and his three brothers and his four sisters (if he had any) were all seriously ill, and that he had to go home absolutely this minute . . . .

It was clear that Cruikshank was nervous – David knew of somebody else who was nervous, too – but he presented a dull solid wall to two straight balls. Then, with extreme caution, he lobbed one up in the direction of long-off, and ran like the devil. 'Come on,' he shouted to Maddox, for he was just as anxious that Maddox should get the bowling as were the rest of Adams's.

Maddox wanted a run as much as anybody, but he was completely taken by surprise at the impudence of this. But there was Cruikshank half way up the pitch, and it meant a wicket lost, if he told him to go back. So he, too, ran like the devil.

The situation only lasted a couple of seconds, but it made up in quality what it lacked in quantity. If long-off, who already had the ball in his hands, had thrown it in to the end from which Cruikshank had started, he had a good chance of getting Maddox run out, while if he threw it in to the bowler, close to him, he had the practical certainty of running Cruikshank out, which was not nearly so important. Simultaneously both wicket-keeper and bowler shouted 'This end!' and he threw it wildly to about the middle of the pitch. And there were fifteen more runs to get to win.

It seemed to David, as he watched, forgetting himself for a moment or two, that Maddox himself was feeling the strain, especially after this last and unmerited escape. He spooned a ball feebly in the air short, but only just short of point; and the next, though he scored two off it, was the most dangerous stroke, and as unlike as possible to his usual crisp cutting. Still, it might be only that there was something dreadfully unexpected about that ball, which caused him to mistime it. But if only he would kindly *not* mistime balls for a little while longer. Then came the last ball of the over, which he hit out at, completely missed it, and was nearly bowled. So Cruikshank had to face the fatal Tomlin.

There ensued some piercing moments. There was an appeal for a catch at the wickets, confidently made, which was not upheld, and Cruikshank proceeded to play like a clockwork doll, imperfectly wound up. After failing to play two balls altogether, he hit out as hard as he could at the third, intending to drive it, and snicked it between his legs for one. But that gave Maddox the bowling again, and off the last ball he scored one, and thus secured the bowling again.

A little faint glimmer of hope came into David's heart. There was a bye for two, which left eleven runs only to get, and perhaps, perhaps he would not have to bat at all. If only Maddox would hit three fours in succession, a feat of which he was perfectly capable, the match would be over, and David thought it would be quite impossible ever to stop shouting again. For nothing in the whole world mattered to him now, except that they should win, and nobody mattered except those two white figures at the wicket. Yet one was Frank, and David so far mastered his trembling knees as to go to the scoring-box to see how many he had made. His score was just 80, so that he could not get his century, even if he scored the rest himself. Rather a pity, but certainly nobody would care less than Frank.

At the third ball he opened his shoulders, and gave a little skip out to drive, and a celestial stroke it was. The ball flew along the ground, rather to the right of long-off, and it seemed as if it must go for four; but that odious fellow just reached it, stopping it with his foot, made a beautiful return, and instead of four it was a single only. And Cruikshank had the bowling.

A roar had gone up on account of the smart fielding of the last ball, and was instantly silent again. Now there went up another, not so soon coming to an end, for Cruikshank's leg-stump had been sent flying. And there were ten more runs to get.

David got up, put on his cap, and then with great deliberation took it off again. He didn't know if he wanted a cap or not, and it was immensely important to settle that. It was sunny, but the sun was still high, and would not really come in his eyes. But he certainly wanted something to drink, for his throat had suddenly become gritty and dry like the side of a match-box, and he wanted to run away and hide, or to do anything in the world rather than cross that interminable stretch of grass, across which Cruikshank was now walking. But as soon as Cruikshank reached the pavilion he would have to go. That impossible feat had to be accomplished.

Bags had been sitting by him, thoughtfully eating cherries, after David had refused them, but it was long since he had had any clear consciousness of Bags or of anyone else except those white figures in the field. But at this awful moment Bags proved himself a friend in need.

'Oh, David, how ripping it will be,' he said, in a voice of complete conviction, 'that you and Maddox win cock-house match for us.'

Up till that moment the possibility had literally not entered David's head: he had been entirely absorbed in the prospect of losing it for them. But this suggestion put a little heart into him, instead of the cold fear.

'By Gad,' he said, and, drawing a long breath, went down the steps on to the level field.

The moment he got moving, even though he was only moving to the place of execution, he found that it was not so impossible as it had appeared in anticipation. It had seemed out of the question at this crucially critical period in the history of cricket, which was more important than the history of the world, to face this. But now there he was, going out all alone, bat in hand, and he did not sink into the earth or fall down with a few hollow groans. And then two other things encouraged him further, neither of which he had contemplated. As his tall, slight figure detached itself from the crowd in front of the pavilion a real cheer went up, not from the boys of his house only, but from the school in general. He told himself that they were not cheering him, David Blaize, but only the last actor in this enthralling piece of drama, in spite of which he felt much the healthier for it. And the second thing that encouraged him was far better, for Maddox, leaving the wicket, had come half-way across the ground to meet him and walk back with him.

'David, old chap, isn't it ripping,' he said (even as Bags had said), 'that it's you and me? Just the jolliest thing that could happen. Don't bother about runs; they'll come all right. Just keep your end up, and don't take any risks. The bowling's absolute piffle, so long as you don't try to hit it.'

Then they had to part company, each going to his wicket.

There were, so David remembered with hideous distinctness, two more balls of the over, and after taking middle and leg he had a look round. The two points that struck him most were that the other wicket seemed nightmarishly close to be bowled at from, and that there were apparently about thirty fielders. But then, as Crawley walked away to get his run, the rest of David's nerve, now that the time for action had come, was completely restored to him. He had never felt cooler nor clearer of eye in his life.

He received his first ball. At first he thought it was going to be a full-pitch, but then he saw it was a yorker. He saw it in time and he heard, sweet as honey to the mouth, the chunk with which it hit the centre of his bat close to the end.

There was no doubt whatever about the second ball: it was a half-volley well outside his leg-stump. David made one futile attempt to be prudent and resist the temptation, but he was quite incapable of it, danced out a yard, and smote for all he was worth. He heard the solid impact of the bat, telling him he had hit it correctly, and – there was the ball, already beyond and high above mid-on. It was not worth while starting to run, since this was a boundary-hit, if ever there was one. And – almost more important – this was the end of the over. Opposite he saw Maddox shaking his fist at him, as the roar of applause went up, mingled with shouts from his particular friends of 'Well hit, Blazes! Smack 'em about, David,' and he swaggered out of his ground, to slap a perfectly true place on the wicket with his bat. He looked up with a deprecatory smile at Frank.

'Sorry, I had to,' he said.

'You little devil!' said the other.

A silence more intense than ever settled down over the ground, as the last shouts consequent on David's immortal feat died away, for Tomlin proceeded to send down perhaps the best over he had ever bowled in his life. Once he completely beat Maddox, and must have shaved the varnish off his bails, and from the rest the batsman made no attempt to score, being quite satisfied with stopping them. At the end Anstruther looked round the field.

'Wace, take an over at Crawley's end, will you?' he said.

Then that period, deadly for a newly arrived batsman, had to be gone through, when the fresh bowler has a few practice-balls, and rearranges the field, and it made David fret. Long-on had to be moved two yards nearer, and one yard to the right: cover-point had to go much deeper, point had to come in a little, and the slips went through a mystic dance. This being concluded, Wace proceeded.

David opened with an appalling stroke, that would have been easily caught by cover, if only Wace had not moved him, and thereupon Wace brought him in again. So David, with an even worse stroke, spooned the ball over his head, so that if he had not been moved the second time, he must have caught it. For this he scored one amid derisive and exultant yells, and Maddox hit at him with his bat as they crossed each other. And there were four more runs to get.

Then the end came. Maddox played two balls with great care, and the unfortunate Wace then sent him a full pitch to leg. There came the sound of the striking bat; next moment the ball bounded against the palings by the pavilion. And Maddox had played his last house-match.

Frank waited to see the ball hit the palings, and then ran across the pitch to David.

'Didn't I tell you so?' he said. 'And wasn't it ripping that you and I should do that? Hullo, they're coming for us. Let's run.'

All round the ground the crowd had broken up wildly shouting, some going towards the pavilion, but others, headed by a detachment from Adams's, streaming out on to the pitch. The two boys ran towards the pavilion, dodging the first few of these, but both were caught and carried in starfish-wise. Then again and again, first Maddox alone, then both together, they had to come out on to the balcony, while the house and school generally shouted itself hoarse for this entrancing finish. Indeed, the honours were fairly divided, for if Maddox's batting had saved the situation today, the situation would have been impossible to save if it had not been for David's bowling yesterday. Then by degrees the crowd dispersed, and the shouting died, and the two sat for a while there, the happiest pair perhaps in all England, blunt and telegraphic with each other.

'David, you little devil!' said Frank. 'Frightful cheek, your hitting that four. Second ball you received, too.'

David gave a cackle of laughter.

'Don't rub it in,' he said. 'I apologized. Juicy shot, too. I say, Tomlin sent you down an over of corkers after that.'

'Nearly spewed with anxiety,' said Frank. 'Absolute limit of an over.'

'Wicked fellow, Tomlin,' quoth David. 'Glad I didn't get any of them.'

'So'm I, damn glad. Else —'

'Of course nobody can bat except yourself,' said David.

'You can't, anyhow.'

'But we won.'

'Have we really? Don't interrupt. I should have added that you can bowl.'

'You can't,' said David, getting level.

'No, filthy exercise. I'll take you down to bathe, if you don't bar washing, and then I'll take you to school shop, and you may eat all there is. Lucky I'm flush.'

'Right oh, thanks awfully,' said David. 'But you won't be flush long.'

They got up to go, but at the door Maddox paused.

'Best of all the days I've had at school, David,' he said.

'Same here,' said David.

School bathing did not begin for another hour, but Maddox had the sixth-form privilege of bathing whenever he chose, and Adams, whom they ran to catch up on their way down, gave David leave to go with him. He had dutifully and delightedly watched every ball of the match, and had helped to carry David into the pavilion as there was no chance of assisting at the entry of Maddox.

'Yes, by all means, yes, you – you blest pair of sirens,' he said, quoting from the Milton Ode which was to be sung at concert at the end of term. 'And take care of David, Jonathan, and don't let him sink from being top-heavy with pride. We shall want him to bowl next year.'

They trotted on for a little, in order to arrive at the bathing-place in the greatest possible heat.

from DAVID BLAIZE
1916

A LOT OF JEALOUSY IN CRICKET

by

Frank Richards

As George Orwell wrote in Inside the Whale, *summing up the world of* The Gem *and* The Magnet: *'The year is 1910 – or 1940, but it's all the same. You are at Greyfriars, a rosy-cheeked boy of fourteen in posh tailor-made clothes, sitting down to tea in your study on the Remove passage . . . After tea we shall sit round the study having a good laugh at Billy Bunter and discussing the teams for next week's match against Rookwood. Everything is safe, solid, and unquestionable. Everything will be the same for ever and ever.'*

To which the 1980s reader can only say, 'Amen'.

'You haven't seen much of my batting,' said Bunter. 'You see, at Greyfriars I'm kept a good bit in the background, so far as games are concerned. There's a lot of jealousy in cricket.'

'Weally, Buntah —'

'That's why you've never seen me play for Greyfriars when we've sent men over to St Jim's, you know. You don't mind my telling D'Arcy the facts, Wharton?'

Harry Wharton laughed.

'I haven't heard you tell him any facts, so far,' he answered.

'Oh, really, Wharton —'

'Well, roll on, old porpoise, if you're going to open the innings,' said Bob Cherry. 'Somebody get ready to chalk up a big round nought on the board.'

'Ha, ha, ha!'

'Oh, cheese it, Cherry! This isn't a time for petty envy,' said Bunter.

'Oh, my hat!'

'The fact is, I expect to be not out, Gussy,' said Bunter. 'You can see that the fellows we're playing aren't much class at cricket. What?'

'Oh deah!' murmured Arthur Augustus, quite distressed. Parker was in hearing, but a trifle like that did not disconcert Bunter. It disconcerted the swell of St Jim's considerably.

'What I want you to do is to keep the innings alive while I score,' explained Bunter. 'All you fellows do the same.'

'The samefulness will be terrific, my esteemed fatheaded Bunter,' grinned Huree Singh.

'Don't you worry about run-getting, Gussy. Leave that to me. Just put in some stone-walling, and don't try on any St Jim's swank, you know.'

Leaving Arthur Augustus D'Arcy quite speechless, Bunter rolled away cheerily to the wickets. Arthur Augustus stood rooted to the ground, gazing after him. Bob Cherry grinned and jogged his elbow.

'Man in, you know,' he said.

'Bai Jove!' gasped Arthur Augustus. 'I – I – I suppose Buntah weally means no offence, you know. But for a fellow who means no offence he has a weally wemarkable way of expwessin' himself.'

And the swell of St Jim's trotted away to his wickets, to stand aside while Bunter received the bowling.

The Combermere men were in the field, and Parker went on to bowl. The estate-office young man rather fancied himself as a bowler; but as a matter of fact, he would not have been very useful against the average man in Harry Wharton's team at Greyfriars. But Bunter was very far from being an average Greyfriars cricketer. When it came to games Bunter was in a class by himself – entirely by himself.

Parker sent down the ball. Bunter spread himself to that ball. He was going to begin by knocking the first ball far and away beyond the boundary. That would be encouraging to his side, and would show the Combermere men the kind of cricketer they had to deal with. No doubt Bunter would have landed a 'sixer' but for the trifling circumstance that his bat missed the ball by about a yard.

Crash!

'How's that?' hooted Parker.

'Ha, ha, ha!'

'Out!'

Bunter stared at his wicket.

The middle stump was out of the ground, and the bails lay low. Even William George Bunter could not deny that it was 'out'. He was prepared to dispute with the umpire if necessary; but really, in this case, there was no room for a dispute. A spread-eagled wicket was not to be argued about, even by a cricketer of Bunter's quality.

'Oh!' ejaculated Bunter.

'Ha, ha, ha!'

'How's that!' shrieked all Parker's men.

'Bai Jove!' gasped Arthur Augustus D'Arcy. 'Bai Jove, this weally does take the bun! I wondah how much wun-gettin' there would be in this match if we left the wun-gettin' to Buntah, as he wequested.'

'Get a move on, fatty!' called out Johnny Bull as Billy Bunter stood staring at his wrecked wicket.

'Extraordinary!' said Bunter. 'What a game this is for flukes!'

'Ha, ha, ha!'

And the lord of Bunter Court carried out his unused bat and left the innings to lesser mortals.

from THE MAGNET
No. 914

HIS LAST TRIUMPH

by

Alec Waugh

Alec Waugh has written that the character of the novelist Robert Southcott, who became an 'established deity' to the urchins watching the cricket match at Fordenden in A.G. Macdonell's England, Their England, *was based on himself (see page 263). It was during the First World War, however, in 1917, that he published his first novel* The Loom of Youth, *a public school novel which created a good deal of controversy.* The Loom of Youth, *along with Ernest Raymond's* Tell England *a few years later, pointed away from 'Mike' and 'Billy Bunter' and 'David Blaize' into a new style of school story which made some attempt to treat the problems of adolescence in a closed community. For all that, the House cricket match in* The Loom of Youth *follows fairly traditional lines.*

The last days of June and the early weeks of July passed calmly. In the mornings he lounged in his study, reading novels, or talking to Morgan. The afternoons went by like a cavalcade, with the white figures on the cricket ground, the drowsy atmosphere of the pavilion, the shadows lengthening across the ground. Then the evenings came, with Morcombe sitting in his study getting helped in his work, or talking about books and people and ideas. The House matches began. A–K senior had an average side, but no one expected them to do very much, and it was a surprise when, by beating Christy's and Claremont's, they qualified to meet an exceptionally strong Buller's side in the final. Foster and Gordon looked forward to their last match at

Fernhurst with the cheerful knowledge that they had no chance of winning, and that therefore they had nothing to fear of disappointment. It would be a jolly friendly game to finish up with . . .

'Foster,' said Gordon, as the two walked down to the field, 'I believe ours is one of the very worst sides that ever got into the final. There are two Firsts, you and I. Collins was tried for the Colts two years ago. There are eight others.'

'Oh, you forget Bray, a fine, free bat with an unorthodox style. But . . . I believe he made fourteen on a House game the other day.'

'Yes, that is a recommendation, of course, but somehow I don't think we shall win.'

'Win!' echoed Foster. 'We shall be lucky if we avoid an innings defeat.'

And this supposition proved still more likely when half-an-hour later the House, having won the toss, had lost three wickets for as many runs. Jack Whitaker, now captain of Buller's, had gone on to bowl first from the end nearest the National Schools. In his first over he clean-bowled Gordon, and in the next he got Foster leg before, and Bradford caught in the slips.

'I foresee,' said Collins, 'that we shall spend most of this game fielding. A poor way of occupying our last few days.'

'That's where I score,' said Gordon; 'the wicket-keeper has no running to do, and, besides, I rather enjoy a game in which there is nothing to lose, no anxiety or anything. It is a peaceful end to a turgid career . . . Oh, well hit!'

Bray had just lifted a length ball off the middle stump over short-leg's head.

'That's the sort of cricket I like,' said Gordon; 'a splendid contempt for all laws and regulations. Heavens! there he goes again!'

A lucky snick flew over the slips to the boundary.

'This is something like,' said Foster, and prepared to enjoy himself.

And certainly Bray's cricket was entertaining. He treated every ball the same; he stepped straight down the pitch with his left foot, raised his bat in the direction of point and then, as the ball was bowled, he pivoted himself violently on his left foot and, going through a complete half-circle, finished, facing the wicket-keeper, with both feet outside the crease, but his bat well over the line. The chief attraction of this gymnastic feat was the unexpectedness of it all. No one knew where the ball would go if it was hit. Once when he timed his shot a little late he caught the ball just as it was passing him and drove it flying past the wicket-keeper's head to where long-stop would have been. The fielding side was always glad to see Bray's back, and it usually did not have to wait long. But today he bore a charmed life. He was missed at point once, twice he gave a chance of being stumped, the ball shaved his wickets times innumerable. But nearly every other ball he managed to hit somewhere. In the pavilion the School House rocked with laughter.

At the other end Davenham poked about scoring singles here and there. The score crept up. Amid cheers in which laughter was blended, the fifty went up. Then Bray, in a particularly gallant effort to steer the ball well outside the off stump round to short-leg, hit all three wickets flying out of the ground. It was a suitable end to an unusual innings.

He received a royal welcome in the pavilion.

'Bray, my son,' said Gordon, 'you are a sportsman. Come to the tuckshop and have a drink. Nellie, mix this gentleman an ice and a lemonade, and put it down to my account. Thank you. Ah, there's Collins. Good luck, Collins; keep your head.'

Two minutes later Collins returned to the pavilion with a downcast face.

'The damned thing broke,' he said, as if he considered breaks illegal in House matches.

The rest of the side played in the usual light-hearted School House spirit. There were some fine hits made, and some scandalous ones, too. It was like a cinematograph show. Everyone slammed about; the Buller's men missed catches galore. Davenport was missed four times in making fourteen. Somehow the score reached respectable heights. Byes helped considerably. The final score was 120.

'And now,' said Collins, 'we have got to field for two hours today. Tomorrow is not a half, so we shall have to field all the time; we sha'n't get a knock till after roll on Saturday. Five hours' fielding. Damn!'

'And it will do you a lot of good, too,' said Foster. 'Are you all ready, House? Come on then.'

A–K Senior filed out into the field. A loud cheer rose from the crowd. The House was amazingly partisan. Whether a House side is losing by an innings or winning by two hundred runs, it is always sure of the same reception when it goes on to the field from its own men. The light had grown rather bad and Foster began bowling with the trees at his back, so as to hide his delivery. At the other end Bradford was to bowl.

The start was sensational.

Buller's sent in Crampin and Mitchell first, two hefty footballers, with strong wrists and no science, who had run up some big scores in the preliminary rounds.

Foster ran up to bowl. Crampin had a terrific swipe. The ball turned from the bat. The bat only just touched it.

'How's that?' roared Gordon.

The finger went up. A ripple of clapping ran along the side of the ground.

'You stick to that,' said Collins, 'and we shall get them out by tomorrow night.'

'Dry up,' said Gordon ironically. 'Can't you see we are going to win? . . . Man in!'

Jack Whitaker came in. He was far and away the most stylish bat in the school, and had scored a lot of runs during the season. He faced the bowling confidently; he had played Foster a hundred times at the nets, and knew his tricks well. He played through the over with ease. The last ball he placed in front of short-leg for a single.

Bradford went on to bowl. He was a House match class of bowler. No idea of length, or direction, only an indefatigable energy and considerable pace. His first ball was a long hop wide on the off. Whitaker banged it past point for four.

The next ball was a full pitch to leg. Collins had to run about a hundred yards to rescue it from the road. Bradford looked fierce. He took a longer run than usual, rushed up to the wicket, and plunged the ball in with all his force. A howl of untuneful applause rose from under the trees. The ball not only happened to be straight, but was also a yorker. Whitaker's middle stump fell flat.

There are times when a panic seizes the very best side, and for the next hour and a half the House had the pleasant experience of watching an unusually strong Buller side rabbit out before a very moderate attack. Buller's side contained four First and two Second Eleven colours, to say nothing of three Colts caps. And yet by six o'clock the whole team was dismissed for 83. There was nothing to account for the rot. Foster and Bradford bowled unchanged. Bradford took six of the wickets, four clean bowled. It was incomprehensible.

'I can't understand it,' said Gordon at tea. 'Bradford was bowling the most utter drivel half the time, I would have given anything to have been batting. And you were not bowling at your best, you know, Foster.'

'I am well aware of that; but, heavens! it was sheer joy. Look at old Collins, down there, beaming at the thought of not having to field tomorrow.'

'It's all right,' mumbled Collins from a huge cup of tea.

'By Jove! wouldn't it be gorgeous if we could win this match, and finish up by beating the Buller crowd at their own game?' said Gordon. 'Damn it all, I don't see why we shouldn't. What we have done once we can do again. They are a better side, I know, but we'll have a damned good shot at winning.'

Of course Buller's laughed at the whole thing.

'It's really rather funny,' they said. 'But, of course, we are in absolutely no danger of losing. We couldn't wreck like that again; and, what's more, we shouldn't let an ass like Bray make so many runs again. We are quite safe!'

The School House kept quiet. They were not going to shout their hopes all over the school. It would look so bad if they got thoroughly beaten in the end. But in the studies and dormitories that night there was only one thought in all their minds – that victory was possible.

The next day it rained the whole time. The courts were flooded with water, the branches dripped with a tired languor. Gordon polished off two exams with masterly speed, and returned to his study.

Saturday morning broke grey and wet. It rained spasmodically till mid-day, and then cleared up. With a sight of relief Gordon walked up the big schoolroom to show up the last piece of work that he would do at Fernhurst. For a last composition it was hardly creditable. A long paper on the *Œdipus Tyrannus* was finished in under an hour. But Gordon had ceased to care for academic distinctions. As he closed the door of the big school, and went out into the cloisters, he realised that a certain stage of his journey was over and done with for ever.

By lunch-time all signs of rain had cleared off, and the sun shone down on an absolutely sodden ground. Runs would be very hard to get. A lead of thirty-seven meant a lot on such a wicket. An atmosphere of nervous expectation overhung the House. Everyone was glad when the meal was over.

The match began directly after lunch. There would be very likely some difficulty in finishing the game that day. Collins and Foster went in first. Gordon had asked to be kept back till later. The start was dull. Foster was taking no risks, and Collins seemed unable to time the ball at all, which was luckily always off the wicket. Ten went up after quarter of an hour's play.

And then Foster, reaching out to play forward, slipped on the wet grass and was stumped. Three balls later Bradford was caught and bowled. It was Gordon's turn to go in. Nearly everything depended on him. If he failed, the whole side would probably collapse. The tail had done miracles in the first innings; but it could not be expected to do the same again.

Gordon took guard nervously. He resolved to play himself in carefully, but he never could resist the temptation to have a 'go.' The first ball was well up, just outside the off stump. Gordon stepped across and let fly. He had forgotten how slow the pitch was. The ball hung; he was much too soon; the ball sailed straight up into the air! Point and cover-point both ran for it. 'Crampin!' yelled out Whitaker. Neither heard; they crashed into one another; the ball fell with a dull thud. The House gave a gasp of relief.

It was a costly mistake. For when once he got his eye in, Gordon was very hard to get out. And, moreover, he was one of the few people who could get runs quickly on a really wet wicket, for the simple reason that nearly all his shots went into the air;

and so he did not find the sodden ground making off drives, which should have resulted in fours, realise only singles.

That afternoon Gordon found the bowling perfectly simple. At the other end wickets fell slowly, but he himself was scoring fast. A hard shot over cover-point sent up his individual fifty, and two overs later he drove a length ball on the off stump past mid-on to the boundary, and the hundred went up amid cheers.

'It is a mystery to me,' said Foster, 'how that man Caruthers ever gets a run at all; he has no defence, and hits straight across everything.'

'Don't let's worry about that,' said Collins; 'sufficient be it that he is hitting these Buller's swine all over the place. Oh, good shot!'

A half-volley had landed first bounce among the masters sitting under the wall. The umpire signalled six.

150 went up.

And then Gordon mistimed a slow yorker, and was clean bowled for 85.

He was received with a storm of clapping; the House lined up cheering as he ran in between the ropes.

'Gratters! Well done!' shouted Foster. 'That's a damned fine knock to finish your Fernhurst cricket days with! Well done!'

Everyone came up and congratulated him. It was a proud moment, in some ways the proudest of his whole career.

A few minutes later another burst of clapping signalled the end of the innings. The side had made 186. Buller's were left with 223 to win. Anything might happen. Just before five Foster led the House on to the field.

The next hour and a half was fraught with delirious happiness and excitement. Foster bowled magnificently, Bradford managed to keep a length; the whole side fielded splendidly. Wicket after wicket fell. Victory became a certainty. Gloom descended over the Buller's side. Round the pavilion infants with magenta hat ribbons yelled themselves hoarse. It was one of those occasions in which eternity seems compressed into an hour. Half-past six came. No one went up to tea, everyone was waiting for the end. At last it came. Whitaker, who alone had been able to withstand the School House attack, over-reached himself, Gordon gathered the ball quickly, the bails flew off. The umpire's hand rose. A wild shriek rose from the crowd. Gordon's last game at Fernhurst was over; his last triumph had come; at last 'Samson had quit himself like Samson.' Through the lines of shrieking juniors the team passed into the pavilion. Gordon began to collect his things, to pack up his bag. He gave it to a fag to carry up.

Collins and Foster and Gordon walked up from the field arm in arm.

'Well, if we stopped on here for a hundred years,' said Foster, 'we shouldn't find a better hour to leave.'

'Yes, the end has made up for any disappointments on the way. It will be a long time before we have as wonderful a time again,' Gordon said, as he passed in the sunset, for the last time, through the gate of the cricket-field which had been, for him, the place of so many happy hours.

from THE LOOM OF YOUTH
1917

RETURN OF A HERO

by

Bruce Marshall

The outcome of this hero's return from the war offers one of the most resonant images in writing about cricket – or any sport for that matter. In the field of school stories, it makes the same sort of impact, and for the same reasons, that was made by Sassoon's Memoirs of a Fox-hunting Man *(1928) and* Memoirs of an Infantry Officer *(1930), Remarque's* All Quiet on the Western Front *(1929), and Graves's* Goodbye to all that *(also 1929).*

Bruce Marshall – who died in 1987, aged eighty-seven – was best known for the Second World War story The White Rabbit. *In the First World War, six days before the Armistice, he was wounded and taken prisoner. Subsequently his leg was amputated.*

Calder had been Captain of Cricket the year before, so he had brought his new wooden leg up to St Kentigern's with him, in the hope that they might allow him to play in the match. He could always field point or slips one over and mid-on the next, and they would be sure to let somebody else run for him. Of course, an odd number of runs would be a nuisance, especially in the middle of an over, but he supposed that they wouldn't mind waiting while he hobbled to the other end of the pitch. It wouldn't be much worse than when Slogger Methuen was batting and he hit a one or a three or a five – better really, for with Slogger it wasn't just one man that had to change his position, but the whole field.

It was not until half an hour before the match started that he put on his leg, because it hurt him rather and seemed heavier than it really was, and he hadn't had much practice on it. 'The only way to learn to walk on an artificial leg,' they had told him at the leg-maker's, 'the only way to learn to walk on an artififical limb is to go into a pub five miles from home and get blotto, and then stagger home.' Yes, but it probably wasn't the way to learn to play in a cricket match, and it certainly wasn't the way to please Tired Tim [the headmaster].

So, putting aside what little Sheila had called the night before his one-two sticks and stripping off his uniform, he stood just-as-he-was-without-one-plea, and was about to put on his sweet soft cricket shirt when he realised that he would have to wear a vest underneath, because of his leg-braces, which would show otherwise and make him look just like a workman. 'Blast and damn,' he cursed, but he put on the vest just the same because he couldn't very well do otherwise, no matter how fuggy he was going to feel.

The leg itself took him some time to adjust, because he was unfamiliar with the strappings and beltings and had only worn it twice before – once to show to his father and once to take his sister out to dinner. Had old Dundas said two or three stump-socks? He had better make it three perhaps, because one never knew how long he might be fielding and his stump might begin to feel sucky after standing about for a long time.

He put on three stump-socks, then experimented with the pick-up and the braces to see how tight he should make them, fastened the pelvic band, pulled on his shirt and up his so sinless flannel trousers, and stood in front of the mirror, all white and two-legged, just as though he had never been wounded and heard the round-faced Australian surgeon say: 'Now, Calder, we're going to fix you up this morning.' To look at him, he thought, even the prettiest of girls wouldn't know that he had got his leg off.

Going down the staircase was difficult, because he had lost his leg on the wrong side for holding the banisters and he had to hold his stick on the same side as his leg. But he managed all right, remembering what old Dundas had told him: 'Always the limb first going down and the limb first going up. It's the only way, remember. A bloke that's amputated above the knee can't expect to do steps and stairs other than baby-fashion.' So baby-fashion he did them, placing artificial leg and rubber-tipped stick on the step immediately below him, and bringing his real leg level with them afterwards and then beginning all over again. And even then he cheated, because boys kept rushing down behind him and then slowed up when they saw him, and he was ashamed of what the newspapers called his glory, and liked neither to keep them back nor to stop and let them pass, so he gave up holding the banister at all, and tried to go quicker that way.

Walking along Marine Parade with Slogger Methuen and Giraffe Warner, he cheated too, placing his right hand in his trouser pocket and attempting to steady the bucket with the ball of his thumb, and trying not to abuse their charity of walking slowly beside him too much. For in front of them fellows and masters in flannels kept streaming and streaming away, like the tail-end of a droughted river hurrying to the sea, and leaving himself and Slogger and Giraffe a puddle that could never catch up or evaporate.

Giraffe Warner, to whom it was but yesterday that Calder had been a small boy to whom he had been teaching *mensa*, said:

'Do you think that it's altogether prudent to try and play?'

Calder, remembering how Giraffe had once beaten him for stealing an apple from Tired Tim's orchard, and how he had said: 'I am going to beat you. I shall give you three cuts. Now cut along and change into your cuts,' said back:

'Of course, sir. I'll be all right once I'm in the Meadow.'

Neither Giraffe nor Slogger knew quite what to say to Calder, being ashamed that he had lost his leg when they hadn't lost theirs, and Calder felt that they would think that he was bouncing if he tried to tell them about the war, so they all said nothing, and walked in a striving, eloquent silence along Marine Parade, along Station Road, through the town, and up Brae Road into the Meadow, which lay all green beneath the sun. Round the field the school, in white shorts and green blazers, lay stretched on their stomachs and stared out over the grass, which stood up before their eyes like tiny, waving men, and speculated as to what Tired Tim was going to say in Assembly after lunch when he sacked Bill Sikes. On the far side, in front of the pavilion, stood or sat the cricketers in snowy groups, the school eleven all in mauve blazers, the Old Boys and masters representing them in blazers striped by a Holy Ghost which had descended in tongues of liquorice all-sorts. Over all the sky stretched, a taut blue dome, against which one could bang infinite, longing, unanswerable prayers.

'Ah, Calder,' said Tired Tim, as Giraffe and Slogger and Calder approached and were absorbed into the main group, 'come and sit down. We were waiting for you.' With an arm that wished it could weep, he took Calder and led him to a seat next Una, who stilly and whitely was sitting and wondering if it was right of her to love Middleton the more for the number of dates stretching like a dapple round his faded First Eleven cap.

'Thanks awfully, sir,' said Calder, bending to flex the lower part of his artificial leg inwards, and smiling unhappily at the gold Una who must so hate and shudder at his creaking, scrunching wooden leg.

'Are you sure you feel up to it?' asked Tired Tim.

'Of course, sir,' said Calder. 'That's to say, if you'll allow me to field slips one over and mid-on the next. I'd like somebody to run for me too, if I might.'

'You'd better ask yourself that, then, Calder. As you're easily the best cricketer among us, we've agreed that you are to be our captain.' Calder blushed for pleasure, and Tired Tim continued: 'But are you sure that you'd better not get somebody to field for you as well?'

'Fielding'll be nothing, sir,' Calder smiled, and felt that Una couldn't be disgusted by him after all. 'Why, I know a chap in the Argyll and Sutherlands, sir, that's got both legs off above the knee and drives a car and goes fishing.'

Both legs off above the knee! Oh, the glory that was Greece! Tired Tim, slashed with pain, turned to Jamieson:

'We seem to be ready,' he said.

Jamieson came up to Calder, who was trying to think of something to say to Una.

'I'll toss, and you call,' he said, taking out a coin and balancing it on the joint of his thumb.

Calder smiled.

'I'd like to know my team first,' he said.

'There are only four Old Boys besides yourself,' Jamieson said. 'Versicle and Blair and Cunningham and Rintoul. That makes five. The rest of the team's made up of masters.' He indicated, with his eyes rather than his hand, Tired Tim, Pogo, Slogger Methuen, Grunter Grierson, Tripehound Torrie, and Wearie Willie, blinking at everybody as though they were the principal parts of Greek verbs which he was frightened he didn't know by heart.

Calder stood up stiffly, ritually.

'Heads,' he said, as Jamieson span the shining coin in the air.

'Heads it is,' said Jamieson.

'We'll bat,' said Calder, and, quite in his old style, he turned to the scorer and dictated the order of batting. Tired Tim, and Tripehound Torrie, he decided, would open the batting, but aloud he called them the Headmaster and Mr Torrie, although he knew that they both knew that he and everybody else thought of them as Tired Tim and Tripehound. He himself, as usual, would go in first wicket down. Then Cunningham. Then the Tyke. Then Slogger. Deliberately he made Rintoul last man in because he knew that he wouldn't mind, and because he knew that Wearie Willie would be no end bucked that it wasn't himself.

Tripehound Torrie was wearing only his blue serge jacket, because he had sent his Cambridge Blue to the laundry and hadn't got it back in time. Glad so soon to be solely in white, he clamped into the pavilion with Tired Tim, to put on his pads. The school team followed, peeling off their mauve blazers as they went. The masters and Old Boys stood in front of the pavilion, like splotches of colour on a painter's palette. Una and Calder were left momentarily alone.

'I'll help you on with your pads,' Una said.

'Please,' he begged.

'There's no please about it,' she said. 'I insist.' She got up and stood before him, in a white silk frock which flowed over her like milk. 'You're going to sit here, and I'm going to fix your pads for you.'

She went from him and his dreams followed her, clinging to her hair like sunlight. It would be very wonderful to be loved by a girl like Una. Perhaps it wasn't entirely impossible. Perhaps one day he would be. Perhaps wooden legs weren't so distasteful to girls as he had imagined them to be. Perhaps the war had really changed things. Perhaps wooden legs were no longer the comic but rather distressing property of dirty old men who stumped about harbours. Perhaps he really was a hero, and perhaps Una was falling in love with him for it. In an enchantment he saw the fielders run out from the pavilion, like a flock of gulls released by God, and Tired Tim and Tripehound Torrie follow to arouse a second applause when the first had subsided. In the same enchantment he saw Una come back, pads and batting gloves in her hands.

She knelt before him, and he saw her long pigtail stretching in a concatenation of joys.

'Shall I put the left one on first?' she asked.

He took the pad from her. 'I think I'll only need the left one,' he said and explained, laughingly: 'You see, the right'd probably stop my rotten knee from bending. And, in any case, if I do a sucky one, I shan't feel anything.'

She handed him the batting gloves and sat beside him.

'Was it very sore, being wounded?' she asked.

'Not at the time,' he said. 'But afterwards it was pretty sucky.'

'You don't mind my asking, do you?'

'Of course not. What makes you ask? Ask about your asking, I mean.'

'I don't know. Just an idea I've got.' She gazed solemnly across her uncertainty, symbolised by white Christs walking on a sea of green. 'Daddy says that men who've been in the trenches don't like talking about them.'

'I like talking about them to you,' he said.

'To me?' She tried to sound unconcerned as well as considerate, crystal while kind.

'Yes, to you. You're different from the old ladies that visit us in hospital, you see. More . . .'

'More what?'

'More understanding.'

'Oh, I'm not understanding really.' She laughed a little. 'Mummy says that I'm a very heartless sort of person at times.'

'I don't think that you ever could be heartless, even if you tried.'

'Oh, couldn't I? That just shows how little you know me, that's all. Why, only last term I made our Mademoiselle blub the way I ragged her. But we were talking about your leg, weren't we? It wasn't *blown* off, was it?'

'No, only cut. I copped a whole packet in the knee.'

'I'm so glad,' she said.

'Why?'

'It seems less terrible somehow,' she said.

From behind the wall appeared the crest of a red parasol, like a sun dawning to warm a pre-Copernican world, and Calder, remembering previous cricket matches, knew that his minutes of intimacy with Una were numbered. For the sun pulled Auntie Babsy-More-Tick-Tick after it, and Auntie Babsy-More-Tick-Tick pulled after her a large daisy that would later turn out to be Shiela, and the large daisy pulled after it a small buttercup which would later turn out to be a yellow duck on wheels. Out on the pitch, Tripehound Torrie clicked Middleton to point for a four. In his linen ephod the umpire moved squarely out to leg, and the fielders changed position, leisurely, inexorably, like a thousand years reflecting in God.

'Here's Mummy,' said Una.

'Is Mrs Petrie well?' Calder asked, remembering that he hadn't seen the Queen Bee on his arrival the night before, and that he had asked neither Tired Tim nor Una about her health.

'Mummy's always well. Sheila's a little dear, isn't she? She calls handkerchiefs "blows" and towels "drys." '

Waddling along the boundary line, Auntie Babsy-More-Tick-Tick, looking like a gigantic plum, drew closer. Sheila, turning from a daisy into a little girl in a print frock, walked gravely at her side, pulling the yellow duck as though it were Monsieur Bergson. Out on the pitch Tired Tim hit Jamieson for a two and ran a three, and wondered if he had been right in saying that the clover-leaf was an adequate symbol of the Trinity.

'Seen the Bishop?' asked Auntie Babsy-More-Tick-Tick as she approached.

'No,' said Una. 'Why?'

'Nothing special. He said he'd be here, that's all.' Catching sight of Calder, the Queen Bee's eyes filled with tears. 'You poor boy,' she said. 'The Headmaster and I – we're all so proud of you.'

Round-eyed and ruminant, Sheila stood before Calder and contemplated him.

'One-two stick man got one-two legs now,' she said.

Calder leant forward to pat her cheek.

'One real leg, one wooden leg, Sheila,' he said.

'One real leg, one woogun leg,' Sheila repeated, nodding each syllable down into her memory.

Out in the field, Jamieson picked up the ball and walked reflectively away from the wicket, as though he were tired of the match and were going home. Then suddenly, digging his right heel into the ground, he turned, extended his right arm downwards and backwards, and came running towards the wicket. Two yards distant from it he slowed up, scraped the grass with both feet, came running on again, stopped, and, as he stopped, let his right arm whirl upwards and forwards. The ball, almost invisible in speed, sped obliquely through the low air towards Tripehound Torrie. A foot distant from his bat it hit the ground, rose again, was spooned greatly up to heaven as Tripehound Torrie clacked to meet it, went sailing in the direction of the Brae Road. 'Hit!' Out on the boundary Spence ran and ran and ran, a panting, bounding whiteness above the heads of the watching school. Running, running, running, his hands went up and out from him, and his body swayed backwards, almost toppled, righted itself, and was still. As though spurted on a jet of water, the ball rose a little way from Spence's cupped hands into the air, fell, and was held for the Middlesex ever. ' 'Held!' ' 'Held, sir!' In the middle of an applause which was not for him, Tripehound Torrie swerved out from his running and began to walk rapidly back towards the pavilion.

'Would you like me to help you?' Una asked as Calder got up to remove his blazer.

'There's nothing to help me with,' Calder said, and sat down again and began to put on his brown and white batting gloves. 'I've only got to wait till old Tripehound Torrie rolls into port and I'll be as right as rain.'

The Bishop, black-aproned and gaitered, appeared from Station Road. For a moment he stood and benignly watched the fielders tossing the ball about among themselves and Tripehound Torrie left-righting his retreat. Then, smiling, he came towards the Queen Bee and Sheila and Una and Calder. The scorer shouted figures to Ogilvie Minimus, who rose from his place in front of the scoring-board, which, by bedecking it with battered tin squares, he made read:

24
1
7

'Dear me,' the Bishop said to them all. 'A wicket down already! What a very good thing it is not the Headmaster who is out, otherwise he might have been too despondent to feel like entertaining me to luncheon. And you are next man in, are you?' he said to Calder. 'Well, I'm sure I wish you better luck than your predecessor.'

'This is Calder, Bishop. He lost his leg in the war and has very pluckily insisted on playing in the match.'

'My poor dear boy!' The Bishop's voice was all silvery and quavering, as though he were blessing people in church. 'But are you sure you can manage?'

'Of course, sir.' Calder stood up as Tripehound Torrie clattered finally into the pavilion. 'Why, I know a chap in the Argyll and Sutherlands, sir, that's got both legs off above the knee and drives a car and goes fishing.'

A righteous war! How often had he told congregations that from pulpits? A righteous war which could be won only by boys of nineteen losing their legs and arms and eyes? Yet our dear Lord had been crucified, and that must have hurt a great deal more, even although He had been God. And our Lord would reward these poor boys in heaven for their sufferings, the German and Austrian boys too, because it probably wasn't their fault that they were fighting against Him. Our Lord would be very wonderful to them all. You could trust our Lord for that.

'Yes, my dear boy,' he said. 'But one sits to drive a motor-car, and to fish one can sit also. And what are you going to do about running?'

'I'm afraid I can't run at all, sir. My amputation's above the knee. But the Headmaster said that it would be all right, and that I could get somebody to run for me.'

'And whom were you thinking of getting to run for you, my dear boy?'

'I was thinking that perhaps Mr Torrie wouldn't mind. I was going to wait till he got his pads off to ask him.'

'My child, as your late Father-in-God I order you to do nothing of the kind. I shall run for you.' He took Calder by the arm and led him from the pavilion. 'And even if I am too old and fat to run very fast, I shall still consider you bound by holy obedience to have me.'

Walking across to the pitch amid a roar of applause which was an echo of the centuries he had made against Loretto and Fettes and Glenalmond, Calder wished rather that the Bishop wouldn't insist on taking his arm. For it was more difficult to walk with a bat than with a stick, and he would have liked to ease his discomfiture by guiding his bucket from the inside of his right trouser pocket. But he felt that to explain this necessity would hurt the Bishop more than it benefited him, so he said nothing, and walked onwards towards the wicket, which seemed to keep on being terribly distant.

Arrived at the wicket, the Bishop stood behind him, to leg, and holding his bat sideways, Calder asked the umpire to give him centre. Heavens, but it was silly of him to be feeling so strange and groggy and sea-sicky. Apart from running, it must be just as easy to play a decent game of cricket on one leg as on two. Old Dundas had said so, and old Dundas ought to know, as he had lost his leg himself and still went bowling every week down at Puddocky.

With renewed confidence, he took his stance, patting his bat into position.

Once again Jamieson picked up the ball and walked reflectively away from the far wicket, and behind Calder the Bishop bent and clapped his hands on both knees beneath his apron, prepared to run should Calder give the word. In front of the pavilion little Sheila gambolled after a bumble bee. 'Sheila would like to sit on bumbul bee,' she aspired. 'Sheila would like to sit on bumbul bee.' Suddenly, digging his right heel into the ground, Jamieson turned, extended his right arm downwards and backwards, and came running towards the wicket. 'Bumble bee sore, no touch bumble bee,' Una said, and watched out across the green. Two yards distant from the far wicket Jamieson slowed up, scraped the grass with both feet, came running on again. Once more Calder patted the bat in its niche, strained to see the ball that would volley from that rapidly whirling arm. The ball came, an easy lobbing one. Calder stepped out to slog it to the boundary. But, as he stepped, his artificial leg gave at the knee and he fell forwards on his face, and the ball went on and passed over the middle stump, flicking the bails off as it passed. There was a groan from the spectators on the bank, and the Bishop ran to Calder to help him up again.

As he walked back to the pavilion with the Bishop, they cheered him even louder than when he had made centuries for them, and the distance seemed even longer than it had coming out, because he knew that they were cheering because they were sorry for him and not because he had played well. 'My poor boy,' said the Bishop as they walked, 'I feel as though it were I and not you who were out,' although even he didn't know quite what he was trying to say. 'Bumbul bee sore, no touch bumbul bee,' said little Sheila, toddling tubbily to meet them. Inside the pavilion, Calder took down his trousers, removed a sock from his stump and placed it between his flesh and the pelvic band, to see if that would make the leg hurt less. Then he went out again, and sat beside the Bishop and the Queen Bee and Una, and saw all the cricket matches in which he would never play.

from PRAYER FOR THE LIVING
1934

THE 'M.C.C.'

by

R.K. Narayan

R.K. Narayan's first novel Swami and Friends *introduced his mythical small town of Malgudi where so many of his novels and stories were subsequently set. In this episode his boy 'heroes', friends again after quarrelling, are deciding to set up their own Malgudi Cricket Club.*

Swaminathan had not thought of cricket as something that he himself could play. He was, of course, familiar with Hobbs, Bradman, and Duleep, and vainly tried to carry their scores in his head, as Rajam did. He filched pictures of cricket players, as Rajam did, and pasted them in an album, though he secretly did not very much care for those pictures – there was something monotonous about them. He sometimes thought that the same picture was pasted in every page of the album.

'No, Rajam, I don't think I can play. I don't know how to play.'

'That is what everybody thinks,' said Rajam. 'I don't know myself, though I collect pictures and scores.'

This was very pleasing to hear. Probably Hobbs too was shy and sceptical before he took the bat and swung it.

'We can challenge a lot of teams, including our school eleven. They think they can't be beaten,' said Swaminathan.

'What! The Board School mugs think that! We shall thrash them. Oh, yes.'

'What shall be call it?'

'Don't you know? It is the M.C.C.,' said Rajam.

'That is Hobbs's team, isn't it? They may drag us before a court if we take their name.'

'Who says that? If we get into any trouble, I shall declare before the judge that M.C.C. stands for Malgudi Cricket Club.'

Swaminathan was a little disappointed. Though as M.C.C. it sounded imposing, the name was really a bit tame. 'I think we had better try some other name, Rajam.'

'What would you suggest?'

'Well – I am for "Friends Eleven".'

'Friends Eleven?'

'Or, say, "Jumping Stars"?' said Swaminathan.

'Oh, that is not bad, not bad, you know.'

'I do think it would be glorious to call ourselves "Jumping Stars"!'

Rajam instantly had a vision of a newspaper report: 'The Jumping Stars soundly thrashed the Board High School Eleven.' 'It is a beauty, I think,' he cried, moved by the vision. He pulled out a piece of paper and a pencil, and said, 'Come on, Swami, repeat the names that come to your head. It would be better to have a long list to select from. We shall underline "Jumping Stars" and "M.C.C." and give them special consideration. Come on.'

Swaminathan remained thoughtful and started, ' "Friends Eleven" . . . "Jumping Stars" . . . "Friends Union" . . .'

'I have "Friends Union" already here,' Rajam said pointing to the list.

Swaminathan went on: ' "Excelsiors" . . .'

'I have got it.'

' "Excelsior Union" . . . "Champion Eleven" . . .' A long pause.

'Are you dried up?' Rajam asked.

'No, if Mani were here, he would have suggested a few more names . . . "Champion Eleven".'

'You have just said it.'

' "Victory Union Eleven" . . .'

'That is very good. I think it is very very good. People would be afraid of us.' He held the list before him and read the names with great satisfaction. He had struggled hard on the previous night to get a few names. But only 'Friends Union' and 'Excelsiors' kept coming till he felt fatigued. But what a lot of names Swaminathan was able to reel off. 'Can you meet me tomorrow evening, Swami? I shall get Mani down. Let us select a name.'. . . .

They sat round Rajam's table in his room. Mani held before him a catalogue of Messrs Binns, the Shop for Sports Goods. He read, ' "Junior Willards Bats, Seven Eight, made of finest seasoned wood, used by Cambridge Junior Boys' Eleven".'

'Let me have a look at it . . .' said Rajam. He bent over the table and said, 'Seems to be a fine bat. Have a look at it, Swami.'

Swaminathan craned his neck and agreed that it was a fine bat, but he was indiscreet enough to say, 'It looks like any other bat in the catalogue.'

Mani's left hand shot out and held his neck and pressed his face close to the picture of the bat: 'Why do you pretend to be a cricket player if you cannot see the difference between Junior Willard and other bats? You are not fit to be even a sweeper in our team.' After this admonition the hold was relaxed.

Rajam asked, 'Swami, do you know what the catalogue man calls the Junior Willard? It seems it is the Rolls-Royce among the junior bats. Don't you know the difference between the Rolls-Royce and other cars?'

Swaminathan replied haughtily, 'I never said I saw no difference between the Rolls-Royce and other cars.'

'What is the difference?' urged Rajam.

Mani laughed and teased, 'Come on. If you really know the difference, why don't you say it?'

Swaminathan said, 'The Rolls costs a lakh of rupees, while other cars cost about ten thousand; a Rolls has engines made of silver, while other cars have iron engines.'

'Oh, oh!' jeered Rajam.

'A Rolls never gives trouble, while other cars always give trouble; a Rolls engine never stops; a Rolls-Royce never makes a noise, while other cars always make a noise.'

'Why not deliver a lecture on the Rolls-Royce?' asked Mani.

'Swami, I am glad you know so much about the Rolls-Royce. I am at the same time ashamed to find you knowing so little about

Willard Junior. We had about a dozen Willard Juniors when I was in Bishop Waller's. Oh! what bats! There are actual springs inside the bat, so that when you touch the ball it flies. There is fine silk cord wound round the handle. You don't know anything, and yet you talk! Show me another bat which has silk cord and springs like the Willard.'

There was a pause, and after that Rajam said, 'Note it down, Swami.' Swaminathan noted down on a paper, 'Vilord june-ear bat.' And looking up asked, 'How many?'

'Say three. Will that do, Mani?'

'Why waste money on three bats? Two will do . . .'

'But suppose one breaks in the middle of a match?' Rajam asked.

'Do you suppose we are going to supply bats to our opponents? They will have to come provided with bats. We must make it clear.'

'Even then, if our bat breaks we may have to stop playing.'

'Two will do, Rajam, unless you want to waste money.'

Rajam's enthusiasm was great. He left his chair and sat on the arm of Mani's chair, gloating over the pictures of cricket goods in the catalogue. Swaminathan, though he was considered to be a bit of a heretic, caught the enthusiasm and perched on the other arm of the chair. All the three devoured with their eyes the glossy pictures of cricket balls, bats, and nets.

In about an hour they selected from the catalogue their team's requirements. And then came the most difficult part of the whole affair – a letter to Messrs Binns, ordering goods. Bare courtesy made Rajam offer the authorship of the letter to Mani, who declined it. Swaminathan was forced to accept it in spite of his protests, and he sat for a long time chewing his pencil without producing a word; he had infinite trouble with spelling, and the more he tried to be correct the more muddled he was becoming; in the end he sat so long thinking of spelling that even such words as 'the' and 'and' became doubtful. Rajam took up the task himself. Half an hour later he placed on the table a letter:

From

M.C.C. (And Victory Union Eleven),
Malgudi.

To
Messrs Binns,
Sportsmen,
Mount Road,
Madras.

Dear Sir,
Please send to our team two junior willard bats, six balls, wickets and other things quick. It is very urgent. We shall send you money afterwards. Don't fear. Please be urgent.
Yours obediently,

CAPTAIN RAJAM (Captain).

This letter received Swaminathan's benedictions. But Mani expressed certain doubts. He wanted to know whether 'Dear' could stand at the beginning of a letter to a perfect stranger. 'How can you call Binns "Dear Sir"? You must say "Sir".'

Rajam's explanation was: 'I won't say "Sir". It is said only to clerks. I am not Binns's clerk. I don't care to address him as "Sir".'

So this letter went as it was . . . .

The M.C.C. and its organizers had solid proof that they were persons of count when a letter from Binns came addressed to the Captain, M.C.C., Malgudi. It was a joy, touching that beautiful envelope and turning it over in the hand. Binns were the first to recognize the M.C.C, and Rajam took a vow that he would buy every bit that his team needed from that great firm. There were three implications in this letter that filled Rajam and his friends with rapture: *(1)* that His Majesty's Post Office recognized their team was proved by the fact that the letter addressed to the captain was promptly delivered to him; *(2)* that they were really recognized by such a magnificent firm as Binns of Madras was proved by the fact that Binns cared to reply in a full letter and not on a card, and actually typed the letter! *(3)* Binns sent under another cover carrying four annas postage a huge catalogue. What a tribute!

The letter informed the captain that Messrs Binns thanked him for his letter and would be much obliged to him if he would kindly remit 25 per cent with the order and the balance could be paid against the V.P.P. of the railway receipt.

Three heads buzzed over the meaning of this letter. The trouble was that they could not understand whether Binns were going to send the goods or not. Mani promised to unravel the letter if somebody would tell him what 'obliged' meant. When they turned the pages of a dictionary and offered him the meaning, he was none the wiser. He felt that it was a meaningless word in that place.

'One thing is clear,' said Rajam. 'Binns thanks us for our letter. So I don't think this letter could mean a refusal to supply us goods.'

Swaminathan agreed with him, 'That is right. If he did not wish to supply you with things, would he thank you? He would have abused you.' He scrutinized the letter again to make sure that there was no mistake about the thanks.

'Why has the fool used this word?' Mani asked, referring to 'obliged' which he could not pronounce. 'It has no meaning. Is he trying to make fun of us?'

'He says something about twenty-five per ccnt. I wish I knew what it was,' said Rajam.

Swaminathan could hardly contain himself, 'I say, Rajam, I am surprised that you cannot understand this letter; you got sixty per cent in the last examination.'

'Have you any sense in you? What has that to do with this? Even a B.A. cannot understand this letter.'

In the end they came to the conclusion that the letter was sent to them by mistake. As far as they could see, the M.C.C. had written nothing in their previous letter to warrant such expressions as 'obliged', 'remit', and '25 per cent'. It could not be that the great firm of Binns were trying to make fun of them. Swaminathan pointed out 'To the Captain, M.C.C.' at the beginning of the letter. But he was told that it was also a part of the mistake.

This letter they put in a cover with a covering letter and dispatched. The covering letter said:

> We are very sorry that you sent me somebody's letter. We are returning this somebody's letter. Please send our things immediately.

The M.C.C. were an optimistic lot. Though they were still unhonoured with a reply to their second letter, they expected the goods to arrive with every post. After ten days they thought they would start playing with whatever was available till they got the real bats, et cetera. The bottom of a dealwood case provided them with three good bats, and Rajam managed to get three used tennis balls from his father's club. The Pea was there, offering four real stumps that he believed he had somewhere in his house. A neat slip of ground adjoining Rajam's bungalow was to be the pitch. Everything was ready. Even if Binns took a month more to manufacture the goods specially for the M.C.C. (as they faintly thought probable), there need be no delay in starting practice. By the time the real bats and the balls arrived, they would be in form to play matches.

Rajam had chosen from his class a few who, he thought, deserved to become members of the M.C.C.

At five o'clock on the opening day, the M.C.C. had assembled, all except the Pea, for whom Rajam was waiting anxiously. He had promised to bring the real stumps. It was half an hour past time and yet he was not to be seen anywhere.

At last his puny figure was discovered in the distance. There was a catch in Rajam's heart when he saw him. He strained his eyes to find out if the Pea had the things about him. But since the latter was coming from the west, he was seen in the blaze of the evening sun. All the twelve assembled in the field shaded their eyes and looked. Some said that he was carrying a bundle, while some thought that he was swinging his hands freely.

When he arrived, Rajam asked, 'Why didn't you tell us that you hadn't the stumps?'

'I have still got them,' protested the Pea, 'I shall bring them tomorrow. I am sure my father knows where they are kept.'

'You kept us waiting till now. Why did you not come earlier and tell us that you could not find them?'

'I tell you, I have been spending hours looking for them

everywhere. How could I come here and tell you and at the same time search?'

A cloud descended upon the gathering. For over twenty hours every one among them had been dreaming of swinging a bat and throwing a ball. And they could have realized the dream but for the Pea's wickedness. Everybody looked at him sourly. He was isolated. Rajam felt like crying when he saw the dealwood planks and the tennis balls lying useless on the ground. What a glorious evening they could have had if only the stumps had been brought!

Amidst all this gloom somebody cast a ray of light by suggesting that they might use the compound wall of Rajam's bungalow as a temporary wicket.

A portion of the wall was marked off with a piece of charcoal, and the captain arranged the field and opened the batting himself. Swaminathan took up the bowling. He held a tennis ball in his hand, took a few paces, and threw it over. Rajam swung the bat but missed it. The ball hit the wall right under the charcoal mark. Rajam was bowled out with the very first ball! There was a great shout of joy. The players pressed round Swaminathan to shake him and pat him on the back, and he was given on the very spot the title, 'Tate' . . . .

Granny's passage had no light. It had only a shaft falling from the lamp in the hall. In the half-darkness, he could not see her face clearly. She lay still. Swaminathan was seized with a horrible passing doubt whether she might not be dead – of stomach ache. He controlled his voice and asked, 'Granny, how is your pain?'

Granny stirred, opened her eyes, and said, 'Swami, you have come! Have you had your food?'

'Not yet. How is your stomach-ache, granny?'

'Oh, it is all right. It is all right.'

. . . Swaminathan was overjoyed to hear this good news. And he expressed his mood of joy in: 'You know what my new name is? I am Tate.'

'What?'

'Tate.'

'What is Tate?' she asked innocently. Swaminathan's disappointment was twofold: she had not known anything of his new title, and failed to understand its rich significance even when told. At other times he would have shouted at her. But now he was a fresh penitent, and so asked her kindly, 'Do you mean to say that you don't know Tate?'

'I don't know what you mean.'

'Tate, the great cricket player, the greatest bowler on earth. I hope you know what cricket is.'

'What is that?' Granny asked. Swaminathan was aghast at this piece of illiteracy. 'Do you mean to say, Granny, that you don't know what cricket is, or are you fooling me?'

'I don't know what you mean.'

'Don't keep on saying "I don't know what you mean". I wonder what the boys and men of your days did in the evenings! I think they spent all the twenty-four hours in doing holy things.'

He considered for a second. Here was his granny stagnating in appalling ignorance; and he felt it his duty to save her. He delivered a short speech setting forth the principles, ideals, and the philosophy of the game of cricket, mentioning the radiant gods of that world. He asked her every few seconds if she understood, and she nodded her head, though she caught only three per cent of what he said. He concluded the speech with a sketch of the history and the prospects of the M.C.C. 'But for Rajam, Granny,' he said, 'I don't know where we should have been. He has spent hundreds of rupees on this team. Buying bats and balls is no joke. He has plenty of money in his box. Our team is known even to the Government. If you like, you may write a letter to the M.C.C. and it will be delivered to us promptly. You will see us winning all the cups in Malgudi, and in course of time we shall show even the Madras fellows what cricket is.' He added a very important note: 'Don't imagine all sorts of fellows can become players in our team.'

His father stood behind him, with the baby in his arms. He asked, 'What are you lecturing about, young man?'

Swaminathan had not noticed his father's presence, and now writhed awkwardly as he answered, 'Nothing . . . Oh, nothing, Father.'

'Come on. Let me know it too.'

'It is nothing – Granny wanted to know something about cricket and I was explaining it to her.'

'Indeed! I never knew Mother was a sportswoman. Mother, I hope Swami has filled you with cricket-wisdom.'

Granny said, 'Don't tease the boy. The child is so fond of me. Poor thing! He has been trying to tell me all sorts of things. You are not in the habit of explaining things to me. You are all big men . . .'

Father replied, pointing to the baby, 'Just wait a few days and this little fellow will teach you all the philosophy and the politics in the world.'

from SWAMI AND FRIENDS
1935

THE LAST OF THE GRAND OLD SERIES

by

R. Gorell Barnes

Warrior's Way, *a fictionalised family chronicle of the years* c. *1880–1940, has cricket in a changing world as one of its subsidiary themes. Here it is expressed through the Eton* v. *Harrow match at Lord's in 1939.*

Mid-July 1939. Optimism and easing of tension were over: Danzig and the whole question not merely of the Polish Corridor but of Poland's existence was being forced by Hitler inexorably more and more into the foreground: though it was rumoured that the Anglo-Russian pact was at long last about to mature, which enabled some hearts to renew their hopes, dense crowds had come thoughtfully, apprehensively to watch the National Service rally in Hyde Park, and prophets, if they were wise and wishful still to have honour, kept silent. But England, in some of her manifestations at all events, remained indifferently England. It was Malcolm's last term at Harrow and, though he had not attained, as he had at one time hoped, to the captaincy, he was a prominent member of a very confident cricket XI – and the confidence was at last justified. Malcolm himself was unlucky: he encountered – so Frederick (his grandfather) very sympathetically and truthfully told him – the best ball bowled in the match in his first over, but personal disappointment gave way on the flood-tide of generous youth to elation at his side's success. At 5.30 on the Saturday afternoon, Lithgow, the Harrow captain, made the winning hit, a fine drive to the Pavilion rails – and then followed pandemonium.

'Let the world do its worst!' cried Frederick, joining wildly in the cheering from the Pavilion upper balcony and looking down with shared excitement at the seething crowds and the orgie of hat-smashings. 'We have again beaten Eton – and decisively! By 8 wickets, by the Lord! Wow! Some victory!'

Then, as he turned away at last, to find Malcolm and search for Diana, Heather, and others, he said soberly to Michael, who was with him and back in his 'teens at heart, even as he himself had been, 'We're a mad race, but it's good to be mad sometimes! I'm glad we've had this, Mike: I wonder whether we shall ever have it again.'

'We'll knock the stuffing out of them again next year, Dad,' asserted Michael with vigour.

'If it's played, old chap – perhaps. But will it be? And, if it isn't, will it ever be again? I wonder. We may have been watching the last of the grand old series.'

from WARRIOR'S WAY
1943

KEEPING A STRAIGHT BAT

A story by

Brian Glanville

Alan Ross, in the introduction to The Cricketer's Companion *(1960), remarked that Brian Glanville was the sort of writer who could render very well the authentic background of professional cricket just as he does that of professional and local footballers in his many, sharply characterised stories. In a rare excursion into cricket Glanville has taken a prep school background, but his story is full of the sorts of irony that school stories, as a genre, usually by-pass.*

'Up she jolly goes!' cried Mr Bright, and threw the football up into the air with a joy, a zeal, that bade fair to send it not only higher than the high wire fence but higher even than the rich green foliage of the chestnut and horse chestnut trees, around the paddock.

The paddock must once have been a lawn tennis court, just as Blackford Court itself had once been a small stately home, but the school, and Mr Bright, used it for cricket and for physical training. Now it was physical training, but with Mr Bright there was nothing so banal as jumping astride, trunk rolling, deep breathing. He had invented his own game, a variant of netball, in which nets gave place to designated goals, along the wire fence. A few jumps, a few knees' bends for formality's sake, then, 'Up she jolly goes!'

Mr Bright had come this summer term, the very spirit of summer. Indeed, it was hard to picture him in winter, when the leaves would wither, chilblains swell on our fingers, and the little, one-eyed, bare-legged, tireless vicar took us for killing runs across the soggy fields. What would Mr Bright do then? Hibernate? He could scarcely migrate. There was a war on, which was why the school had been evacuated to this safe, tranquil corner of the Midlands.

Mr Bright was what he himself might well have described as a fine figure of a man, lean and lank and brown, well over six feet tall, fifty-two, perhaps, with a full head of short, grey hair, and what might have been called, again appropriately, a military bearing. He was a man who, even then, in the early nineteen-forties, was clearly sliding out of fashion, a man for whom life was a cricket pitch, a thing of straight bats, stiff upper lips, and keeping one's end up on a sticky wicket. At the same time, and even we prep-school boys could feel it, there was something that divided him from the hierarchy of our schoolmasters, with their astringent self-sufficiency, their military ranks and medals. He was at once more amiable than they and less intractable. The Headmaster, with his moustache, his Military Cross, his ruddy cheeks, his sporadic explosions – '*Tense*, boy!!' – and Mr Remington, the Deputy Head, with his green tweed plus-fours, his covertly exercised manual skills, his old man's tetchiness; these, we somehow sensed, were irreducible, they would be what they were wherever you put them, the life of the school whirled round them as around two rocks. Mr Bright's was a different kind of imperviousness. He was as changeless as they, but not as impregnable.

He came from Kent, we certainly knew that. 'A Man of Kent, boys,' he must have told us fifty times, 'Not a Kentish Man. There's all the difference. Difference of geography, difference of character.' Prep schoolmasters, especially in the war, were a little like soldiers of the Foreign Legion; one did not probe their pasts. With such exceptions as the Headmaster, Mr Remington, and the seamed, resilient Miss Patterson, a handful of old boys waiting for their call up, they came from the blue and went back into the blue, remembered for a phrase, an anecdote, an eccentricity.

Mr Bright, unlike the Headmaster and Mr Remington, both of whom were captains, did not have a rank, or did not use one, despite his soldierly stance; strange in a man his age, teaching in a prep school, a man of his fervent, unimpeachable patriotism.

'The only good German is a dead 'un,' he would say, decisively, sitting erect, each lunch time, at the end of one of the long, oak tables in the panelled dining room. The teachers each had their allotted place at top or bottom of these tables, fixed and immovable, like suns, while around them, place by place, day by day, we, the boys, revolved like planets.

Aphorisms poured, crisp and staccato, from Mr Bright's lips: 'Many a good man's dug his grave with a knife and fork. Either at your throat or at your feet, the Hun.'

But, above all, fluent and seraphic, he would talk of cricket, and it was this which made him irresistible to me. At that time, I was in love with the romance of cricket, happy to play, but happier still among its pantheon of heroes: Hutton, Compton, Edrich, Hammond, Hobbs and Hendren; from the past, legendary, bearded Dr Grace. Of this magic world, Mr Bright was prophet, celebrant and propagandist. He knew, actually knew, Bill Edrich, the Middlesex and England all-rounder, now, appropriately, an Air Force pilot, with whom he had played, actually played. He was a friend, a personal friend, of Arthur Gilligan, the old captain of Sussex. 'Arthur Gilligan told me . . . Arthur Gilligan always said . . . Arthur Gilligan used to believe . . .'

'Oh, Gilligan, Gilligan, Gilligan!' grumbled crabby Mr Remington, in a stage whisper. He had been the cricket master, but now had been dethroned. Off with the old, on with the passionately enthusiastic new! Enthusiasm! That was Mr Bright's essence and watchword, boyish enthusiasm, so easily communicable to boys. This in itself differentiated him from the senior staff, for whom enthusiasm was a kind of crime. Mr Remington himself, on his better days, was a mine of marvellous reminiscence, reaching back into the nineties, but his style was closed and curmudgeonly, a thing of cautions and deflations. 'Gilligan!'

'But sir, he played a lot with Bill Edrich!'

'So he says, sir, so he says!'

Mr Bright showed no such malice to Mr Remington – he

simply swept over him like a wave. Mr Remington was a sceptic, Mr Bright had faith; it was the corollary of his enthusiasm. Because he believed that we could all bowl, bat, field, bowl, bat and field, we did: the good impressively, the moderate competently, the inept sufficiently. In the paddock, of a summer evening, he would bounce slip catches to us off the heavy roller, and we would hold them, though they stung; even those of us whom Mr Remington had scornfully dismissed as hopeless.

In the big, cowpat-ridden field at the back of the house, an eighteenth-century house, brick-walled, parapeted and bow-windowed, he laid down new wickets, put up practice nets, where he batted and bowled with us. 'Feet, feet! That's the secret! Don't let the willow take root!'

He seemed always to be dressed in white: white, open-necked shirts, white flannels yellowed a little by honourable usage, white pads worn like armour.

It was a good summer, the sun shone almost every day, and this, too, seemed a tribute to Mr Bright; how could even the weather resist such shining optimism?

'The finest sound in the world!' he cried, supple and sinewy in the nets, thrashing ball after ball into the netting: off drives, leg drives, sweeps, pulls, hooks, cuts, glances.

'Rabbit killer!' Mr Remington sneered.

'Finest in the world,' said Mr Bright. 'Leather on willow, willow on leather, when you *middle* it!'

The first eleven played its first match, against a bigger school, St Ignatius, which usually beat us. This time, we beat them. Mr Bright bought rock cakes and ginger beer for the first eleven; Mr Remington's pale, saurian eye dwelt on them as though to turn the feast to stone and vinegar. But Mr Bright was unaware of him, he was revelling in our triumph, still dressed in his rusty flannels, his white sweater with its Kent insignia, his multi-coloured cricket club blazer.

'May I, Headmaster?' he asked, going to the centre of the top table, and when the Headmaster solemnly nodded, raised his arms to quiet us all and said, 'Boys, I was very proud of you. You won. I expected you to win. But more than that, you played the game!'

The Headmaster's face was inscrutable, Mr Remington's a study in astonished disdain. 'You kept a straight bat and a good length,' said Mr Bright. 'Arthur Gilligan used to say to me, when he was captaining England, "Keep a good length, and the wickets will take care of themselves!" A straight bat in cricket and a straight bat in life, then the runs will come, boys, the runs will come!'

It was a crescendo that invited applause, but there was no applause, only uneasy anticlimax – we were unused to such incitements – and the Headmaster's gruff, 'Thank you, Mr Bright. Well done, boys.' The sentiments were surely his own. The delivery was not.

The first eleven continued to win matches. Mr Remington continued to mutter on the sidelines, Cassius to Mr Bright's Caesar, Wicked Fairy at his feast. Yet there was more to it than envy. His sour asides at table, in his classroom set among the woods, at cricket matches, grim beneath an oak, had also a tinge of sombre prescience.

Mr Bright did not teach the top class. He taught English, geography, maths and scripture to the smaller boys, though one guessed that these must be mere parentheses, so many transient tea intervals, in an eternal game of cricket.

One hot July day, when the sun blazed through the great, stone-arched windows of the dining room, dancing on the cutlery, he came to lunch more euphoric than ever. 'I've heard from Arthur Gilligan!' he said. 'He's coming down to Dorrington Manor for a cricket weekend. That's only fifteen miles from here. I'll ask him to bring a team to play us.'

'Oh, sir, that's marvellous, sir!'

From that moment, Gilligan became a Godot, his arrival hourly expected, constantly postponed.

'Any news of Arthur Gilligan, sir?'

'He's coming, definitely coming.'

'Next week, sir?'

'No, he can't manage it next week. Possibly the week after.'

It was about this time that I received my new copy of *Wisden's Almanac*, biscuit-coloured then, limp-covered, *ersatz* and attenuated, but still the cricketer's Bible, an initiate's orgy of statistics: batting averages, bowling averages, history, records.

'I'm in there,' said Mr Bright, with casual modesty, when I showed it to him. He cocked an eye at the ceiling, as if embarrassed by his fame.

'Are you, sir?'

'Oh, yes, you'll find me in there. Last season. Played for Bill Edrich's Eleven against Kent, at Folkestone.'

Mr Bright in *Wisden*! Glory, celebration, vindication! What better evidence that he was, triumphantly, the real thing? I bore the book off to the school library, found an armchair in a quiet corner, frantically turned the pages, but discovered nothing. Certainly the match had been played, a one-innings match, in the wartime manner, in which W.J. Edrich's Eleven had batted first, made 198 for 6, declared and put in Kent, who had scored 156 for 7 when stumps were drawn on a drawn game. Edrich himself had made a bold 66, but of Mr Bright's name, not a mention. Should I tell him? Could I confront him with it?

It was as torment, and to confront him was to challenge his word, not to confront him was to live in doubt. It was, as I can see in retrospect, the first blemish on credulity, leading to an eventual, uneasy resolution.

It was a week before I could get up courage to go to him: 'Sir, I can't find your name in *Wisden*, sir!'

It was the first time I had ever seen him other than exuberant, the first time I had seen him frown. 'I'm there,' he said, 'I'm there,' and took the book from me, opened it, turned the pages with a sombre resolution.

'Page two hundred and thirty-six,' I heard myself say, faintly.

'Here you are,' he said, at last, and held the book out to me, the short, clean, shining nail of his index finger resting on a name: *his* name. He had not bowled that day, he had not batted, he had caught nobody, but beneath the statistics of Bill Edrich's Eleven's innings, one could clearly read: A.R. Gover, L. Gray and C. Bright did not bat.'

'There,' he said.

A Pyrrhic victory. It was not that he was now discredited, only that one was alive to new dimensions, other ways of seeing him, even if they were not Mr Remington's. Stand here, and he was still a hero; stand there, and he was mildly comic. Even among us, the boys, acquaintance had bred a certain impatience; we could not match such devouring enthusiasm forever.

'Keep a straight bat!' said the older boys, scathingly. There was a sense in which he seemed to be playing his own game, of which we were merely adjuncts. But the cricket team continued to win, and Mr Bright continued to talk of Arthur Gilligan, who was indubitably coming; next week, next month – next year, if not this.

I was leaving at the end of the term, for my public school. Obscurely guilt-ridden, I shook hands with Mr Bright on my last morning, but the blue eyes shone with their old exuberance, and his great hand enclosed mine in manly good fellowship. 'Good luck,' he said. 'Remember, keep a straight bat, and the runs will come!' We would meet again, we were both quite sure. Mr Bright lived hard by Hythe; my family was always renting summer cottages in Kent. We would speak again about Edrich and Gilligan.

That summer, however, my family went on holiday to Sussex, and it was almost a year before I heard again of Mr Bright. Richards, a boy younger than myself, arrived in the Easter term at my public school. I met him one morning as we filed out of the great, stone hangar of a chapel, and talked to him about our old school: the Headmaster, Remington. 'And Bright?' I asked.

'Oh, him,' said Richards. 'He's gone.' He was a small, dark, pumpkin-headed boy with spectacles. He had not been in the cricket team but, like myself, merely on the admiring verge.

'Gone?' I said, surprised.

'Kicked out. He was beating the younger boys in class. Hit them with a blackboard pointer when they got things wrong.'

'Mr Bright?' I said, yet in some curious way I was not astonished, had somehow been ready for shocks, disillusionment, perhaps through that first disillusionment, with *Wisden*. Beating little boys. I could even imagine it.

'Right-ho. Come out and take your medicine. Take it like a

man. There, that's it! All over! Wasn't so bad, was it?' And possibly a handshake.

But public school, with its initial, overpowering size and scope, ten times as many people, most so much older, larger than oneself, swept away thoughts of prep school, and of Mr Bright.

I thought of him again only the following summer, when my father announced that he had taken a cottage near Hythe. My heart jumped. Hythe! Mr Bright! I wanted to see him, it would be fun to see him. He may have beaten little boys, but he had always been kind to me, never sarcastic, vindictive, impatient, contemptuous, as every other teacher had been, at one time or another. I would run across him, I was sure, and I had a picture of him in his archetypal blazer and flannels, smiling his incorrigible smile.

The cottage we had rented stood in a road just off the busy coast road, two-storeyed, stuccoed, built some time in the twenties. Five hundred yards away, in a much larger house, a permanent residence, lived the Levinsons, with whose son I was expected to be friends. His father was a gown manufacturer who had prospered in the war.

I visited them. The son was my own age, fourteen, but went to day school, a dark, plump, pink-checked, knowing boy, with opaque brown eyes, who wasn't interested in cricket. Did I play bridge? he asked. Did he know Mr Bright? I wondered.

'I know him,' he said scornfully. 'We all know *him* round here.'

What would come next? I wanted to stop him, but knew I had to hear, knew, too, that nothing pleasant could emerge from that prematurely disenchanted face.

'Went round everyone last Christmas promising he'd get them whisky. Got money off them all, then they never saw the whisky.'

'Are you sure?' I said.

'Of course I'm sure. My old man got done for a tenner. Oh, he's known round here, all right.'

I hated him for telling me, yet I believed him, just as I had believed Richards. These were missing pieces, locking into a jigsaw left incomplete when I left prep school.

'He's known round here, all right.'

I had meant to look for him, but wouldn't seek him now. Yet meet him I did, in the apposite setting of a Kentish lane, steep and green, canopied thickly by its summer trees, down which I sped on my bicycle, only to stop in full flight as I saw him at the bottom.

'Mr Bright!'

He'd recognised me, too. 'Hallo!' he cried, dressed not in his flannels and striped blazer but in faded corduroys, a white shirt buttoned at the sleeves.

It was a moment of ecstatic reunion, delight so strong that it swept all else aside: rumour, disgrace, humiliation. Certainly there was no trace of inhibition as he beamed at me, shaking my hand. How was I? How was my cricket? Good to see me! Splendid! There was no resisting him.

I felt then, but couldn't formulate, the power and pathos of his innocence. Mr Remington was old and crabbed, Levinson was wise before his time. They had both been right, and yet were both so wrong.

'Been keeping a straight bat, eh?' asked Mr Bright. 'That's it! That's right! That's the ticket!'

Originally titled 'Up she jolly goes'
from LOVE IS NOT LOVE
1985

PART THREE

THE VILLAGE GREEN AND OTHER COMMONS

CRICKET IS A CONFIDENCE TRICK

by

A.C.H. Smith

I sometimes feel there are more leg-spinners in cricket fiction than in real cricket nowadays – and certainly in first-class cricket. But the reason is not far to seek. Leg-spin bowling is a fascinating but difficult craft, and when it is operating, there is always something happening – runs and/or wickets. Hence its attraction to Mike Marqusee (see page 17) and to Anthony Smith, who likes to turn a few very slow ones himself.

Seventy-three for four. Not too good.

The sixth batsman was identified by Jacquetta as a Pakistani poet. He had a sound batting style. Runs came slowly, but now there was a solidity about the partnership. The village captain made a double bowling change, bringing on his leg-spinner, Dicky Lee, and yet another slow left-armer, a tall man who gave it plenty of air and seemed to be getting some turn. With a pair of sound batsmen playing a pair of accomplished bowlers, the cricket was not spectacular to the casual watchers on the terrace, but absorbing to those who knew the game.

Charley did not talk much to Jacquetta. He was particularly watching Dicky Lee, seeing how he opened his chest for the googly, and reckoning that the top-spinner must be the one he bowled a bit quicker and flatter. Craven took no chances, but drove solidly when he saw the half-volley. The Pakistani looked as though he could reproduce one of the eternal innings with which the subcontinent has sprinkled the record books.

And then a familiar thing happened. The left-armer lost control of a delivery, it reached the Pakistani full toss at waist level, he swung too greedily at it, and square leg took a long but not difficult catch.

As Charley walked in, at ninety-eight for five, he felt like a stateless person again. Of course, he would have to find himself batting with Craven, entering a relationship of trust and encouragement with him this afternoon. He took one leg, and looked at the field, trying to decode it. A long-off, for the one held back. Long-on and deep mid-wicket for the hit against the spin. Slip and point, of course, and two each side saving one. He would just have a look at it, for a while. There was no hurry. After a few overs, he would go for the drive between cover and mid-off. He played out two balls, getting plenty of bat behind them, and the umpire called 'Over'.

Craven had been in some forty minutes for about fifteen, but he was taking no chances. His eyes narrowed at the ball in flight, and as in the nets he played late, not committing himself forward or back until he was satisfied he had read the length. Lee's fourth ball was short. Craven moved across on the back foot, played it firmly forward of point, and called Charley for a brisk single to cover.

While Charley took guard, the village captain had a discussion with the bowler. A number seven batsman could be attacked. Two grabbers were in for the wrong'un, one fine, one so square that the umpire had to cross to the off side. Slip, gully, point, stretching their fingers to meet. Shortish extra, and two out behind him saving one. Wide mid-on. Again, Charley was going to watch it at the start. Then, his best chances looked like driving straight, dabbing, and anything short enough he would get across and hammer between his short square leg's ankles until he was shifted out.

Dicky Lee ran up and delivered with jerky joints. His arm came over quicker than you'd expect, but he released the ball early, so that it was hard to adjust the rhythm of the backlift and downswing to what should be the reciprocal rhythm of the delivery. As the first ball came towards him, Charley could hear it humming. He got his front foot right out to the pitch, but his head had not gone with it, and the ball broke clean past the bat, missing off stump, and leaving Charley looking awkward. The village captain at once brought extra up to silly. 'Tight as you like,' he called.

Right, you presumptuous bastard, Charley thought, I'll show you. Left shoulder, left elbow, head still, let it come to you, don't commit yourself too early, wrist down the line, *wait*. On the back foot if you can. The next ball came down a little quicker than the first. Charley got everything into the appointed place, but the ball shot through low, flicked bat and pad, and dropped between the two short legs. The fielders gestured and sighed, not believing his luck. Charley didn't need their hustling. He knew he'd failed to read the top-spinner. A few weeks earlier, he had scored fifty-five in a works match. Now, here he was, among strangers who gave him no credit, looking like a virgin in a scrum. What an endlessly difficult game it was. One thing the old public school mob were right about, it was character-forming like nothing else, except maybe going over the top at Ypres.

The village team were in good heart, chatting cheerfully to each other. Craven offered no counter-companionship from the other end, which may have been just as well, taking the long view. What he did do was drive two excellent fours past mid-off, in the next over. The field was adjusted in respect.

Charley faced Lee again. He watched the hand. The wrist came over pointing towards cover. He read it as a standard leg break, correctly, and played it quietly back to the bowler. The next was similar, tossed higher. He got his head over it, and stopped it dead. The third ball came from a wrist facing him. He got everything behind it and, as he expected, it came through quick and low, either the top-spinner or the googly, it didn't matter too much. The fourth was a leg break, the fifth unquestionably the wrong'un. He stopped both. The last was tossed right up to him. He took a step down the pitch, then changed his mind, and simply blocked the full toss. He could hear the snickers behind him. Next over, he vowed, you wait.

Craven took a single from the left-armer's last ball. Charley approved of him for not apologizing to his partner. He took another single from Dicky Lee's fifth ball, and Charley, still on nought, faced the last. He saw the wrist cocked towards him, and the ball well up. Confident that he had read the googly, he leaned on an on-drive, and with relief saw it run crisply out to the vacant mid-wicket area, for two. Not many of those watching, probably few even of the fielders, would have appreciated the analysis and technique that produced the modest shot, he thought, but he did, which was important. Dicky Lee must do, which was more important still. The whole of cricket was a confidence trick.

Craven, well set now, used his feet to the left-armer's second ball, and off-drove it for three. Charley played easily forward to the next ball, and was clean bowled through the gate. It was the old story, like all cricket's stories, he reflected, walking back. You concentrate on the difficult thing, bring it off, preen yourself a little, relax, and the fellow at the other end does you with his arm ball. You ought to have worked it out past mid-on for a couple. Next time. Only tomorrow. And here comes Fitzknight on cue with a silver tray of lemon drinks, and you rattle the hard-luck-old-chap smile on his face by nabbing one as he goes past.

'Well batted,' Jacquetta greeted him.

'A little gem,' he agreed.

from EXTRA COVER
1981

THE END OF THE SEASON IN SINJI

by

J.L. Carr

J.L. Carr is the author of several novels including A Month in the Country *and* The Battle of Pollocks Crossing. *Also, as a publisher of 'unlikely dictionaries', he has brought out his own* Carr's Dictionary of Extra-ordinary English Cricketers, *a little gem.*

In A Season in Sinji *Flanders, a keen and knowledgeable cricketer but only an Aircraftsman in rank, starts a unit team, 697 Squadron XI, to play other units in West Africa. Then a new adjutant, Turton, turns up to take part. Or take a hand? Long before Turton even obtained his commission, his and Flanders's paths had crossed.*

The last but one game of my campaign was already fixed – against the Liberator Squadron. The Semi-Final you might call it, because, if we lost there really wasn't much point in playing the Station XI.

This game, the Liberator Squadron one, is worth telling about because from it sprang all the later trouble. So this is what happened. Slingsby and I could never pick a side until the last minute because of bods being wanted for duty, and I was in the Section one morning when the C.O. came round on one of his snap inspections. He never really looked at things, but I suppose he felt he ought to be seen now and then.

'Ah,' he said, 'Aircraftsman Flanders! Flanders, I've been hearing about your cricket side. You've been doing jolly well. Yes, jolly well. I'm very pleased that you fellows have organised some recreation. Far too many nowadays wait for someone to entertain them. Yes, jolly good! Playing the Liberator crowd too I hear?'

'Yes, sir.'

'Ah, good! Yes, well, there's a couple of my officers would like a game. You can find places for them? Both tell me they played for their schools. 1st XI men. Now, can you manage that, Flanders?'

You couldn't hum and haw with your C.O. A wink is as good as a kick from him.

'Yes, sir,' I said as cheerfully as I could manage.

'Good man, good man! Mr Oates – I think you'll find him a jolly useful bat. And the Adjutant. You know Turton of course. Good! I trust you'll lick them, Flanders.'

And off he went, walking-stick and all, saying 'Jolly good!'

I looked around for Wakerly to laugh. It had been the sort of scene he delighted in. Then I went to break the news to Slingsby.

We felt the depressing effect of this soon enough in the shape of an oral message to Slingsby (not me) by an Orderly Room toady – 'The Adj. says you all have to wear shirts in the game tomorrow . . .' (Of course, in that climate, as soon as we airmen were off duty, we stripped down to the waist, wearing only shorts and pumps.) Wearing the shirts against our normal custom wasn't too bad: it was the irritation of him wedging himself into the side and then interfering. But there was no getting out of it, and we wore them.

I won the toss and batted. I'd never found a competent partner, so I put the new officer, Oates, in Number Two. He was a dead loss – dollied up a catch the fourth ball of the first over, having nearly run me out in the third. But their bowling was very plain, straight up and down stuff and, though the other wickets fell regularly, I stayed and made my biggest score (in Africa) – 124 not out, and we declared at 201 for 8. (Well, if I don't say it nobody else will – it was a concert performance; my timing was dead-on and the last fifty came in twenty-five minutes. In fact, I scored 18 in the last over and ended the innings by hammering a ball only just short of a length round over long-leg. It went like a rocket, a six, struck high up on the trunk of a palm tree and bounced back like a golf ball and hit a spectator. You only get a dozen innings like that in twenty years' batting.)

Neither Slingsby nor Trader were in form though, and when one of the Liberator sergeants, a thickset man with a black moustache, and an airman called Hawke-Jones got set, the runs kept coming at an uncomfortably steady pace until they were 175 for 7 and no sign of the partnership breaking. Then I panicked and, instead of trusting my side, I switched myself into fielding positions where I imagined the catches were likely to go. So I wasn't controlling the game any more – just being pushed along by the current of events.

Then Turton shouted across at me, 'Flanders, I should like an over.' Frankly, I'd forgotten him. He was up to his Budmouth antics, of course; he *had* to be different. The best he could do here was to tie knots in the four corners of a handkerchief, like farm-labourers at home sometimes did, and to wear it as a sun-hat.

'Next over, then,' I said.

I know I shouldn't have done. A captain should let no one dictate to him on the field. That I did was a measure of the flap I'd got myself into.

And the impossible happened. In the first over he clean bowled the sergeant and the incoming batsman and, an over later, finished off the side. Just plain straight balls such as Slingsby, Stone and Trader had been belting down all afternoon.

As we walked off, Slingsby looked across at me. 'Jam!' he said.

The new officer stopped. 'Thanks for the game, Flanders,' he said. 'Sorry I didn't help much.'

Turton, of course, just *left*. Full stop!

So there we were. One more game and we'd be there. Everything had worked out to plan. Slingsby must have suddenly guessed what was passing through my mind because he suddenly began to bawl,

One more river and that's the River of Jordan,
One more river, there's just one more river to cross.

Slingsby singing! It must be his nerves, I thought. So I wasn't the only one who'd panicked? Good!

The old hands had told us what the Rains were like, how you never were really dry, how your shoes went green and the mosquitoes multiplied. So I drew a deep breath as you might say, and fixed a date for the last game. It had been a long, long trail from that first nervous match against the Stores Section.

For my liking, there was a lot too much interest in this last match. Our being unbeaten had been noticed at last and it got around that this final victory over the Rest of the Station was what we'd been working towards. There was a lot of speculation in the billets and a fair amount of betting, with the odds, naturally, very much against us. Plainly, it had caught everyone by surprise, this quiet little campaign working itself out unnoticed. Men I scarcely knew, N.C.O.s and one or two squadron officers, stopped to discuss the chances. Even the posting of the Commanding Officer and arrival of a new one didn't catch their interest more. And, in the billet, I saw erks taking a quick look as though they'd never seen me. I had to take a grip of myself. . . .

I had worked it out that, once the breeze began to blow in from the west – that is across the mangrove swamps from the sea – it would stay in that quarter and would win the game for us. Trader, with his high left-arm action, bowling from the Guard Room end would use it to float the ball towards the slips, and their batsmen would follow it round and tickle it into Slingsby's big hands. And Slingsby himself, from the Work Area end, with the palm trees masking the ball, would jerk his fast off-breaks into their bodies and I'd be waiting at silly mid-on. It was a blessed breeze.

I borrowed a timber frame from Ground Defence (from which they used to hang a bag of straw to practise bayonet plunging) and I fitted this up across the popping crease. Then I chalked a cross chest high on the sack and, after work, set on Trader and Slingsby bowling short to lift the ball. And, out of the corner of my eye, I saw Maidstone and Fife stop to watch. I knew it would worry them, because find me the batsman who likes the ball up at him, especially when it's moving in or away. We packed it in then because it had been for their benefit, not Trader's nor Slingsby's, that I set the thing up.

The day before the game the breeze still blew. If anything, it had veered a couple of points and was coming in from forward short-leg towards gulley which was better than I'd dared hope, putting a sharper drag on off-breaks and carrying the out-swingers with a keener nip from the matting. As I've said before, I like working to a plan: it gives you that extra confidence in a panic. Of course, you never can rule out luck in any game, cricket more than most, but it's plain madness to bank on it.

That week, most of the Catalinas were away on dispersal so that we were slack in the section and I was sitting under our mango tree getting the benefit of the breeze, feeling a bit weak at the knees thinking about this final game. I felt sure that the Station XI were so damned confident of winning that *their* only plan would be simplicity itself – get rid of me and then massacre the others. It was a great responsiblity.

I was pondering the horrors of being out first ball or first over, and all my careful plans over the past months collapsing like a pack of cards into a ridiculous heap, when Slingsby came.

I could see he was blazing mad; he was so pale.

'Turton's made himself captain,' he said, his voice trembling.

I was staggered. Then I went cold and I began to shake in all my limbs: something I can never remember happening before. Outside old time history books, I couldn't even begin to imagine anything like this happening.

'He can't,' I said. 'It's our team. It isn't *his* team.'

'Not according to him. He's called it *The* 697 Squadron XI.'

He hurried me off to the board outside the squadron offices.

The full force of what he'd done didn't hit me until I saw his name heading the list and my own near the bottom, and a Squadron Ldr. Rumm I'd never heard of – a new flight commander it turned out – and saw that Henty and Cork had been pushed out, both only run-of-the-mill players who couldn't be relied on to score ten between them and only really able to stop the ball with their legs. But loyal lads who'd come all the way up with us.

'Ah, Flanders, looking over the Team?' Turton had come up behind us. I could think of nothing to say: I felt stunned. 'After the way you let things get out of hand in the Liberator Game, it was thought in the Mess that I'd better run things,' he said. 'Quite a strong side. If we all pull our weight we should give them a good game.'

I still could only stare stupidly at the board and Slingsby at his feet as he walked off. Oddly enough, in the middle of this horror, I thought what a tactical blunder he'd made putting Slingsby No. 8 and replacing Wood as vice-captain by one of the officers. There was always a chance they might have deserted me but, now he'd given them a back-hander apiece, they weren't likely to forgive him any more than I was.

But '*Ah, Flanders, it was thought in the Mess that I'd better run things . . .*' I'll hear it till my dying day and still feel the baffling heat of the squadron street and my own coldness. It was like a scene from a Western. He'd done it! Usurped our weeks of work and planning just like that! He had all the authority and power he could use, but he had to take over our little corner too! Damn and blast him!

By next morning, I'd settled into depression. There didn't seem to be a thing I could do about this abominable business. In the day-to-day routine of service life, you had to suffer fools and put up with rations of inhumanity from N.C.Os. and officers without answering back. But interference with leisure – that was something new. I'll be frank: I didn't care now if we lost or won. This wasn't the Game we'd been planning and preparing for, the Game that made sense of all the other games we'd won. I've spoken of this before so I'll not labour it.

But, even so, I'd have gone on and played the game, shelving all responsibility of course, but played as I always played, if it hadn't been for the S.H.Q. Sergeant, Fife. I was sitting just inside the Section door, when he poked his head in and said, 'Ready for the thrashing we're going to give you Thursday, Flanders?'

'You'll not be giving *me* one,' I said. 'I'm not captain and it's not my team.' But he laughed and went off laughing. And you could tell from the attitude of his cronies that it was me they had it in for, to smash *my* side and put *me* in my place among the fragments. Little Wood put it into words. 'They're going to crucify us,' he said. That was pitching it a bit thick; I don't care for scriptural words taken from their setting.

I half-heartedly tried to persuade the temporary corporal to insist that I couldn't be spared from duty on Thursday, but he had his ear close to the ground and knew what was going on. Only a sharp bout of malaria could save me from the bitterest pill I'd ever had to swallow. One or two of the lads and Slingsby came round to the billet but, honestly, I couldn't bring myself to talk about it. I still felt numb.

And, when it came to the afternoon itself, I didn't know where to put myself. As skipper, there'd been so much to see to – last minute tactical arguments with Slingsby, jollying up the nervous ones, screwing up my own will to win as I took the over-elaborate pains with my kit I always indulged in (because you have to *think* the game before you play it). It was awful not going out to toss with Maidstone, just waiting to be told what it was to be, bat or field. As it turned out it was *field* – Turton had won the toss and put them in. (That showed how little confidence he had in us!)

Maidstone opened for them and, after he'd been missed by Turton in the slips (where Slingsby should have been) in Trader's first over, they never looked back. Trader and Slingsby were good bowlers; in fact very good. But on asphalt, accuracy wasn't enough. I don't want to appear immodest, but they needed me to direct their fire-power from mid-off and he'd stuck me third man and long-on so that the refinements of the game (if there were any) were lost to me.

About the tenth over, remembering his success against the Liberator Squadron, he put himself on at one end and the new officer, Rumm, at the other. But, as anybody who understood the game could see, Maidstone and Co. with their tails up were a very different kettle of fish, and they put the pair of them to the sword, Maidstone particularly taking anything over-pitched and thumping it like a cannonball through the covers and making massive pulls out of short balls. It was butchery.

I won't prolong the agonizing details – they hurt me still. It was enough to see Slingsby looking half crazy, furiously pushing his long forelock back over his brow, or to have to listen to their supporters making as much row as a cup-tie. The Station side really stuck it in deep and then twisted. At half-past five they declared at 217 for 3.

'Christ!' Stone said, and put his head in his hands and rocked to and fro in misery on the bench under the acacia trees.

'Well, chaps,' Turton said in his jerky way, 'it's a lot. But, if they got 'em, so can we.'

He pinned up the batting order. S/Ldr. Rumm and F/O Oates numbers one and two, then Stone, then myself, Wood, Turton himself, Slingsby and so on. We didn't talk much as we sat there waiting. As a matter of fact, I was feeling pretty normal up till then, nothing like as nervous as I usually was. It was Fife and what he said that sent the balloon up. The Station went out, tossing the ball around one to the other and laughing but *he* couldn't resist rubbing it in to pay off old scores. He paused by the bench where I was sitting with Wood and Slingsby. 'Take your beating like a man, Flanders,' he said. Only the three of us heard him. The man was a sadist.

I didn't say anything. This is important because of what came afterwards. I didn't need to as I glimpsed the faces of the other two as they glared at his back.

But he could laugh all right; second ball of the first over down went Rumm's bailiwick. He'd missed one of Angus's and that usually was fatal. Oates didn't last much longer, and it was two wickets for three runs when I went in, and, then, when poor Stone had been caught at point, it was three for five. Wood came waddling in (he was slightly bow-legged) and began to drop his bat like a hen-house shutter, even though Fife, bowling really fast, soon nipped his fingers. It was no joke. Then the poor kid was hit again and his hands began to run blood. I'd tried to get him out of the habit but, this time, he forgot all I'd told him. Let's face it: he didn't know how to lift his bat *and* stay in. And Fife knew his limitations and bowled at them.

But Wood gritted his teeth (I heard him!) and stuck it out. And, watching him from the other end, I felt (as you might say) a sudden lightening of the spirit. I nearly laughed aloud. What it amounted to was that this backstreet London kid who'd learnt his cricket in an elementary school playground had swallowed my pep talks over the past two months and was carrying them out mechanically. It made me suddenly ashamed too. So when this awful over stopped and he was wringing his blood fingers, I called gently, 'Good lad, Woody!' and winked at him and he must have got the message when I lowered my stance and then let everything more than three inches wide of the off stump go through to the wicket-keeper. After that, I only tried to score a single an over just to keep him from the chopping block.

You might say that this was the crisis of the match. In ten overs we scored but eight runs. And suddenly Turton stood up, cupped his hands and yelled, 'Get a move on, Flanders.' I didn't look directly at him, because I could see the other lads sitting up looking cheerful for the first time with Slingsby jumping up and down behind him. Next over, Wood missed one and was lbw and in came Turton. He glared down the pitch at me and called sharply, 'We'll have some quick singles.' And, in fact, he glanced his very first ball gracefully to leg, his favourite shot I suppose, and came racing down at me. 'Come on, come on, man,' he shouted. I didn't move and he reached my end, stuck his face no more than a foot from mine and yelled like a maniac, 'What the hell are you playing at, Flanders!' But Maidstone had moved quietly round from the slips to short fine-leg and the ball had gone straight into his hands.

The silence was electric. Turton suddenly knew something had gone wrong. He looked round and saw the ball being tossed gently into the air. 'I'm afraid you're out, sir,' the umpire said.

The Station still kept at it. With five wickets down, I suppose they still thought they had a half chance of winning. But they must have seen the writing on the wall when Slingsby came in and began to smother everything. He more or less sat astride his bat as though he'd taken up permanent residence in the crease. It was growing dark by now and Fife had just about lost control of himself, so that I heard Maidstone say quietly to him, 'Steady on, man, you'll kill somebody.'

Then Turton intervened for the last time. He advanced a few

yards on to the field of play and called, 'Flanders, you are to retire.'

I didn't shift and he called again. The game just stopped. But I know the rules. A captain can make an entire side declare, but he can't winkle out one player. It would have been fatal to have argued this out with him though. So I didn't look at him and stayed put and took my guard.

'Play on,' said the umpire, and Maidstone gave me a shy grin. Slingsby got a glancing blow on his head and, after that, didn't know whether he was coming or going and just went through the motions as taught in Ossett and District. Ten minutes later, you could hardly see who was in the long-field or even at extra cover and every third ball I was being rattled in the ribs. But we wouldn't appeal against the light.

Then, all at once, the game stopped. The umpires looked at one another and lifted the bails. And that was an end to it. It was crazy and silly and funny. 217 for 3 them, 27 for 5 us. A draw!

from A SEASON IN SINJI
1967

THE RING-IN

A story by

Dal Stivens

Born in Blayney, New South Wales, in 1911, Dal Stivens is a novelist, short-story writer, painter and naturalist who has been described as 'a one thing at a time perfectionist'. He has published five novels of which A Horse of Air *– about a mystical search for a rare bird, the night parrot – won a major Australian prize, the Miles Franklin Award; and eight collections of stories. These range from the social realism, à la Steinbeck, of* The Tramp and other stories *(1936) to the author's fascination with the essentially oral tradition of the tall, Bush tale, and a distinct comic gift often expressed in the mingling of realism and surrealism. These latter qualities, apostrophised by one literary historian as 'playful exaggerations', are frequently combined to excellent effect in Dal Stivens's cricketing tales which have been collected in* The Demon Bowler and other cricket stories *(1979).*

He was the greatest batsman of all time; he was Trumper, Bradman, Macartney, Hobbs, Hutton and Woolley and everyone else united in one transcendental master. And he played only one match in his life. (Or so J.V.B. Rawlinson, who was my uncle, used to declare.) And, moreover, all that opulence was squandered in a bush match in outback Australia. It should have been lavished in a score of games at Lord's, The Oval, Old Trafford, Headingley, Sydney, Cape Town, Melbourne, Adelaide, Durban, Kingston, Georgetown, Bombay, Calcutta . . . (The names of the great grounds rolled like poetry from J.V.B. Rawlinson's lips, caressed and cossetted so that you had sudden visions of white figures crinkling in the sunlight and flickering over bright green turf.)

There was a kind of retribution in it, Rawlinson used to think, as though the sport of cricket had taken a revenge on him – or had shown itself in a startling and mysterious way, because he had allowed himself to be rung in this particular bush match. Rawlinson was, of course, the famous Rawlinson, perhaps the greatest spin bowler that Australia, or even the world, has seen. His deeds are legendary. On his best days he was almost unplayable. He frequently troubled Trumper. On this occasion, just before the opening of the New South Wales season and the start of first-class club games in Sydney, J.V.B. Rawlinson went for a short holiday with a friend who was a wheat farmer. He was twenty-seven at the time, slim, dark, and at his peak. It was an overnight journey from Sydney and he slept badly. He got out of the slow, smoky train about 11 a.m. the next day and, carrying his luggage, walked along the hot, gravelly station. He had gone about twenty yards when his friend followed by three men came through the gate. After the hand-clasps, his friend introduced him, with a vigorous wink, as 'Bill Jackson' to the others.

He explained later, 'We'll have a little fun and ring you in when we play Mundabilla tomorrow. There'll be no harm in it because it's only a picnic match. But it'll be funny to watch you go through them – but not too easily, Jack. We'll play act a bit.'

My uncle said he didn't like the idea, but allowed himself to be talked into it. After all, it seemed harmless enough. But the next day, when the team of which his friend was captain was out for 162 and they took the field – well, then, it struck Rawlinson as being a bit condescending. Rawlinson had had to disguise his batting – he was, as you know, quite good as bowlers go. He frequently made his forties and fifties in Tests. And now he had to hide his superb fielding and catching. He deliberately muffed several drives and he put down a catch.

'I felt – well – that I was committing sacrilege of some sort,' he said. 'It was as though I was desecrating something – you could call it the spirit of the game.' This was something real to

Rawlinson – something that brooded not only over Sydney and Lord's, but over village green games in England and over the dusty country grounds of South Africa, the West Indies, India and Australia. It was here in this oval hacked out in the Australian bush from the encircling hardy dwarf eucalyptus.

When Mundabilla were none for seventy – his friend's idea of a joke was to let them go so far – Rawlinson was put on to bowl, and he felt worse than ever. He could (he said) have gone through the team in under three overs – or so he thought at the time – and instead he had to ham. It was (he said) the most difficult bit of bowling he had ever done. He had, of course, superb control and he could and did bowl long hops and full tosses. The difficulty – and the hurt – was spiritual. He felt mean and it wasn't funny at all, though his friend was enjoying it hugely.

In any class of cricket, good leg-spin is the hardest to play. It's the type of bowling which separates the men from the boys. The wicket was coir matting, but Rawlinson had played on it during country tours in Australia and in India. He quickly adjusted his right-arm spin to the increased bounce and turn.

'You can't use the seam in leg-spinners because the ball bounces too high to hit the stumps,' he explained. 'But otherwise coir matting is a gift to a spinner.'

After three overs by Rawlinson, the other team were six down for 85. Rawlinson had taken four of the wickets with a mixture of good and deliberately bad balls. Two batsmen, he said, got out to balls they should never have touched.

Rawlinson wasn't concentrating very hard when he started his fourth over. He was wishing that his friend the captain had let him go off as he wished. About the fourth ball he suddenly began to notice the batsman opposing him. He was tall, fair, beautifully built, and he leapt down the pitch and smashed the ball through the covers so fast that the fieldsman had not moved a yard when the ball hurtled past him. The fifth ball was one of Rawlinson's best. He hadn't intended it but a man can't control everything he does. It was Rawlinson's famous over-spinner which looked like a leg-spinner but spat straight through. Rawlinson had claimed most of the great batsmen leg before wicket with this ball. It was tremendously difficult to detect and its speed off the pitch was cobra-swift. But the new batsmen met it firmly in the middle of the bat. It ran out past mid-off, and they took two.

Rawlinson was now studying the fair-skinned batsman. His stance was poised, relaxed. His body was compact and controlled. It flowed into his strokes. He played the ball very late, as nearly all class players do. Rawlinson's next ball was a good length, dipping a little to the left and breaking swiftly from the leg stump. The batsman went back and shortened its length and square cut it for four.

The next ball (Rawlinson said) wasn't a really bad one, but the batsman hit it over the bowler's head for six with immense power and grace. It made Rawlinson think of Trumper or Woolley. There was no straining. The magisterial bat had swept through to the ball and smashed it back over the bowler's head into the wheatfield beyond the ground.

During the next few overs by the other bowlers and Rawlinson, they saw the full range of the batsman's imperious strokes – seemingly delicate late-cuts which spirited the ball bullet-swift to the fence, sovereign square cuts which thrust the ball swerving in a swift red arc to the boundary, brisk pulls and trenchant hooks, and necromantic leg glances where the bat barely flickered as the batsman rose on his toes and the ball was magically halfway out to the fence before anyone realised it had happened. It was poetry, ballet, the matador's grace, said Rawlinson. 'I've seen them all – the great dancers and the great fighters of the bulls. And I should know,' he added. He was an admirer of the bullfight, and he had once drawn my attention to the fact that only cricket and bullfighting had inspired any considerable literature. He had contributed a scholarly monograph to an English literary journal on the subject.

Rawlinson was a student of cricket, and I have often seen him watch a batsman for an over and then unerringly say where he had learnt his game and what his masters and models had been. 'There's a tradition of batsmanship,' he said. 'A great batsman influences those who come after. I can see the heritage of

Trumper in some present-day batsmen. They haven't his genius, of course, but there's a glimmer of the master in some of their strokes. I couldn't trace this chap's genealogy but I am positive about one thing. He hadn't learnt his cricket in the bush.'

By this time Rawlinson was asking questions of the other batsman. Who was this player? The other batsman didn't know. The brilliant stroke-maker had never played for Mundabilla before, but he thought he came from a farm a fair way out of town.

The spiritual disquiet had now left Rawlinson, as he related. Here was a batsman worthy of any bowler in the world. Rawlinson now bowled his best. And it was *his* best. Against anyone else it would have been one of Rawlinson's days, but the tall batsman countered everything Rawlinson could devise. 'He called the tune,' Rawlinson said. 'His footwork alone was enough to make you go into rhapsodies. He moved close to the ball with his head right over it. There was never the waste of a movement. He played as Mozart must have played the pianoforte – "like flowing oil", was how he said it should be done. He quietly stole the strike, too.'

The score meanwhile was mounting rapidly. It rose to 150. The two other batsmen had been dismissed.

Once Rawlinson got a faint edge, but the ball went safely to ground. And once the batsman made an error. Rawlinson had no idea of what the batsman's score was at this stage – perhaps in the seventies or eighties – but he seemed suddenly to get a little reckless. It was almost as though he was growing tired, not physically but mentally, of batting. It was almost certainly the touch of the artist in him, said Rawlinson. He'd done it all. Scores didn't count, and they don't with some of the great batsmen. It's what you do and how you do it that matter. Whatever the explanation, the batsman now began coming out of his crease to meet Rawlinson almost as the ball left the bowler's hand. Rawlinson caught him cold. He dropped one short and it should have been a stumping. The batsman was set for a drive and he was stranded, feet down the pitch, and the ball was five feet short of him.

'I was pleased and I was also sorry,' Rawlinson said. 'He was finished, or anyone else would have been. I've never seen anything so fast in my life. Somehow in mid-stroke he stopped his bat, and he late-cut that ball with all the grace and power you'll ever see. It was as though that had been the stroke he intended to play! It was superb.'

Rawlinson's farmer friend and captain had been growing increasingly upset by the turn of events. With a set face he constantly urged Rawlinson to bowl the side out. He was frantic when the other side drew to within four of victory. Rawlinson was angry. He realised that a deceit had been practised on him. He had allowed himself to be rung in on what was not a friendly picnic game, but more in the nature of a grudge match.

The other side won of course. The batsman who had never played for his team before straight drove Rawlinson for four. Rawlinson said he had scarcely straightened up before it had flashed past him along the ground.

Afterwards in the pavilion there were the drinks and congratulations. Rawlinson found them a bit nauseating, but some might say he was a bit over-sensitive. And perhaps he put too much emphasis on what happened next. He made a point of approaching the brilliant batsman and quietly congratulated him. There, too, Rawlinson displayed exquisite taste. 'You would insult a great batsman if you praised him,' he said. 'He knew what he had done. And, remember, I was just another country team bowler called Bill Jackson, though I think he knew better.'

The two talked together, discussing the game. I fancy they had the respect for each other that supreme masters have for each other. Rawlinson had a sense of guilt about the masquerade and he, not surprisingly, put more emphasis than is warranted on what happened next. He asked the batsman his name.

'Bill Jackson,' he said, with what Rawlinson claimed afterwards was an enigmatic smile.

Rawlinson, though imaginative, was not given to superstition, but this answer shook him badly. 'Could I – or cricket – have been punished in this way for hubris – for pride?' he asked. 'Bill Jackson – or whatever his real name was – never played again. Never before and never afterwards. And what's more, he just disappeared after that one day. We tried our best to trace him. How do you explain that?'

There's the story as J.V.B. Rawlinson – and others – told it to me.

from THE DEMON BOWLER AND OTHER CRICKET STORIES
1979

THE BRENSHAM VILLAGE SIDE

by

John Moore

In Brensham Village *we are in the West Country in the 1930s, but also on the borders of fiction and fictionalisation. 'I have built upon a ground-plan and framework of truth,' the author wrote, 'but I have purposely played fast and loose with chronology and topography and have not hesitated to make what Byron called a short armistice with truth where it would have been embarrassing to write about living people.' Armistice or no, a sizeable portion of the book is devoted to 'the Cricket team', the individuals in which ring idiosyncratically true; while the match against the detested Woody Bourton side is decided, in the best tradition of literary cricket matches, only in what would anyway have been the last over.*

Perhaps I should never have got to know much about Brensham but for the accident that I was not a very good cricketer. When I left school I returned to Elmbury and was articled to my uncle, who was an auctioneer. I joined the Elmbury Cricket Club, which played competent and rather solemn games on Saturday afternoons and which didn't take long to discover that my rightful place in the batting-order was last. But so competent and solemn were the earlier batsmen that they very rarely got out; and in practice I hardly ever batted at all.

Now Brensham, whose parson was tolerant and broadminded (as was to be expected of one who kept live-bait in his font), sometimes played cricket on Sundays; and one day Mr Chorlton invited me to join the team. The Brensham standard was not so high as Elmbury's; and I was put in fifth wicket down. Moreover the previous batsmen, whose approach to the game was light-hearted and happy-go-lucky, smote the ball hard, high, and often, so that before long they were all caught in the deep. Within half an hour of the start of the innings I found myself walking to the wicket. This unfamiliar experience was so intoxicating that I was heartened to swipe the first ball over the bowler's head for six. The next one bowled me middle-stump; but I had had my fun and I walked back cheerfully to the pavilion where Mr Chorlton, Briggs the blacksmith, and Sammy Hunt were chuckling and clapping. 'That's the sort of innings we like to see at Brensham,' they said. After the match we all went to the 'Adam and Eve' and played darts; and I drank more beer than a seventeen-year-old is supposed to be able to carry. Sammy Hunt, who was the captain of the team, invited me to play for it regularly; and since whatever loyalty I possessed to the Elmbury Club had been dissipated by beer I gladly accepted.

Thereafter, on Saturdays and Sundays throughout the summer, I made my way to the small square cricket-field which lay between the orchards and the river; at first by bicycle, later upon an old ramshackle Triumph, and, once or twice when the Triumph broke down, on horseback. The spectacle of a young man in blazer and white flannels, carrying a bat, trotting down the village street on a lanky chestnut didn't at all surprise the people of Brensham; for almost everybody in the place was a horseman, and the neighbouring farmer's sons would often ride to the village dances in white waistcoast and tails. And already I was accepted as belonging to the village; for they had known me as a boy, buying cattie-lackey at Mrs Doan's shop or wandering over the hill where the keepers employed by the Syndicate spoke of me and my three friends as 'they young Varmins'. In the 'Adam and Eve' after a cricket-match, an old man wearing the traditional velveteens came up to me grinning and said: 'I knows thee. Thee be one of they young Varmins.' So although I was technically a 'foreigner' (for I lived four miles away, and even the people of neighbouring Dykeham, just across the river, were considered foreigners) I was permitted a sort of honorary membership of the Brensham community.

Thus I got to know it and love it as well as I did Elmbury; I played cricket and darts, drank beer, sang in the pubs, fished, rode, shot, and boated with the crack-brained people of Brensham until my ways became woven with theirs; and thus I learned gradually, sentence by sentence and paragraph by paragraph, the story of what went on beneath the roofs.

The Cricket-Ground

I used to think that the cricket-field at Brensham, on a blue afternoon in May, must surely be one of the pleasantest places in the world; and certainly, when I travelled about the world, I found few places pleasanter. About the time of the first match, the apple-blossom came out, and the willows put on their young green. The first cuckoo arrived and started calling from the small adjacent meadow which was appropriately named Cuckoo Pen. There were cuckoo-flowers in this meadow too, a silver-lilac carpet of them, so that we did not know whether it was called after the bird or the flower. Lapwings had their nests there, and sometimes we found the mottled eggs when we were looking for a ball which had been skied, Brensham-fashion, right over the tops of the willow-trees.

To match the newness of the spring, Mr Chorlton had repainted the pavilion in green-and-white. Against the very fresh green of the pitch – the floods had lain on it for weeks at midwinter – the white lines of the creases showed sharp and clear. And how white in the spring sunshine were the flannels well-creased after months in bottom-drawers, the umpires' coats, the new-blanco'd pads and cricket-boots! How bright were the many-coloured blazers, and Mr Chorlton's Harlequin cap, and Mr Mountjoy's I Zingari! . . .

Smells and sounds: the sweet linseed-smell of bat-oil, and an indefinable clean smell (waterweed and foam?) which came from the weir and the lock just up-river. The gillyflower smell which blows in little brief gusts all over Brensham when there is a wind. The satisfying smack of a well-oiled bat hitting a ball during a knock-up before the game. The first bees buzzing in the apple-blossom. And in the willow-branches ubiquitous the endlessly repeated *chiff-chaff, chiff-chaff, chiff-chaff, chiff*, of the little yellow-olive bird from across the sea.

Clatter of plates in the lean-to hut behind the pavilion: the Helpers were already preparing the tea. These Helpers were a personable lot: Mrs Doan's daughter Sally, the young wife of the landlord of the 'Adam and Eve', and two merry little blondes, Mimi and Meg, from the 'Horse Narrow'. We were proud of them, because they always excited the wonder and admiration of visiting teams. We were also proud of their teas, which were not teas in the sedate drawing-room sense, but were more like Hunt Breakfasts, for they consisted of home-made meat pies, wonderful salads – lettuces, tomatoes, spring onions, watercress from the same stream in which we sometimes lost our cricket-balls – and generally a ham, home-smoked at the 'Adam and Eve' and decorated with paper frills and parsley so that it looked like a picture out of Mrs Beeton. The tea interval was always a long one at Brensham.

And now the captains have tossed and Sammy Hunt leads us out to field. Sammy has a completely bald head, which at the beginning of the season appears startlingly white; but he scorns to wear a hat, and as the season progresses his pate becomes rubicund, and then gradually goes brown, until by mid-August it is the colour of an overwintered russet apple. Mr Chorlton, of course, wears his Harlequin cap, the gayest cap in cricket, but it's old and faded and it's the very same cap, he tells us, in which he ran about the field for hours, in 1895, chasing the ball which Archie MacLaren hit so mercilessly when he scored 424 against Somerset. Mr Mountjoy, who wears his I Zingari cap, must have been a useful cricketer too in his young days; but he can't run very fast or bend very quickly, and his old eyes – so sharp at spotting the chiff-chaff in the willow-tree – are too slow to follow the ball which comes quick off the pitch and breaks away. Therefore his innings generally end with a loud *snick* and a yell of 'How's that?' from the delighted wicket-keeper; and as the umpire's finger goes up Mr Mountjoy mutters sadly: 'Oh Lord, that awful noise again!'

Sammy begins to arrange his field, doing so with humanity and a sense of the fitness of things. Thus Mr Mountjoy, since he can't run far, goes to mid-off and to save him walking between overs takes point when the bowling is from the other end. Mr Chorlton, who can't or won't run at all, keeps wicket; and another elderly member of the team, a retired engineer called Hope-Kingley, alternates between mid-on and square leg. But Briggs the blacksmith, who has huge horny hands with which he sometimes bends a six-inch nail for fun, must stand at forward short-leg or in the deep, and take what's coming to him; the village policeman goes in the slips, because, says Sammy, that's a suitable place for a bobby – 'they catch you out when you're not looking'. Billy Butcher, who is the village ne'er-do-weel and drunkard, is sent to long-leg in the hope that a bit of running about will do him good; and the 'boys', a collective term for any youths whom the secretary has roped in at the last moment to make up the team, are distributed round the boundary where with luck some high hits will harden up their palms. As for Sammy himself, he will be anywhere and everywhere, wherever the catches come low and hard, wherever the new red ball races towards the boundary there will be Sammy's bald head bobbing after it; for he is like a good general who turns up unexpectedly wherever the fight is hottest.

Our Secretary, a small, wiry market-gardener called Alfie, takes the ball for the first over. Joe Trenfield, our umpire and the landlord of the 'Horse Narrow', counts his six pennies and drops them one by one into the pocket of his smock. Dai Roberts the postman opens his score-book at the pavilion window and licks the point of his pencil.

'Play!' says Joe: and the season begins. . . .

The Match Against Woody Bourton

It was delightful to watch those three extraordinary and lovable spectators sitting together on the bench that was only just long enough for them: Goaty Pegleg with his impressive white beard and his wooden peg held out straight in front of him, looking extremely salty and piratical although he's never seen the sea, nor, in fact, travelled more than twenty miles from Brensham; the Colonel in his green tweeds which merged into the leafy background so that his figure lacked definition and you only noticed the fire-red, gnome-like face, the badger-grizzle moustache, the bright humorous blue eyes; and the scarecrow lord, Lord Orris, whose panama hat had not worn as well as the Colonel's deerstalker, so that he gave the impression of having, literally, straws in his hair.

I remember a match at which I was a spectator, because I had sprained my ankle in a fall from my motor-bike. I remember it better than all the other matches, perhaps because the looker-on sees most of the game, or perhaps because it had such a comic and glorious ending, or perhaps again because it happened on the loveliest June day you could possibly imagine, a day of blue and green and gold, and of light breezes, gillyflower-scented, and lullaby sounds of bees, wood-pigeons, and far-away cuckoos. The sky was immaculate, hedge-sparrow-egg-blue; the mowing-grass rippled in all the water-meadows along the river and like green foam were the leafy orchards on the lower slopes of the hill. Buttercups along the unmown edges of our ground were a frieze of gold which gilded white cricket boots and the turn-ups of flannel trousers.

The match was against a team called Woody Bourton and it was a match we particularly wanted to win; for the plain reason that we detested Woody Bourton, whose captain was a dull humourless stone-waller, whose one-eyed umpire had never been known to give an l.b.w. against his own side, and whose wicket-keeper appealed almost ceaselessly in a cracked voice like that of a raven prophesying doom. Do not let yourself be misled by romantic writers into the belief that village cricket is played in a cheerful, 'sporting' spirit of 'Never mind who wins'. I have said that when we took the field we were Brensham going to war. Therefore we minded very much who won. And especially we should mind if we were defeated by Woody Bourton who were known to us as Bloody Bourton. They had beaten us (or, as some said, their umpire had beaten us) the previous year; and we thirsted for revenge.

But from the first ball, which took Mr Chorlton's off stump out of the ground, things went ill for us. Sir Gerald Hope-Kingley, who was next in, ran out Mr Mountjoy and shortly afterwards ran out himself. ('Like two old hens scampering up and down the wicket they are,' commented Dai.) Sammy Hunt batted for a while with the heroic determination of one who maintains a crumbling citadel against an innumerable enemy; then the wicket-keeper appealed for a catch and up went the loathèd umpire's cigarette-stained finger. Sammy walked slowly back, his bald head bright scarlet, which meant, we rightly guessed, that he was furious about the verdict. Alfie went out, had his stumps knocked flying, and returned to spread alarm and despondency among 'the boys'. 'He's bowling helluva fast,' said Alfie, who frequently employed this curious adjective. Banks, who batted next, was so cast down by Alfie's report that he jumped out of the way of his first ball, which took the bails off.

So far we had lost six wickets for thirty runs, most of which were byes off the fast bowler. Then there was a brief gallant stand by Briggs, the blacksmith, and Billy Butcher. Briggs for once in a way forgot his ambition to chop every ball County-fashion between the slips; he threw caution to the winds, took hold of his bat by the top of the handle as one would hold a sledge-hammer – and used it as a sledge-hammer. He had a private reason for disliking the Bloody Bourton captain: the man was Conservative Agent for the constituency. So when Briggs smote the ball, he felt that he was smiting the Tories. Thus inspired he walloped it three times to the boundary and once over the willow-trees: three fours and a six, eighteen runs for Brensham, four hearty blows struck for the proletariat.

Billy Butcher, as it happened, was suffering from an appalling hangover: he'd had a bad bout which had lasted three days and hadn't yet, we suspected, come to an end. But he cocked his cap at a defiant angle and jauntily took his guard, brandished his bat at the first ball in a devil-may-care gesture, missed it altogether, and received the ball on the inside of his thigh. It came quick off the pitch, and it must have hurt badly; but Billy only grinned, pointed his bat at the fast bowler, and called out: 'Hey, mind my courting tackle, if you please!' This made the bowler laugh, and brought a faint smile even to the sombre face of the Bloody Bourton captain. The next ball was a loose one, and Billy cut it over slip's head for an accidental four. Encouraged, he began to play the fool, and his clowning provoked, irritated and thoroughly put off the opposing players, who dropped him twice and let him make several runs from overthrows. Then, unexpectedly in the middle of his clowning, the poetry appeared. Billy would have been a very fine batsman indeed if he could only have achieved the necessary co-ordination between hand and eye; the whisky got in the way of that. Today, however, he suddenly pulled himself together and made three successive strokes in which the timing was quite perfect. They were sublime: they were a poet's strokes. The first was a drive through the covers which flowed like a slow river with lovely, lazy grace. The next was a cheeky glance to leg carried out as casually as if it had been an impertinent aside during a serious conversation. The third was a glorious pull off his middle stump made with a sort of despairing gaiety, a laughing challenge to the gods, a wild unorthodox defiant shot which you realized, if you knew him well, was Billy cocking a snook at the world. The ball went sailing over the brook and into the buttercups beyond. 'Oh, lovely, lovely, lovely!' cried Lord Orris, clapping his thin pale hands. The Colonel, wiping the mouth of his flask, muttered: 'By God, I'll have a drink on that one,' and did so. A full half-minute later Goaty Pegleg, travelling slowly in the Fourth Dimension, declared loudly: 'He's hit a six.'

But the effort of co-ordination had been too much for Billy. He failed to see the next ball until it hit his pads, which were plainly in front of the wicket. 'Howzat?' croaked the Raven, and Joe, after a moment's hesitation to show Bloody Bourton that he could have got even with their umpire if he had liked, reluctantly gave Billy out. After that the innings soon ended; three hobbledehoys, unlucky victims of Alfie's press-gang, made three runs between them and Briggs, trying to hit another six for Labour, was caught in the deep. Brensham was all out for seventy-nine and the teams came in to tea.

I remember the cuckoo which called all tea-time from a willow-tree in Cuckoo Pen; and the background of bees and woodpigeons and gillyflower scent on the soft light airs. I remember the Colonel's Ionian laughter at some remark of Billy Butcher's, and old Orris's gentle manners and gentle smile. I remember Mrs Hartley's ham with the golden breadcrumbs on it, and a ridiculous garden-party hat which Mimi wore, and Meg confiding her film-ambitions to Mr Chorlton who listened gravely and didn't smile even when she said: 'They told me I was ever so photogenic.' I remember Sally Doan plying Billy with meat-pies and whispering to him urgently: 'Now you must *eat*' – and I remember wondering if she were in love with him. How absurd and disastrous if she were! But then Joe Trenfield, who'd been a Sergeant-Major before he took the 'Horse Narrow', looked at his watch and said: 'Come along, boys! Late on parade!' and Sammy led our team out into the field.

Now Bloody Bourton had an hour and a half in which to score eighty runs. They could have done it easily; but being Bloody Bourton they scratched and scraped and niggled and fiddled about, as Dai put it, so that by half-past five – we drew stumps at six, which was opening-time – they had only scored forty for the loss of three wickets. The game looked like ending in a dreary draw; but Bloody Bourton, realizing too late that they would have to score much faster in order to have a chance of winning, suddenly began to hit; and hitting was not in their nature. After Mr Mountjoy had missed an easy catch, because he was listening to the curlews and the drumming snipe in the meadows beyond Cuckoo Pen, Alfie Perks took two wickets in the same over. And still the Bloody Bourton batsmen went out for the runs. A curious sort of desperation had overtaken them; for they delighted as a rule to make little pernickety shots along the ground, to score in singles, and to keep their opponents running about in the hot sun for two or three hours while they enjoyed themselves in their prim puritanical cautious way. But now they waved their bats wildly at every ball and called each other frantically for short runs. I heard Mr Chorlton say to Mr Mountjoy between overs: *Quem Deus vult perdere, prius dementat*; and sure enough next ball he was able to stump a batsman who had run half-way down the pitch to one of Alfie's leg-breaks and missed it altogether.

Six wickets for fifty-one, and twenty minutes to go! Sammy, who must be in the forefront of the battle always, put himself on to bowl, pounded down to the wicket with his bald head flaming, and yorked his man with the last ball of the over. Then Billy missed a catch; and our hearts sank. 'It iss the whisky and the pubs and the profane goings-on,' said Dai primly, 'this iss the ruination of cricket in Brensham!' We suffered another set-back a moment later, when Mr Chorlton appealed for a catch and the one-eyed umpire (who might have been blind in both eyes, and stone-deaf as well, for all the notice he took of our appeals) remained motionless as if rooted to the ground, stared stonily in front of him, and took no notice. The Bloody Bourton captain, taking heart, scored a couple of fours, and sixty went up on the score-board. Things looked bad; but a few minutes later Sammy took another wicket with a yorker and at ten to six the ninth man was stumped by Mr Chorlton. The last man walked out to the wicket as slowly as he dared and as eagerly as if he went blindfold towards the scaffold, snicked a two and a four off Sammy, and got a present of another four from one of Sir Gerald's overthrows. The score was seventy-two when Alfie bowled a long hop to the Bloody Bourton captain, who astonished even himself by hitting it for six.

This was the last over, the Bloody Bourton wanted two runs to win. Even the Colonel sat up tensely and put his flask away in his pocket. Everybody was on his toes with the solitary exception of Briggs, who was standing deep at long-on where for a long time he had had nothing to do. I noticed a faint blue haze hanging about him in the still evening air; I looked again, and perceived that Briggs was lighting his pipe.

Alfie came up to the wicket with his familiar hop, skip, and jump, tousled fair hair falling into his eyes. The Bloody Bourton captain, whose success in hitting a six had gone to his head, ran down the pitch and hit the ball a full toss. He caught it awkwardly high up on the blade of the bat but it was a hefty clout all the same, and the ball flew high towards long-on. Everybody looked at Briggs; but Briggs, with his big hands cupping a match, was still puffing away at his pipe. The whole team yelled at him. Sammy shouted terrible sea-oaths at the top of his voice. I shouted, the Colonel shouted, even Lord Orris shouted in his small piping voice. Only Goaty Pegleg, who had not yet tumbled to what was happening, remained silent. At last Briggs looked up, and saw the ball falling towards him. He did not move.

Without hurry he put the box of matches into his left pocket and the pipe into his right pocket. Then, as one who receives manna from heaven he extended his enormous hands in front of him. The ball fell into them, the strong fingers closed as if they would squeeze it out of shape. Finally, still without hurry, he removed his pipe from his pocket lest it burn his trousers.

When the cheering was over there was a little silence while Joe Trentfield pulled up the stumps and the team came back towards the pavilion. Then Goaty Pegleg announced in a loud voice *urbi et orbi:* 'He's caught it! We've won!' as if he were an astronomer who watches the stars through a telescope and sees, a hundred light-years after the event, the flaming destruction of a far-distant sun which, at the moment of earth-time when he witnesses it, has long been black and dead.

So off go Bloody Bourton with perfunctory handshakes and insincere smiles and with black hatred in their hearts. 'It was a good game,' we say, rubbing it in. 'Just the right sort of finish,' they agree without enthusiasm. Mr Mountjoy hurries off to his Evening Service – he's two minutes late already. The Colonel mounts his motor-bike and chugs off towards the 'Swan'. Lord Orris untethers from the gate Tom Pearce's grey mare and rides slowly back towards his ruined mansion. Goaty Pegleg stumps away, the girls wash up the tea-things, Mrs Hartley puts back her ham in its muslin bag. The persistent cuckoo, whose voice is breaking already, calls his last throaty cuck-cuck-cuck-oo from the top of the willow-tree.

'And now,' says Sammy Hunt, wiping the sweat-beads off his bald head, 'now for a pint at the "Adam and Eve", and a game of darts!'

from BRENSHAM VILLAGE
1946

THE NOVICE: DOWN UNDER

A story by

Denzil Batchelor

Denzil Batchelor, who died in 1969, was a versatile author, journalist and broadcaster who, at one period, was Sports Editor of Picture Post. *His generous enthusiasm is expressed in his many books, notably his 'cricketing lives' biography of one of his heroes, C.B. Fry. His other great hero was Arthur Mailey. His two volumes* The Game Goes On *and* Days Without Sunset *mix Test match accounts, essays and fiction. This story, from the former book, is set in Australia where he frequently visited and stayed long periods.*

Between a couple of shops you could see the purple glow of Sydney from halfway down the high street on the way to the Look Out. A mile on, and the world hadn't a house on its huge horizon, let alone a city, only the three colossal crags towering like blunted spires above the valley where every tree in the illimitable forest was a clear-defined speck in the flood lighting. Bob Maitland had thought maybe a bit of a stroll as far as the Look Out would set a guy off to sleep after a beaut film like that at the Olympic. Myrna Loy (once again) had sabotaged his allegiance to the sheilah in the ham-and-beef shop whom he'd taken dancing the last three weeks running, the nearest thing to monogamy he'd achieved in all his fifteen years. The only advantage Shirley had over Myrna was her teeth. Shirley's were the prettiest teeth in the world: Myrna's only the second prettiest.

As he slouched along the road to the Look Out, pondering on

Miss Loy's advantages over Shirley, he threw his pocketful of stones one by one at the targets among the dim trees that throned the roadside. Thirty-four out of forty-seven hits, and most of them about stump high. It wasn't too bad at all. When he reached the parking-place at the Look Out he'd just a couple of chunks of blue metal left. A bonzer little park they'd made up there, overlooking the prodigious expanse of valley where huge mists floated no larger than white rose petals beneath the great blunted peaks of minor ranges towering out of the plain thirty miles away, with the forests still clinging to their shoulders and crests like swarms of ants. A bonzer little park. Beds of geraniums, and Swiss summerhouses and crazy paving and little painted metal dwarfs dotted all about the gardens.

By golly! if that wasn't a flaming cat, crouching under a figure of Dopey in front of the car park. His hand went to his pocket. He had a sacred duty towards cats – and this one vanished with an eldritch squeal into the bush. He had now leisure to hope he hadn't cracked one of the poor beast's ribs. It was just that a fellow'd got to be absolutely dead sure of his throw-in, hard and fast and true from extra cover, which was where they'd be sure to put him, a beaut fielder like he was.

He filled his coat pocket with another fifty chunks of blue metal for the return journey home.

He had always known it would be a blazing blue day for his first match for Gowrie. And a blazing blue day it was – just the sort of weather to send them winking fast over the outfield, and pick up real cheap boundaries. Not that there'd be many cheap boundaries going against Koolahra – about the hottest thing in the whole Blue Mountains Intermediate League, Koolahra was, and specially sultry in the fielding department.

On the way to the ground he ran into old Bluey Crosfield. With a bit of luck they might let him open up the innings with old Bluey.

'Listen, Blue,' he said, 'if you and I open up together, for Jeez sake show a bit of life chasing the short 'uns. I watched you last Saturday, and, stone the crows, you might have had the blinking infantile paralysis the way you was going for the runs. I reckon if me and my cobber, Ted Bellhorn, had been in together while you and Nose was there we'd have got another twenty – thirty.'

Blue was never one of the chaps who appreciate helpful, constructive criticism. 'I'm captain today,' said Blue, 'and you won't be opening any innings with me, Bobbie boy. Number eight is where you'll bat, and remember to come to me for a word of advice before you go in.'

After that, of course, you couldn't be surprised when a fellow like Blue goes and loses the toss right at the first go off.

The matting wicket was pitched on the little clearing between two armies of ring-barked gums, naked and deathly white even on a midsummer morning: corpses and not ghosts those armless, leafless trunks of trees were. Here and there at the edge of the paddock the outcrop of the ubiquitous grey rock showed. The sun beat mercilessly on the unshielded trestle spread with piles of stiffening pies and sandwiches, the tea urn and the pin of beer. Back of that chaps sat in the narrow shade of isolated trees, and in the small wooden hut where the scorers crowded. But that was a sun-trap, where you were baked, and most fellows preferred to be grilled in the open.

Koolahra had a goodish pair of opening batsmen – one tall and fair, the other short and dark – and they set about the Gowrie bowling in earnest. The darkie was the Koolahra Council schoolmaster, and it was said that if he'd the guts to take a chance he could have got him a job in Sydney's Northern Suburbs with the absolute certainty of a good trial for the Gordon first grade side. No one knew where such a chance might lead to. A bloke might find himself on the old S.C.G. before the season was out, being bowled at by half the pick of Australia, and if he showed a bit of form, then . . .

'It's a fact, I tell you,' Bob had promised his father, who thought all time spent on cricket – if it came to that, all time spent out of the coal mine – was so much time wasted.

'A fact, is it?' the old man had grunted sombrely. 'And do you know what a fact is? A fact's a lie and a half.'

All the same, it was a fact. Wasn't that the way the Don himself had begun? A string of hundreds for Moss Vale right up here in the Blue Mountains, so that everybody said there was no one in the locality (except a young bowler called O'Reilly in the next door township) who could stop him from getting a double century, if he had the mind to it. That had led to an invitation to Sydney. That, and his fielding. Gossip said there wasn't a whole cat anywhere round Moss Vale when he was a schoolboy polishing up his throw-in.

Be that as it might, Darkie Davis wasn't another Don, for when the invitation came from Sydney he'd turned it down flat on the grounds that he hadn't any cream flannel trousers, had never heard of any schoolmaster in the mountains who had any, and the risk was too great for him to go wasting the money. A lot of people said he was wise. After all, hadn't he got what every right-thinking Aussie went through the University to get out of his degree: a job in the Civil Service? One out of every six had it – it was worse (or better, according to your point of view) than pyorrhœa.

And now here was Darkie Davis showing them all how to play cream-flannel cricket in a pair of old grey trousers. A flick of fine leg off the fast bowler for 3. A lovely full-blooded drive off a half-volley into the jumble of grey boulders that marked the boundary behind the bowler's arm. And a hook off the end of his nose which was signalled 4 before mid-wicket had spun round on his heel to chase after the red blur.

The long fair streak was a bit more pedestrian. He didn't relish the slinger, but with the machine-like leg-break off the matting he could deal like an accountant settling a long-division sum. Still, in the end it was the leg-breaker, producing his bit of a bosey that could rarely be trusted to strike a length, who got him stretching and caught off his glove at slip.

All the while, as the game wore on and the score rattled up and up on the trunk of the gum, young Bob was thinking about one thing, and one thing only. Shirley, of course! Would she or would she not come? She'd sworn she couldn't be bothered; but there was the field filling up now, and a score of soldiers from the camp at Mittagong were already stretched full length on the ground, knotted handkerchiefs over their wet crowns. Be sure she'd come! What else was there to do at Gowrie on a Saturday arvo, with her having seen the picture at the Olympic and both the films on at Wattle Hill?

And suddenly – there she was. Wearing her blue dress too, the one he'd always put ace high. God! she was glamorous in that blue dress. She rated higher in it with him than as a sweater girl even.

60 for 1. He went up to Blue as they were crossing over and said: 'Cripes, Blue, things aren't too good. Better give me an over.'

Blue gave him the old raspberry,

'I've been practising up my blowing, Blue, dinkum.'

But of course Blue didn't take as much notice of that as he would have of the buzz of a blowfly.

And then the astounding thing happened – he himself had to go and drop a catch. He just would never know how and why that had come about. Yes, it was a snorter all right; but who'd ever heard of him dropping a catch, however fast it came at him off the face of the bat?

'Hey, Blue,' he said when they crossed at the end of the over, 'you got to put me on now, cobber. You got to put me on now.'

Blue's gaze roamed the little band of spectators. There was Shirley, having the time of her young life with the Koolahra team's fast bowler. 'It's no good, boy,' he said. 'That guy bats number nine. You'll never get him away from her that way. I couldn't keep you on long enough. Honest, I couldn't.'

He was right. They never left each other's sides during the morning. And at lunch the silly cow went halfway round the ground to get mustard to put on her beef sandwiches.

Just before the teams went out again Bob strolled up to her – casual like. 'Hullo, Shirley, so you've turned up after all?' he said, as if he hadn't been looking at her all morning, with that spinning catch coming at him and all.

'Oh, hullo,' she drawled: you couldn't see the famous teeth at all. Myrna Loy stuff. Cool as a cucumber; and she'd put pink on her finger-nails. Her mother wouldn't half hand out pink somewhere else if she caught her – a kid of fifteen.

'Come to see me do my couple of hat-tricks? Never get less than a couple here at Gowrie,' said the fast bowler.

Bob remembered now; the chap was a wag. At a Sunday picnic once he'd seen that chap over talking to the women after lunch, when all the men had gone off to one end of the paddock to talk stock and the drought, and all the women had gone off to the opposite end to talk whatever it was that women did talk about. What a bloke! He'd show him – him and his girl friends and his hat-tricks.

It was three o'clock before they got Darkie Davis out, and even then there was some doubt whether short leg had really got his hand under the ball before it touched the chocolate dust of the cricket field. Eighty-seven, he'd got. That made his average 75·35 – second highest in the Blue Mountains Intermediate League.

By half-past three the whole side was finished with. It was something that Arthur Saville, the slicked-up fop of a fast bowler, should have gone for a blob. Something, but not much. 'Always get a blob here at Gowrie,' he'd said as he came in. 'Always get a blob – and never less than a couple of hat-tricks.'

The girls had all giggled at that, silly half-wits. And Shirley had giggled loudest.

And now Gowrie's first pair was marching to the wicket. Cripes, would you believe it, Blue had picked on that old fool Clem Huskinson to open the innings with him. Clem's only claim to interest, in Bob's opinion, was that he was the one chap he had ever seen batting in a beard – but not for long. He was the youngest and only surviving child of a very large family. His grandfather, nearly fifty years before Clem's old man had been born or thought of, was one of the party under Blaxland who had blazed a trail through the Blue Mountains, linking the fertile valley of the Macquarie with the wooden-hutted main street of Sydney by a line of track running between the hundred million gum trees of uncharted infinity. The old boy had died as far away as a lunar landscape from the sun-dappled grey cottage of his birth in a Dorset village: by the shores of that never-ending reed-blanketed swamp that had been the dismal finish of the dreams of a huge inland sea at the mouth of the stripling Macquarie. But old men still spoke his historic name reverently, though he had not lived to strike north across the Liverpool Plains to where, past the foothills of the New England Range, the luckier Oxley and his little band had seen beyond the illimitable forests of gum trees the first sapphire sparkle of the basking Pacific.

'That's Clem Huskinson,' they told visitors to the township's little boarding-houses, Lazidaze and Eeziwaze – 'Clem Huskinson, whose grand-dad was one of Blaxland's party that founded Bathurst and were the first to open up the interior of Australia.' Old Clem reckoned that it was still good for a couple of schooners a day from strangers in the nameless pub at the corner of the long, featureless main stret: that, and the fact that he himself claimed to have seen Blackham keep without a long stop to the fast bowling of Turner in the long ago.

There he was now, the old has-been – not even a has-been, only a grandson of a has-been – pottering about taking guard, as if that would make any difference to where his wicket would be in a couple of overs' time. Bob hated old-timers, and by an unlucky fate Gowrie seemed to be packed with stale but monumental figures. That pair sitting on a tree trunk outside the scorers' hut, for example, clapping feebly and uttering soft bleats of applause when their old dope of a cobber trotted creakily across the pitch for a fluky single. Harry Hawkes and Harry Makins! A precious pair. Lived in Gowrie all their dull lives, except that Harry Hawkes had gone to South Africa as a trooper with a rabble of Australian volunteers in the Zulu War, and old Makins had spent a year in New Australia, the Socialist paradise founded in Brazil by a poetess which had exploded at the climax of a crescendo of squabbles and financial collapse. Harry Hawkes was another of those schooner-earners with that dreary story of how in South Africa he and his dog had been bushed for ten days with Zulus on the prowl all round, until in the end, out of sheer starvation, he'd been compelled to kill and eat his tyke, which had, ironically enough, rejoiced in the same of Sausage. Neither Harry could tell a Mosquito from a Liberator, and neither seemed to think it mattered.

The older generation! Best out of the way, thought Bob. Wait till he reached school-leaving age. Head for Sydney like a homing pigeon, he would; if necessary, get taken on in one of the new motor factories until he could earn a satisfactory living out of being an amateur cricketer. Why, cripes, you could go racing six days a week from Sydney, and spend all Sunday getting as brown as your boot on Bondi Beach, where only last year, on his holiday, he'd been lucky enough to see a surfer bitten in half by a shark. Only let them wait till he grew up! He'd show them! The new Australia wasn't going to be any Old Men's Home for softies and dreamers, not if he was going to have anything to do with it. It would be a roaring great factory, a hundred per cent alive, with the latest in jet-propelled cars to whizz you down to sun-bathe or to the cricket ground as soon as you'd put your work behind you.

It was queer, perhaps, that there was any cricket ground in such futurist dreams; but there was. A field where a better than Bradman should eclipse the latest hero, as he in turn had eclipsed Trumper. A field whereon no English team should ever win a Test Match again: and yet, somehow, the fierce tension of the eternal struggle between the two teams should never be relaxed.

Koolahra's fast bowler was cracking them down at old Blue: you'd got to give it him, take him away from the sheilahs where he carried on like he was a performing poodle, and he was a proper little trimmer, right enough.

'He can toss 'em up a bit, your boy friend,' he flung at Shirley.

She wasn't interested. She was chattering away, nineteen to the dozen, to her friend Lauren Jukes, from the chemist's. 'Ever such a lovely boy, Lauren. Well, I mean he really does remind you a *bit* of Alan Ladd, only he's a bit more sophisticated in a way. And he's got a motor-bike of his own already, and when he's twenty-one he's to have a half share in the shop —' She broke off to applaud enthusiastically her little cock-sparrow of a fast bowler, preening himself on having uprooted old Clem's off stump after a couple of near misses; but it was doubtful if she had seen the ball.

Two more wickets fell quickly. By the time they broke up for cups of tea and a puff at a cigarette things weren't looking too clever for Gowrie. Only 19 on the board and 3 of 'em gone already. Even Bluey'd had a smack over the fingers that had made him sort of cautious about pushing out his forward stroke to the little fast fellow.

After tea Bob lay in the shimmering heat haze and began to wonder what would happen to him when his turn came. Which wouldn't be long, from the look of things. Four gone for less than 50 – three of them to the speed merchant, who wasn't losing any of his nip off the matting, for all that he must have bowled close on a dozen overs.

The way he looked at it, the best thing for him to do was to knock the little chap off his length. Though it was true he'd never played in a man's match before, he didn't believe for a moment that this bloke was any faster than Reg Carpenter, in the school team. Cripes, hadn't Reg broken a stump in the match against the kids from Moss Vale? You didn't see this little guy breaking any stumps. Well, then, wasn't it the cold, hard truth that he'd straight-driven Reg for three fours running in a pick-up only last Thursday? He began to consider whether he'd be wiser to jump out to drive the fast bowler (his own technique), or step back, turn and hook him shoulder high to the square-leg boundary (Bradman's way). A bit of both, perhaps. He hardly looked at the disposition of the field at all; and when the bowler kept a whole over dead on the middle and off stumps, his only mental reaction was that two of the balls were short enough to be hooked and three over-pitched enough to be driven. He even felt a little pang of jealous annoyance when old Blue took a cut for four off the last ball of the off-breaker at the other end to send the fifty up. It all tended to diminish the glory that he would shortly be winning. That was what came of not being sent in first.

The fast bowler had already proved himself the deadliest attacker Gowrie had seen that season. Now he suddenly seemed to acquire an even stronger charge of malevolent electric energy. He bounded to the wicket full of the spirit of sheer destruction. You couldn't see the flash of the ball against the chocolate out-field. The next thing you knew was the thud upon the pad and the anguished howl of appeal. But you couldn't startle Vince Hargreaves, the Gowrie policeman, into a snap decision like that. Not until the fast bowler had turned his back on him and was starting to plod off to the end of his run did his rumbling 'Not Out' emerge.

There was no appealing about the next ball. Only the leg

stump showed above the ground, like a glimpse of a spar from a sunk ship on the crest of the wave. Now there was only Turcan, the publican, between Bob and his hour. He got up to fetch his pads from the scorer's hut. He hadn't started to buckle on the first before the wicket was a shambles again. Same ball and – next ball.

All round the ground they were clapping, some even cheering. They were all set for the hat-trick. All Gowrie was there – squatting or lolling round the edge of the field licking their lips in anticipation of a hat-trick against their own side. Such glamour does success possess.

He noticed, as he took guard, that square leg was deep and well placed to stop any but the most lightning hook. Behind the bowler there was no one – no one except Shirley and her mob of girl friends, fallen silent now, their big made-up eyes fixed on the pitch as hungrily as if it were the screen itself. All set, then, for the straight drive, if only the little fop would dish one well up.

But as the ball shot from the bowler's hand, Bob knew – knew with every pore of his body, every fibre of his being – that his enemy had sent him down the ball of all balls his soul craved. The ball he used to dream about at nights – or lie awake lusting after, not daring to sleep lest the vision of it should fade: a fast half-volley. Dead straight, of course – but unless there was a spice of risk where was the fun in this fool game?

His left leg lunged forward. He flung back his bat in an imperious swing, and swept down on the impious ball in a drive of annihilating power. As he felt the ball slip away from him like a thunderbolt switched into reverse gear, time stood still.

He saw Shirley lose interest in the game the moment she realised her little fancy man wasn't going to get any spectacular hat-tricks. She turned round to continue her jabber to Lauren.

And the ball rose towards her in a steep climb, like an avenging bolt from the machine. He had got under that half-volley, and here was no humdrum four to explode those vain hopes of a hat-trick. Here was a stupendous sixer – a super-climax piled upon climax.

Up and up she steepled; and idle was the scamper of mid-on

to the edge of the field. There! She was falling; down she came at last.

There was a warning scream. Too late! Shirley half sprang from her seat. Lauren squealed in panic, and pushed her friend straight into the descending atom.

Then there were several loud shrieks: all from Lauren. Shirley lay like a log on the ground.

There were people rushing to her from all over the field. The scorer's hut emptied out. Only Vince Hargreaves, the umpire, remained at his post, slowly raising his prodigious arms above his head like a man doing setting-up exercises as he signalled the major boundary.

By the time Bob got to her side, Shirley had recovered. She sat up, her head in Lauren's lap, whimpering, dazed. Her jaw was dabbled with blood. Blood gushed from her mouth.

There in the dust beside the ball lay one of the lustrous front teeth. It was the opinion of well-placed spectators that she had swallowed the other.

'Where am I? Where am I?' she kept gasping. Some realistic reporter explained that her friend, losing her head, had pushed her into the biggest sixer seen on the Gowrie ground that season, as it descended.

Poor Shirley burst into tears. Tears washed the blood from her chin, and fresh blood washed the tears.

'Oh, Gert, you never,' she moaned; and again: 'Oh, Gert, you done it now.'

So another beautiful friendship was over; for Lauren had been inflexibly rechristened nearly a year ago; and she hated all her girl friends with longer memories.

They led Shirley weeping from the field. Never in the rest of her blighted life would she tell anyone what was in her heart: which was that she had always known that Bob Maitland was the one boy in the world for her, and that she very clearly realised that her beautiful teeth were the supreme lure she possessed in a community where most of the girls lost theirs with their maidenhood almost immediately on entering their teens.

The game went on. The fast bowler had lost all his devil now. He didn't seem to care what happened, and after Bob had driven him for two more fours and a six in his next over he was taken off, never to bowl again in that match.

Nobody seemed to have much heart in what remained of the game: nobody except, of course, Bob himself. It was most unfortunate that after he'd made 38 in less than half an hour he should have been caught off a lovely on-glide that long leg had put out his hand to in a purely formal gesture, never anticipating for a moment that there was any danger of getting within a foot of the ball. He worried about getting out like that for the rest of the afternoon. (By the by, for the record, Gowrie lost easily. He gave the fact but a momentary consideration; did not, however, waste a split of a second in worrying over it. To do him justice, they had certainly never been expected to win.)

So that was Bob Maitland's first real cricket match. The night it was over he went to bed early – after a tree-basting walk to the Look Out to keep his eye in – and he lay awake half the night anticipating a letter from the New South Wales Cricket Association inviting him down to Sydney for a trial. Hardly this season, perhaps, but it might easily come next year. After that it would perhaps take him two years to force his way into the Test team – the selectors hung on to old hands with sentimental tenacity.

Just before he went to sleep it flashed across his mind that it was a pity that Shirley had lost her lovely front teeth, her chief attraction. Oh, well, there were plenty of girls with pretty teeth – Lauren's weren't bad, for instance. And when, in a couple of years or so, he'd settled in Sydney, there'd be bound to be lots more living conveniently near to the cricket ground.

from THE GAME GOES ON
1947

ENGLAND, THEIR ENGLAND

by

A.G. Macdonell

That the village cricket match from England, Their England *took its inspiration from some of the cricket played by The Invalids, founded by the poet and Literary Editor Sir John Squire, is attested by the novelist Alec Waugh who was himself in part the model for the elegant 'crack' Mr Southcott. What is more important, however, is that Archie MacDonell drew a superbly funny picture of village green cricket in a series of tableaux by exaggerating its qualities to the nth degree, yet just stopping this side of impossibility. In any collection of fictional writing about cricket it has to be included for its sheer hilarity and wit – a combination which Macdonnell (who was killed in an air-raid in 1941 at the age of forty-five) never quite achieved so well elsewhere. When, for example, in* How like an Angel, *he tried to satirise bodyline, the result was curiously lacking in humour and plausibility. Or perhaps bodyline just is not funny.*

At twenty minutes to 3, Mr Hodge had completed his rather tricky negotiations with the Fordenden captain, and had arranged that two substitutes should be lent by Fordenden in order that the visitors should field eleven men, and that nine men on each side should bat. But just as the two men on the Fordenden side, who had been detailed to the unpleasant duty of fielding for both sides and batting for neither, had gone off home in high dudgeon, a motor-car arrived containing not only Mr Hodge's two defaulters but a third gentleman in flannels as well, who swore stoutly that he had been invited by Mr Hodge to play and affirmed that he was jolly well going to play. Whoever stood down, it wasn't going to be him. Negotiations therefore had to be reopened, the pair of local Achilles had to be recalled, and at ten minutes to 3 the match began upon a twelve-a-side basis.

Mr Hodge, having won the toss by a system of his own founded upon the differential calculus and the Copernican theory, sent in his opening pair to bat. One was James Livingstone, a very sound club cricketer, and the other one was called, simply, Boone. Boone was a huge, awe-inspiring colossus of a man, weighing at least eighteen stone and wearing all the majestic trappings of a Cambridge Blue. Donald felt that it was hardly fair to loose such cracks upon a humble English village until he fortunately remembered that he, of all people, a foreigner, admitted by courtesy to the National Game, ought not to set himself up to be a judge of what is, and what is not, cricket.

The Fordenden team ranged themselves at the bidding of their captain, the Fordenden baker, in various spots of vantage amid the daisies, buttercups, dandelions, vetches, thistle-down, and clumps of dark-red sorrel; and the blacksmith having taken in, just for luck as it were, yet another reef in his snake-buckle belt, prepared to open the attack. It so happened that, at the end at which he was to bowl, the ground behind the wicket was level for a few yards and then sloped away rather abruptly, so that it was only during the last three or four intensive, galvanic yards of his run that the blacksmith, who took a long run, was visible to the batsman or indeed to anyone on the field of play except the man stationed in the deep field behind him. This man saw nothing of the game except the blacksmith walking back dourly and the blacksmith running up ferociously, and occasionally a ball driven smartly over the brow of the hill in his direction.

The sound club player having taken guard, having twiddled his bat round several times in a nonchalant manner, and having stared arrogantly at each fieldsman in turn, was somewhat surprised to find that, although the field was ready, no bowler was visible. His doubts, however, were resolved a second or two later, when the blacksmith came up, breasting the slope superbly like a mettlesome combination of Vulcan and Venus Anadyomene. The first ball which he delivered was a high full-pitch to leg, of appalling velocity. It must have lighted upon a bare path among the long grass near long-leg, for it rocketed, first bounce, into the hedge and four byes were reluctantly signalled by the village umpire. The row of gaffers on the rustic bench shook their heads, agreed that it was many years since four byes had been signalled on that ground, and called for more pints of old-and-mild. The other members of Mr Hodge's team blanched visibly and called for more pints of bitter. The youngish professor of ballistics, who was in next, muttered something about muzzle velocities and started to do a sum on the back of an envelope.

The second ball went full-pitch into the wicket-keeper's stomach and there was a delay while the deputy wicket-keeper was invested with the pads and gloves of office. The third ball, making a noise like a partridge, would have hummed past Mr Livingstone's left ear had he not dexterously struck it out of the ground for six, and the fourth took his leg bail with a bullet-like full-pitch. Ten runs for one wicket, last man six. The professor got the fifth ball on the left ear and went back to the Three Horseshoes, while Mr Harcourt had the singular misfortune to hit his wicket before the sixth ball was even delivered. Ten runs for two wickets and one man retired hurt. A slow left-hand bowler was on at the other end, the local rate-collector, a man whose whole life was one of infinite patience and guile. Off his first ball the massive Cambridge Blue was easily stumped, having executed a movement that aroused the professional admiration of the Ancient who was leaning upon his scythe. Donald was puzzled that so famous a player should play so execrable a stroke until it transpired, later on, that a wrong impression had been created and that the portentous Boone had gained his Blue at Cambridge for rowing and not for cricket. Ten runs for three wickets and one man hurt.

The next player was a singular young man. He was small and quiet, and he wore perfectly creased white flannels, white silk socks, a pale-pink silk shirt, and a white cap. On the way down in the char-à-banc he had taken little part in the conversation and even less in the beer-drinking. There was a retiring modesty about him that made him conspicuous in that cricket eleven, and there was a gentleness, an almost finicky gentleness about his movements which hardly seemed virile and athletic. He looked as if a fast ball would knock the bat out of his hands. Donald asked someone what his name was, and was astonished to learn that he was the famous novelist, Robert Southcott himself.

Just as this celebrity, holding his bat as delicately as if it was a flute or a fan, was picking his way through the daisies and thistle-down towards the wicket, Mr Hodge rushed anxiously, tankard in hand, from the Three Horseshoes and bellowed in a most unpoetical voice: 'Play carefully, Bobby. Keep your end up. Runs don't matter.'

'Very well, Bill,' replied Mr Southcott sedately. Donald was interested by this little exchange. It was the Team Spirit at work – the captain instructing his man to play a type of game that was demanded by the state of the team's fortunes, and the individual loyally suppressing his instincts to play a different type of game.

Mr Southcott took guard modestly, glanced furtively round the field as if it was an impertinence to suggest that he would survive long enough to make a study of the fieldsmen's positions worth while, and hit the rate-collector's first ball over the Three Horseshoes into a hay-field. The ball was retrieved by a mob of screaming urchins, handed back to the rate-collector, who scratched his head and then bowled his fast yorker, which Mr Southcott hit into the saloon bar of the Shoes, giving Mr Harcourt such a fright that he required several pints before he fully recovered his nerve. The next ball was very slow and crafty, endowed as it was with every iota of finger-spin and brain-power which a long-service rate-collector could muster. In addition, it was delivered at the extreme end of the crease so as to secure a background of dark laurels instead of a dazzling white screen, and it swung a little in the air; a few moments later the urchins, by this time delirious with ecstasy, were fishing it out of the squire's trout stream with a bamboo pole and an old bucket.

The rate-collector was bewildered. He had never known such a travesty of the game. It was not cricket. It was slogging; it was wild, unscientific bashing; and furthermore, his reputation was in grave danger. The instalments would be harder than ever to collect, and Heaven knew they were hard enough to collect as it was, what with bad times and all. His three famous deliveries had been treated with contempt – the leg-break, the fast yorker, and the slow, swinging off-break out of the laurel bushes. What on earth was he to try now? Another six and he would be laughed out of the parish. Fortunately the village umpire came out of a trance of consternation to the rescue. Thirty-eight years of umpiring for the Fordenden Cricket Club had taught him a thing or two and he called 'Over' firmly and marched off to square-leg. The rate-collector was glad to give way to a Free Forester, who had been specially imported for this match. He was only a moderate bowler, but it was felt that it was worth while giving him a trial, if only for the sake of the scarf round his waist and his cap. At the other end the fast bowler pounded away grimly until an unfortunate accident occurred. Mr Southcott had been treating with apologetic contempt those of his deliveries which came within reach, and the blacksmith's temper had been rising for some time. An urchin had shouted, 'Take him orf!' and the other urchins, for whom Mr Southcott was by now a firmly established deity, had screamed with delight. The captain had held one or two ominous consultations with the wicket-keeper and other advisers, and the blacksmith knew that his dismissal was at hand unless he produced a supreme effort.

It was the last ball of the over. He halted at the wicket before going back for his run, glared at Mr Harcourt, who had been driven out to umpire by his colleagues – greatly to the regret of Mr Bason, the landlord of the Shoes – glared at Mr Southcott, took another reef in his belt, shook out another inch in his braces, spat on his hand, swung his arm three or four times in a meditative sort of way, grasped the ball tightly in his colossal palm, and then turned smartly about and marched off like a Pomeranian grenadier and vanished over the brow of the hill. Mr Southcott, during these proceedings, leant elegantly upon his bat and admired the view. At last, after a long stillness, the ground shook, the grasses waved violently, small birds arose with shrill clamours, a loud puffing sound alarmed the butterflies, and the blacksmith, looking more like Venus Anadyomene than ever, came thundering over the crest. The world held its breath. Among the spectators conversation was suddenly hushed. Even the urchins, understanding somehow that they were assisting at a crisis in affairs, were silent for a moment as the mighty figure swept up to the crease. It was the charge of Von Bredow's Dragoons at Gravelotte over again.

But alas for human ambitions! Mr Harcourt, swaying slightly from leg to leg, had understood the menacing glare of the bowler, had marked the preparation for a titanic effort, and – for he was not a poet for nothing – knew exactly what was going on. And Mr Harcourt sober had a very pleasant sense of humour, but Mr Harcourt rather drunk was a perfect demon of impishness. Sober, he occasionally resisted a temptation to try to be funny. Rather drunk, never. As the giant whirlwind of vulcanic energy rushed past him to the crease, Mr Harcourt, quivering with excitement and internal laughter, and wobbling uncertainly upon his pins, took a deep breath and bellowed, 'No ball!'

It was too late for the unfortunate bowler to stop himself. The ball flew out of his hand like a bullet and hit third-slip, who was not looking, full pitch on the knee-cap. With a yell of agony third-slip began hopping about like a stork until he tripped over a trussock of grass and fell on his face in a bed of nettles, from which he sprang up again with another drum-splitting yell. The blacksmith himself was flung forward by his own irresistible momentum, startled out of his wits by Mr Harcourt's bellow in his ear, and thrown off his balance by his desperate effort to prevent himself from delivering the ball, and the result was that his gigantic feet got mixed up among each other and he fell heavily in the centre of the wicket, knocking up a cloud of dust and dandelion-seed and twisting his ankle. Rooks by hundreds arose in protest from the vicarage cedars. The urchins howled like intoxicated banshees. The gaffers gaped. Mr Southcott gazed modestly at the ground. Mr Harcourt gazed at the heavens. Mr Harcourt did not think the world had ever been, or could ever be again, quite such a capital place, even though he had laughed internally so much that he had got hiccups.

Mr Hodge, emerging at that moment from the Three Horseshoes, surveyed the scene and then the scoreboard with an imperial air. Then he roared in the same rustic voice as before:

'You needn't play safe any more, Bob. Play your own game.'

'Thank you, Bill,' replied Mr Southcott as sedately as ever, and, on the resumption of the game, he fell into a kind of cricketing trance, defending his wicket skilfully from straight balls, ignoring crooked ones, and scoring one more run in a quarter of an hour before he inadvertently allowed, for the first time during his innings, a ball to strike his person.

'Out!' shrieked the venerable umpire before anyone had time to appeal.

The score at this point was sixty-nine for six, last man fifty-two.

The only other incident in the innings was provided by an American journalist, by name Shakespeare Pollock – an intensely active, alert, on-the-spot young man. Mr Pollock had been roped in at the last moment to make up the eleven, and Mr Hodge and Mr Harcourt had spent quite a lot of time on the way down trying to teach him the fundamental principles of the game. Donald had listened attentively and had been surprised that they made no reference to the Team Spirit. He decided in the end that the reason must have been simply that everyone knows all about it already, and that it is therefore taken for granted.

Mr Pollock stepped up to the wicket in the lively manner of his native mustang, refused to take guard, on the ground that he wouldn't know what to do with it when he had got it, and, striking the first ball he received towards square leg, threw down his bat, and himself set off at a great rate in the direction of cover-point. There was a paralysed silence. The rustics on the bench rubbed their eyes. On the field no one moved. Mr Pollock stopped suddenly, looked round, and broke into a genial laugh.

'Darn me —' he began, and then he pulled himself up and went on in refined English, 'Well, well! I thought I was playing baseball.' He smiled disarmingly round.

'Baseball is a kind of rounders, isn't it, sir?' said cover-point sympathetically.

Donald thought he had never seen an expression change so suddenly as Mr Pollock's did at this harmless, and true, statement. A look of concentrated, ferocious venom obliterated the disarming smile. Cover-point, simple soul, noticed nothing, however, and Mr Pollock walked back to the wicket in silence and was out next ball.

The next two batsmen, Major Hawker, the team's fast bowler, and Mr Hodge himself, did not score, and the innings closed at sixty-nine, Donald not-out nought. Opinion on the gaffer's bench, which corresponded in years and connoisseurship very closely with the Pavilion at Lord's, was sharply divided on the question whether sixty-nine was, or was not, a winning score.

After a suitable interval for refreshment, Mr Hodge led his men, except Mr Harcourt who was missing, out into the field and placed them at suitable positions in the hay.

The batsmen came in. The redoubtable Major Hawker, the fast bowler, thrust out his chin and prepared to bowl. In a quarter of an hour he had terrified seven batsmen, clean bowled six of them, and broken a stump. Eleven runs, six wickets, last man two.

After the fall of the sixth wicket there was a slight delay. The new batsman, the local rate-collector, had arrived at the crease and was ready. But nothing happened. Suddenly the large publisher, who was acting as wicket-keeper, called out, 'Hi! Where's Hawker?'

The words galvanized Mr Hodge into portentous activity.

'Quick!' he shouted. 'Hurry, run, for God's sake! Bob, George, Percy, to the Shoes!' and he set off at a sort of gallop towards the inn, followed at intervals by the rest of the side except the pretty youth in the blue jumper, who lay down; the wicket-keeper, who did not move; and Mr Shakespeare Pollock, who had shot off the mark and was ahead of the field.

But they were all too late, even Mr Pollock. The gallant Major, admitted by Mr Bason through the back door, had already lowered a quart and a half of mild-and-bitter, and his subsequent bowling was perfectly innocuous, consisting, as it did, mainly of slow, gentle full-pitches to leg which the village baker and even, occasionally, the rate-collector hit hard and high into the long grass. The score mounted steadily.

Disaster followed disaster. Mr Pollock, presented with an easy chance of a run-out, instead of lobbing the ball back to the wicket-keeper, had another reversion to his college days and flung it with appalling velocity at the unfortunate rate-collector and hit him in the small of the back, shouting triumphantly as he did so, 'Rah, rah, rah!' Mr Livingstone, good club player, missed two easy catches off successive balls. Mr Hodge allowed another easy catch to fall at his feet without attempting to catch it, and explained afterwards that he had been all the time admiring a particularly fine specimen of oak in the squire's garden. He seemed to think that this was a complete justification of his failure to attempt, let alone bring off, the catch. A black spot happened to cross the eye of the ancient umpire just as the baker put all his feet and legs and pads in front of a perfectly straight ball, and, as he plaintively remarked over and over again, he had to give the batsman the benefit of the doubt, hadn't he? It wasn't as if it was his fault that a black spot had crossed his eye just at that moment. And the stout publisher seemed to be suffering from the delusion that the way to make a catch at the wicket was to raise both hands high in the air, utter a piercing yell, and trust to an immense pair of pads to secure the ball. Repeated experiments proved that he was wrong.

The baker lashed away vigorously and the rate-collector dabbed the ball hither and thither until the score – having once been eleven runs for six wickets – was marked up on the board at fifty runs for six wickets. Things were desperate. Twenty to win and five wickets – assuming that the blacksmith's ankle and third-slip's knee-cap would stand the strain – to fall. If the lines on Mr Hodge's face were deep, the lines on the faces of his team when he put himself on to bowl were like plasticine models of the Colorado Canyon. Mr Southcott, without any orders from his captain, discarded his silk sweater from the Rue de la Paix, and went away into the deep field, about a hundred and twenty yards from the wicket. His beautifully brushed head was hardly visible above the daisies. The professor of ballistics sighed deeply. Major Hawker grinned a colossal grin, right across his jolly red face, and edged off in the direction of the Shoes. Livingstone, loyal to his captain, crouched alertly. Mr Shakespeare Pollock rushed about enthusiastically. The remainder of the team drooped.

But the remainder of the team was wrong. For a wicket, a crucial wicket, was secured off Mr Hodge's very first ball. It happened like this. Mr Hodge was a poet, and therefore a theorist, and an idealist. If he was to win a victory at anything, he preferred to win by brains and not by muscle. He would far sooner had his best leg-spinner miss the wicket by an eighth of an inch than dismiss a batsman with a fast, clumsy full-toss. Every ball that he bowled had brain behind it, if not exactness of pitch. And it so happened that he had recently watched a county cricket match between Lancashire, a county that he detested in theory, and Worcestershire, a county that he adored in fact. On the one side were factories and the late Mr Jimmy White; on the other, English apples and Mr Stanley Baldwin. And at this particular match, a Worcestershire bowler, by name Root, a deliciously agricultural name, had outed the tough nuts of the County Palatine by placing all his fieldsmen on the leg-side and bowling what are technically known as 'in-swingers.'

Mr Hodge, at heart an agrarian, for all his book-learning and his cadences, was determined to do the same. The first part of the performance was easy. He placed all his men upon the leg-side. The second part – the bowling of the 'in-swingers' – was more complicated, and Mr Hodge's first ball was a slow long-hop on the off-side. The rate-collector, metaphorically rubbing his eyes, felt that this was too good to be true, and he struck the ball sharply into the untenanted off-side and ambled down the wicket with as near an approach to gaiety as a man can achieve who is cut off by the very nature of his profession from the companionship and goodwill of his fellows. He had hardly gone a yard or two when he was paralysed by a hideous yell from the long grass into which the ball had vanished, and still more by the sight of Mr Harcourt, who, aroused from a deep slumber amid a comfortable couch of grasses and daisies, sprang to his feet and, pulling himself together with miraculous rapidity after a lightning if somewhat bleary glance round the field, seized the ball and unerringly threw down the wicket. Fifty for seven, last man twenty-two. Twenty to win: four wickets to fall.

Mr Hodge's next ball was his top-spinner, and it would have, or might have, come very quickly off the ground had it ever hit the ground; as it was, one of the short-legs caught it dexterously and threw it back while the umpire signalled a wide. Mr Hodge then tried some more of Mr Root's stuff and was promptly hit for two sixes and a single. This brought the redoubtable baker to the batting end. Six runs to win and four wickets to fall.

Mr Hodge's fifth ball was not a good one, due mainly to the fact that it slipped out of his hand before he was ready, and it went up and came down in a slow, lazy parabola, about seven feet wide of the wicket on the leg-side. The baker had plenty of time to make up his mind. He could either leave it alone and let it count one run as a wide; or he could spring upon it like a panther and, with a terrific six, finish the match sensationally. He could play the part either of a Quintus Fabius Maximus Cunctator, or of a sort of Tarzan. The baker concealed beneath a modest and floury exterior a mounting ambition. Here was his chance to show the village. He chose the sort of Tarzan, sprang like a panther, whirled his bat cyclonically, and missed the ball by about a foot and a half. The wicket-keeping publisher had also had time in which to think and to move, and he also had covered the seven feet. True, his movements were less like the spring of a panther than the sideways waddle of an aldermanic penguin. But nevertheless he got there, and when the ball had passed the flashing blade of the baker, he launched a mighty kick at it – stopping to grab it was out of the question – and by an amazing fluke kicked it on to the wicket. Even the ancient umpire had to give the baker out, for the baker was still lying flat on his face outside the crease.

'I was bowling for that,' observed Mr Hodge modestly, strolling up the pitch.

'I had plenty of time to use my hands,' remarked the wicket-keeper to the world at large, 'but I preferred to kick it.'

Donald was impressed by the extraordinary subtlety of the game.

Six to win and three wickets to fall.

The next batsman was a schoolboy of about sixteen, an ingenuous youth with pink cheeks and a nervous smile, who quickly fell a victim to Mr Harcourt, now wideawake and beaming upon everyone. For Mr Harcourt, poet that he was, understood exactly what the poor, pink child was feeling, and he knew that if he played the ancient dodge and pretended to lose the ball in the long grass, it was a hundred to one that the lad would lose his head. The batsman at the other end played a fourth ball of Mr Livingstone's next over hard in the direction of Mr Harcourt. Mr Harcourt rushed towards the spot where it had vanished in the jungle. He groped wildly for it, shouting as he did so, 'Come and help. It's lost.' The pink child scuttered nimbly down the pitch. Six runs to win and two wickets to fall. Mr Harcourt smiled demoniacally.

The crisis was now desperate. The fieldsmen drew nearer and nearer to the batsmen, excepting the youth in the blue jumper. Livingstone balanced himself on his toes. Mr Shakespeare Pollock hopped about almost on top of the batsmen, and breathed excitedly and audibly. Even the imperturbable Mr Southcott discarded the piece of grass which he had been chewing so steadily. Mr Hodge took himself off and put on the Major, who had by now somewhat lived down the quart and a half.

The batsmen crouched down upon their bats and defended stubbornly. A snick through the slips brought a single. A ball which eluded the publisher's gigantic pads brought a bye. A desperate sweep at a straight half-volley sent the ball off the edge of the bat over third-man's head and in normal circumstances would have certainly scored one, and possibly two. But Mr Harcourt was on guard at third-man, and the batsmen, by nature cautious men, one being old and the sexton, the other the postman and therefore a Government official, were taking no risks. Then came another single off a mis-hit, and then an interminable period in which no wicket fell and no run was scored. It was broken at last disastrously, for the postman struck the ball sharply at Mr Pollock, and Mr Pollock picked it up and, in an ecstasy of zeal, flung it madly at the wicket. Two overthrows resulted.

The scores were level and there were two wickets to fall. Silence fell. The gaffers, victims simultaneously of excitement and senility, could hardly raise their pint pots – for it was past 6 o'clock, and the front door of the Three Horseshoes was now as wide open officially as the back door had been unofficially all afternoon.

The Major, his red face redder than ever and his chin sticking out almost as far as the Napoleonic Mr Ogilvy's, bowled a fast half-volley on the leg-stump. The sexton, a man of iron muscle from much digging, hit it fair and square in the middle of the bat, and it flashed like a thunderbolt, waist-high, straight at the youth in the blue jumper. With a shrill scream the youth sprang backwards out of its way and fell over on his back. Immediately behind him, so close were the fieldsmen clustered, stood the mighty Boone. There was no chance of escape for him. Even if he had possessed the figure and the agility to perform back-somersaults, he would have lacked the time. He had been unsighted by the youth in the jumper. The thunderbolt struck him in the midriff like a red-hot cannon-ball upon a Spanish galleon, and with the sound of a drumstick upon an insufficiently stretched drum. With a fearful oath, Boone clapped his hands to his outraged stomach and found that the ball was in the way. He looked at it for a moment in astonishment and then threw it down angrily and started to massage the injured spot while the field rang with applause at the brilliance of the catch.

Donald walked up and shyly added his congratulations. Boone scowled at him.

'I didn't want to catch the bloody thing,' he said sourly, massaging away like mad.

'But it may save the side,' ventured Donald.

'Blast the bloody side,' said Boone.

Donald went back to his place.

The scores were level and there was one wicket to fall. The last man in was the blacksmith, leaning heavily upon the shoulder of the baker, who was going to run for him, and limping as if in great pain. He took guard and looked round savagely. He was clearly still in a great rage.

The first ball he received he lashed at wildly and hit straight up in the air to an enormous height. It went up and up and up, until it became difficult to focus it properly against the deep, cloudless blue of the sky, and it carried with it the hopes and fears of an English village. Up and up it went and then at the top it seemed to hang motionless in the air, poised like a hawk, fighting, as it were, a heroic but forlorn battle against the chief invention of Sir Isaac Newton, and then it began its slow descent.

In the meanwhile things were happening below, on the terrestrial sphere. Indeed, the situation was rapidly becoming what the French call *mouvementé*. In the first place, the blacksmith forgot his sprained ankle and set out at a capital rate for the other end, roaring in a great voice as he went, 'Come on, Joe!' The baker, who was running on behalf of the invalid, also set out, and he also roared 'Come on, Joe!' and side by side, like a pair of high-stepping hackneys, the pair cantered along. From the other end Joe set out on his mission, and he roared 'Come on, Bill!' So all three came on. And everything would have been all right, so far as the running was concerned, had it not been for the fact that Joe, very naturally, ran with his head thrown back and his eyes goggling at the hawk-like cricket-ball. And this in itself would not have mattered if it had not been for the fact that the blacksmith and the baker, also very naturally, ran with their heads turned not only upwards but also backwards as well, so that they too gazed at the ball, with an alarming sort of squint and a truly terrific kink in their necks. Half-way down the pitch the three met with a magnificent clang, reminiscent of early, happy days in the tournament-ring at Ashby-de-la-Zouche, and the hopes of the village fell with the resounding fall of their three champions.

But what of the fielding side? Things were not so well with them. If there was doubt and confusion among the warriors of Fordenden, there was also uncertainty and disorganization among the ranks of the invaders. Their main trouble was the excessive concentration of their forces in the neighbourhood of the wicket. Napoleon laid it down that it was impossible to have too many men upon a battlefield, and he used to do everything in his power to call up every available man for a battle. Mr Hodge, after a swift glance at the ascending ball and a swift glance at the disposition of the troops, disagreed profoundly with the Emperor's dictum. He had too many men, far too many. And all except the youth in the blue silk jumper, and the mighty Boone, were moving towards strategical positions underneath the ball, and not one of them appeared to be aware that any of the others existed.

Boone had not moved because he was more or less in the right place, but then Boone was not likely to bring off the catch, especially after the episode of the last ball. Major Hawker, shouting 'Mine, mine!' in a magnificently self-confident voice, was coming up from the bowler's end like a battle-cruiser. Mr Harcourt had obviously lost sight of the ball altogether, if indeed he had ever seen it, for he was running round and round Boone and giggling foolishly. Livingstone and Southcott, the two cracks, were approaching competently. Either of them would catch it easily. Mr Hodge had only to choose between them and, coming to a swift decision, he yelled above the din, 'Yours, Livingstone!' Southcott, disciplined cricketer, stopped dead. Then Mr Hodge made a fatal mistake. He remembered Livingstone's two missed sitters, and he reversed his decision and roared 'Yours, Bobby!' Mr Southcott obediently started again, while Livingstone, who had not heard the second order, went straight on. Captain Hodge had restored the *status quo.*

In the meantime the professor of ballistics had made a lightning calculation of angles, velocities, density of the air, barometer-readings and temperatures, and had arrived at the conclusion that the critical point, the spot which ought to be marked in the photographs with an X, was one yard to the north-east of Boone, and he proceeded to take up station there, colliding on the way with Donald and knocking him over. A moment later Bobby Southcott came racing up and tripped over the recumbent Donald and was shot head first into the Abraham-like bosom of Boone. Boone stepped back a yard under the impact and came down with his spiked boot, surmounted by a good eighteen stone of flesh and blood, upon the professor's toe. Almost simultaneously the portly wicket-keeper, whose movements were a positive triumph of the spirit over the body, bumped the professor from behind. The learned man was thus neatly sandwiched between Tweedledum and Tweedledee, and the sandwich was instantly converted into a ragout by Livingstone, who made up for lack of extra weight – for he was always in perfect training – by his extra momentum. And all the time Mr Shakespeare Pollock hovered alertly upon the outskirts like a Rugby scrum-half, screaming American University cries in a piercingly high tenor voice.

At last the ball came down. To Mr Hodge it seemed a long time before the invention of Sir Isaac Newton finally triumphed. And it was a striking testimony to the mathematical and ballistical skill of the professor that the ball landed with a sharp report upon the top of his head. Then it leapt up into the air a foot or so, cannoned on to Boone's head, and then trickled slowly down the colossal expanse of the wicket-keeper's back, bouncing slightly as it reached the massive lower portions. It was only a foot from the ground when Mr Shakespeare Pollock sprang into the vortex with a last ear-splitting howl of victory and grabbed it off the seat of the wicket-keeper's trousers. The match was a tie. And hardly anyone in the field knew it except Mr Hodge, the youth in the blue jumper, and Mr Pollock himself. For the two batsmen and the runner, undaunted to the last, had picked themselves up and were bent on completing a single that was to give Fordenden the crown of victory. Unfortunately, dazed with their falls, with excitement, and with the noise, they all three ran for the same wicket, simultaneously realized their error, and all three turned and ran for the other – the blacksmith, ankle and all, in the centre and leading by a yard, so that they looked like pictures of the Russian *troika*. But their effort was in vain, for Mr Pollock had grabbed the ball and the match was a tie.

And both teams spent the evening at the The Horseshoes, and Mr Harcourt made a speech in Italian about the glories of England and afterwards fell asleep in a corner, and Donald got home to Royal Avenue at 1 o'clock in the morning, feeling that he had not learnt very much about the English from his experience of their national game.

from ENGLAND, THEIR ENGLAND
1933

GAUVINIER'S LAST GAME

by

Hugh de Selincourt

Although it was published in 1924 Hugh de Selincourt's The Cricket Match *is probably still the best single novel written about cricket in general and village cricket in particular. He followed it with a collection of stories called* The Game of the Season, *also about Tillingfold in Sussex. 'Gauvinier's last game' follows his captain-hero Paul Gauvinier into his farewell match for the village. Not surprisingly, when he comes in to bat it is at a moment of some crisis, and not a little emotion.*

71 – 5 – 22.

Once more the whole character of the game had changed. Forty-one more runs were needed: and the two set batsmen had been fooled out. There was young Jack, true . . .

And Gauvinier was walking in. Damned if I could look in his direction. There came suppressed clapping, suppressed, yet eager: aching to cheer him: fearful of putting him off his game.

I looked up to see him taking his block. Young Farringdon went back to slip. I could hardly force myself to look at the first ball. I couldn't bear to see his stumps disarranged or a silly little catch hit up off the first ball. Still I had to look. Do you know, I said aloud, 'Oh, thank God!' when he hit that first ball clean and true for an easy single. Then one for young Jack: and he had the bowling again. A long hop on the off – he's got it, got it with all his strength, it'll reach the boundary, must – damn that accursed thick grass – but they've run three. My heavens! it was good to hear the yell of delight which greeted that shot. Pent up, my

God! and then we had a chance to let it loose. It was let loose. See him striding between the wicket with those long legs, using every inch of his length to spare his wind. If he and young Jack got going we should be all right.

But young Jack took a tremendous whack at the next ball, blind certain of a six; the bat was a fraction of an inch out of place: hit the ball a shade on the edge, and up it went higher and higher, a huge height into the air, and underneath stood Vereker, moving with unhurrying stride to the exact spot where it must fall, and did fall into his safe hands.

I must have missed some shots in my excitement, for I thought the score-board must be wrong in displaying the figures.

84 – 6 – 1.

I went into the box to consult old Francis, who was past speech of any kind, in his frantic anxiety that Gauvinier should make runs: he muttered unprintable appellations. He was rather keen on Gauvinier. So was I. I cleared out. But everywhere there was the same intensity of feeling. Unbearable. I almost wished the old swine *had* got out first ball and not be keeping us hanging on tenterhooks – waiting, looking, hoping. At any rate we should have been done with it.

Freddie Winthrop came hurrying out, sworn to keep his end up. These two had made many a decent stand together. Would they once more? Judging by his set face, it wouldn't be Freddie's fault if they didn't.

The next ten minutes were agonizing: the tenseness of the rope when two exactly balanced teams are straining at the pull. A sort of vibrant stillness in which Gauvinier's voice sounded loud, calling after every ball, *No* or *Wait*, for he says something at every ball bowled, old-fashioned perhaps but right, dead right. Only ones came, and those slowly. The old skipper took himself off, spoke to Vereker, who moved his arm up and down, decided it was mostly stiffness, not a strain, and went on to bowl.

He bowled Gauvinier a maiden. I suppose the delivery of six balls can only last an allotted time; but they seemed to last an eternity, though Gauvinier seemed to be seeing them perfectly, and using his reach without any hesitation. Two singles came off Farringdon's next over, each loudly applauded. The score crawled up. And there followed another long, long maiden to Gauvinier. I could not believe my eyes to see him playing, thus patiently, without flurry, like a good example from a good book; but the strain of watching it was terrible. Two singles and a two off Farringdon, and each run was cheered like a six: men were walking up and down in their excitement: wiping their faces: scratching themselves: pommelling each other like little boys: it was ridiculous to see.

And once more Gauvinier was standing ready for Vereker. And look! a wild roar burst from every man as we saw the ball rise . . . the man in the deep stepping back, stop at the hedge, and the ball bounce in the road and up again so that Gauvinier saw it on the bounce, over the hedge: a little high for a perfectly safe six but a glorious smack. Motor horns hooted; men kept on shouting; a little girl by their car waved her arms about madly. Stillness for the next ball: played quietly back. Then a bad long hop. Gauvinier withdrew and with all his might smote it into the hedge, well out of reach of the man in the deep: another roar of joy went up.

Damnation! the old beggar was going to pull it off after all, was he?

Sid Smith called out: 'And just once more, please!' and everyone burst out laughing. Vereker was taken off; changed places with the old skipper.

Freddie, after a leg-bye, took a couple off him; that sent up the hundred. Twelve more, by Gum! But there came another halt: a single here, a single there. Neither bowler gave anything away. And then Freddie, trying to smother a straight one, got right in front of his wicket and was out l.b.w.

105 – 7 – 5.

Sam Gault came in. Four more runs, and Sam was stumped.

109 – 8 – 1.

Then Sid Smith came out to join his skipper, stooping on his way to pick a bent for chewing to a shout of laughter. Hit the last ball of the over for two. It was a tie.

You should have heard the yell that greeted Gauvinier's next shot off young Farringdon, as good a drive as he has ever made, far past extra-cover – into the thickest of thick grass. He was shaking all over after running that three – the winning hit. It was twenty minutes past six.

They went on playing. We talked and laughed, at perfect ease at last, all strain gone. Soon Sid patted up a catch to Vereker, and came running out. Charlie came in for a knock, and while he was still in, the umpire called his last over.

Lord God! how Gauvinier was cheered. Some were for carrying him in. We flocked round him.

He rushed off to his womenfolk – jumped on to the running-board, leaned into the car, shaking hands, saying, 'What did I tell you? Still going strong?'

He came back: he was pouring with sweat – panting, shaking – to take off his pads. Old Francis called out, 'Forty not out. And not too bad for you, metty.'

A small boy helped him take his pads off; his hands were shaking. Dick Culvert stood by him.

'I'm going to slip off now.'

'Yes, just a minute.'

He took him by the arm and guided him to the small changing room. All the team were there. They started shaking hands with him. There was hardly room to move – such a tight little packed crowd. He was pushing out, when the General began to speak and we all crowded back to make some small gap. Gauvinier sat down, bewildered, still sweating, bowed his head.

The General spoke slowly and with genuine feeling. Of what Gauvinier had done for the cricket, of his example of sportsmanship – all the familiar things, you know: but none of them sounded in the least familiar under the circumstances.

Gauvinier, right in the thick of it as it were, bowed his head lower and lower. The General stopped and presented the silver inkstand, which Gauvinier stood holding.

He began to speak in reply: began very well – 'All those pleasant things said . . . but of course it's the fellows one plays with make the game . . .' Then he stopped suddenly, swallowed. His face puckered: he managed to articulate 'Thank you very much,' and burst out at the little changing-room door, clutching the inkstand.

That's the story of the game.

'If it had been arranged for me,' Gauvinier said, 'it could not have been more perfect. All I wanted. To hit a six. To have another little stand with Freddie and Sid: to come off – and I was physically beaten: too knock-kneed to bowl – too blear-eyed to see. Do you see what I mean?' I did in a way. But the fact is that he is superstitious, and superstitious in a way that I don't really very much like. But, dear God! How he treasures that inkstand!

from THE GAME OF THE SEASON
1931

A COUNTRY-HOUSE MATCH AND SOME LOOKERS-ON

by

E.R. Eddison

A Fish Dinner in Memison *is the second volume of the Zimiamvian trilogy, a work which sets up its own imagined world à la Tolkien and uses the nature of time as a principal theme. If this seems an unlikely setting for a cricket match, let the author explain. 'The plain "daylight" parts of my story cover the years from April 1908 to October 1933 while, as for the month that runs contemporaneously in Zimiamvia . . . it is sufficient to reflect that the main difference between earth and heaven may lie in this: that here we are the slaves of time, but there the Gods are the masters.'*

E.R. Eddison's achievement in this episode – he was a retired civil servant and something of a littérateur *– is to distil the essence of Edwardian country-house cricket during cricket's Golden Age (usually regarded as the twenty years preceding the First World War). As Rowland Bowen comments in* Cricket: A History of its Growth and Development throughout the World, *'that it is fiction does no harm, for it tells us what such cricket was like – or perhaps what it was thought to be like, and that is more important if we are to understand why the age is called the Golden Age.'*

'Time, you know, is a curious business,' said Lord Anmering, tilting his head forward a little to let the brim of his panama hat shade his eyes; for it was teatime, and the afternoon sun, from beyond the cricket field below, blazed out of cloudless blue full in their faces. 'Love of money, we're told, – root of all evil. Gad! I think otherwise. I think Time strikes deeper.'

Lady Southmere replenished the vacuum with one of the more long-drawn, contemplative, and non-committal varieties of the inimitable transatlantic 'Aha'.

'Look at Mary,' he said. 'Look at me. If I wasn't her father: wasn't thirty-two years her senior. Wouldn't I know what to do with her?'

'Well, I dare say you would.'

'Easy enough when they're not your own,' he said, as they walked on slowly, coming to a halt at the top of two flights of shallow steps that led down to the field from the gardens. 'But when they are, – By Jove, that's the style!' The ball, from a magnificent forward drive, sailed clean over the far fence, amid shouts of applause, for six. 'If you let your boy go and smash my melon-houses, knocking the bowling about like that, I'll tell you, I'll have no more to do with him. We mustn't forget,' he said, lower again: 'she's very young. Never force the pace.'

'O but don't I just agree? And the very dearest, sweetest—'

'You know her, well as I do. No, you don't, though. Look there,' putting up his eye-glass to examine the telegraph board: 'eighty. Eighty: a hundred and sixty-three: that's eighty-four to win. Not so bad, with only three wickets down. It's that boy of yours is doing it: wonderful steady play: nice style too: like to see him make his century. You know our two best bats, Chedisford and that young Macnaghten, didn't add up to double figures between 'em: Hugh's got his work cut out for him. Look at that! pretty warm bowling. A strong team old Playter's brought us over this time from Hyrnbastwick: Jove, I'd like to give 'em a whacking for a change. Well, Hugh and Jim seem settled to it. Would you like to come down over there: get a bit of shade?'

'I would like to do anything anbody tells me to. This is just too perfect.' She turned, before coming down the steps, to look back for a minute to the great west front of Annering Blunds, where it ranged beyond green lawns and flower-beds and trim deep-hued hedges of clipped box and barberry and yew: long rows of mullioned windows taking the sun, whose beams seemed to have fired the very substance of the ancient brickwork to some cool-burning airy essence of gold. This wing, by Inigo Jones, was the newest part, masking from this side the original flint-built house that had been old Sir Robert Scarnside's whom Henry VIII made first Earl of Anmering. Round to the right, in the homepark, stood up, square and grey, Anmering church tower. A sheltering wood of oak, ash, beech and sycamore was a screen for hall and church and garden against the east; and all the midsummer leafage of these trees seemed, at this hour, impregnate with that golden light. Northwards, all lay open, the ground falling sharply to the creek, salt marshes and sand-dunes and thence-away, to the North Pole, the sea. Southwards and landwards, park and wood and meadow and arable rose gently to the heaths and commons: Bestarton, Sprowswood, Toftrising. Lady Southmere, waiting on the silence a minute, might hear as under-tones to the voices of the cricket field (of players and lookers-on, click of wood against leather as the batsman played) the faint far-off rumour of tide-washed shingle, and, from trees, the woodpigeon's rustic, slumbrous, suddenly started and suddenly checked, discourse: *Two coos, tak' two coos, Taffy, tak' two coos, Taffy tak'* —. From golden rose to larkspur a swallowtail butterfly fluttered in the heat. 'Just too perfect for words,' she said, turning at last.

They came down the steps and began walking, first north, and so round by the top end of the cricket field towards the tents. 'I'll make a clean breast of it,' she said: 'twenty-six years now I have been English and lived in the Shires; and yet, Blunds in summer, well, it gets me here: sends me downright home-sick.' Just as, underneath all immediate sounds or voices, those distant sea-sounds were there for the listening, so in Lady Southmere's speech there survived some pleasant native intonations of the southern States.

'Home-sick?' said Lord Anmering. 'Virginia?'

'No, no, no: just for Norfolk. Aren't I English? and isn't your Norfolk pure England as England ought to be?'

'Better get Southmere to do an exchange: give me the place in Leicestershire and you take Blunds.'

'Well, and would you consent to that? Can you break the entail?'

'My dear lady,' he said, 'there are many things I would do for you—'

'But hardly that?'

'I'm afraid, not that.'

'O isn't that just too bad!' she said, as Jim Scarnside, playing forward to a yorker, was bowled middle stump.

Fifty or sixty people, may be, watched the game from this western side where the tents were and garden chairs and benches, all in a cool shade of beech and chestnut and lime and sycamore that began to throw shadows far out upon the cricket field: a pleasant summer scene as any could wish, of mingled sound and silence, stir and repose: white hats and white flannels and coloured caps and blazers contrasting here and there with more formal or darker clothes: a gaiety of muslin frocks, coloured silks, gauzes and ribbons, silken parasols and picture hats: the young, the old, the middle-aged: girls, boys, men, women: some being of the house-party; some, the belongings of the eleven that had driven over with Colonel Playter from Hyrnbastwick; some, neighbours and acquaintance from the countryside: wives, friends, parents, sisters, cousins, aunts. Among these their host, with Lady Southmere, now threaded his way, having for each, as he passed, the just greeting, were it word, smile, formal salutation or private joke: the Playter girls, Norah and Sybil, fresh from school: old Lady Dilstead, Sir Oliver's mother, and his sister Lucy (engaged to Nigel Howard); young Mrs Margesson, a niece of Lord Anmering's by marriage: Romer, the bursar of Trinity: Limpenfield of All Souls': General Macnaghten and his wife and son: Trowlsey of the Life Guards: Tom and Fanny Chedisford: Mr and Mrs Dagworth from Semmering: Sir Roderick Bailey, the Admiral, whose unpredictable son Jack had made top score (fifty) for the visiting eleven that morning: the Rector and his wife: the Denmore-Benthams: Mr and Mrs Everard Scarnside (Jim's parents) and Princess Mitzmesczinksy (his sister): the Bremmerdales from Taverford: the Sterramores from Burnham Overy: Janet Rustham and her two little boys: Captain Feveringham; and dozens besides.

'Sorry, uncle,' said Jim Scarnside, as their paths met: he on his way to the pavilion. 'Ingloriously out for three.'

'I was always told,' Lady Southmere said, 'you ought to block a yorker.'

'My dear Lady Southmere, don't I know it? But (I know you won't believe this), it was all your fault.'

'That's very very interesting.'

'It was.'

'And please, why?'

'Well. Just as that chap Howard was walking back the way he does to get properly wound up for one of those charging-buffalo runs that terrify the life out of a poor little batsman like me—'

'Poor little six foot two!' she said.

'Just at that instant, there, on the horizon, your black and white parasol! And I remembered: Heavens! didn't Mary make me promise that Lady Southmere should have the first brew of strawberries and cream, because they're so much the best? and isn't it long past tea-time, and here she comes, so late, and they'll all be gone? So there: and Nigel Howard sends down his beastly yorker. Is it fair? Really, Uncle Robert, you ought not to allow ladies to look on at serious cricket like ours. All very well at Lord's and places like that; but here, it's too much of a distraction.'

'But dreadfully awkward,' said she, laughing up at him, 'not to have us to put the blame on? Jim!' she called after him as they parted: he turned. 'It was real noble and kind of you to think about the strawberries.'

'I'm off to rescue them.' And, using his bat like a walking-stick, he disappeared with long galloping strides in the direction of the tea-tent.

St John, next man in, was out first ball. This made an excitement, in expectation that Howards should do the hat-trick; but Denmore-Bentham, who followed, batted with extreme circumspection and entire success (in keeping his wicket up, though not indeed in scoring).

'Who's this young fellow that's been putting up all the runs? Radford? Bradford? I couldn't catch the name?' said an old gentleman with white whiskers, white waistcoat, and that guinea-gold complexion that comes of long living east of Suez. His wife answered: 'Lord Glanford, Lord Southmere's son. They're staying here at the house, I think. And that's his sister: the pretty girl in pink, with brown hair, talking now to Lady Mary.'

His glance, following where hers gave him the direction, suddenly came to rest; but not upon Lady Rosamund Kirstead. For Mary, chancing at that instant to rise and, in her going, look back with some laughing rejoinder to her friends, stood, for that instant, singled; as if, sudden in a vista between trees, a white sail drawing to the wind should lean, pause, and so righting itself pass on its airy way. A most strange and singular look there was, for any perceiving eye to have read, in the eyes of that old colonial governor: as though, through these ordinary haphazard eyes, generations of men crowded to look forth as from a window.

Glanford, with a new partner, seemed to settle down now to win the match by cautious steady play, never taking a risk, never giving a chance. When, after a solid half hour of this, a hundred at last went up on the board, the more cavalierly minded among the onlookers began to give rein to their feelings. 'Darling Anne,' Fanny Chedisford said, arm in arm with Lady Bremmerdale, 'I simply can't stick it any longer; poke, poke, poke: as soon look on at a game of draughts. For heaven's sake, let's go and drown our sorrows in croquet.'

'Croquet? I thought you agreed with Mary—'

'I always do. But when?'

'When she said it was only fit for curates and dowagers, and then only if they'd first done a course in a criminal lunatic asylum.'

'O we're all qualified after this. Try a foursome: here's Jim and Mr Margesson: ask them to join in.'

'Did I hear someone pronounce my name disrespectfully?' said Jim Scarnside. Fanny laughed beneath her white parasol. 'Ah, it was my much esteemed and never sufficiently to be redoubted Miss Chedisford. You know,' he said to Cuthbert Margesson, 'Miss Chedisford hasn't forgiven us for not making it a mixed match.'

'Broom-sticks for the men?' said Margesson.

'Not at all,' said Fanny.

Jim said, 'I should think not! Come on: Margesson's in next wicket down. It does seem rather cheek, when he's captain, but after all it's his demon bowling made him that, and his noted diplomacy. Let's take him on and coach him a bit: teach him to slog.'

Anne Bremmerdale smiled: 'Better than croquet.' They moved off towards the nets.

'Are you a bat, Miss Chedisford? or a bowler?' said Margesson.

'Well, I can bat more amusingly than this': Fanny cast a disparaging glance at the game. 'My brothers taught me.'

'All the same,' Margesson said, 'Glanford's playing a fine game. We shall beat you, Lady Bremmerdale. How is it you didn't bring your brother over to play for Hyrnbastwick?'

'Which one? I've five.'

'I've only met one. The youngest. Your brother Edward, isn't it?'

'She couldn't bring him because she hasn't got him.'

Fanny said, 'I thought he was staying with you now at Taverford?'

'Not since early May.'

'He's the kind of man,' said Jim, 'you never know where he is.'

Fanny looked surprised. 'I'd have sworn,' she said, 'it was Edward Lessingham I saw this morning. Must have been his double.'

'Antipholus of Ephesus,' said Jim: 'Antipholus of Syracuse.'

'About eight o'clock,' said Fanny. 'It was such a dream of a morning, all sopping with dew, I'd got up with the lark and walked the dogs right up onto Kelling Heath before breakfast. I'd swear no one in these parts had that marvellous seat on a horse that he has. So careless. My dear, I'll bet you anything you like it was he: galloping south, towards Holt!'

'Really, Fanny, it couldn't have been,' said Anne.

'There are not many young men you'd mistake for him,' said Fanny.

Jim said to them, 'Talking of Kelling Heath, I'll tell you an idea of mine; why can't we get up a point-to-point there this autumn? What do you say, Cuthbert?'

'I'm all for it.'

'I tackled Colonel Playter about it today at lunch: very important to get him, as M.F.H., to bless it: in fact, he really ought to take it over himself, if it's to be a real good show. He likes the idea. Did you sound Charles, Anne?'

'Yes I did: he's awfully keen on it, and means to get a word with you this evening. Of course you could have a magnificent run right over from Weybourne Heath to Salthouse Common, and back the other way; pretty rough and steep, though, in places.'

Fanny accepted the change in subject. May be she thought the more.

Bentham was out: caught at the wicket: six wickets down for 109, of which Glanford had made 60 off his own bat. Margesson now went in, and (not because of any eggings on of impatient young ladies – unless, indeed, telepathy was at work – for Glandford it was who did the scoring), the play began to be brisk. Major Rustham, the Hyrnbastwick captain, now took Howard off and tried Sir Charles Bremmerdale, whose delivery, slowish, erratic, deceptively easy in appearance, yet concealed (as dangerous currents in the body of smooth-seeming water) a puzzling variety of pace and length and now and again an unexpected and most disconcerting check or spin. But Glanford had plainly got his eye in: Margesson too. 'We're winning, Nell,' said Lord Anmering to his niece, Mrs Margesson. 'A dashed fine stand!' said Sybil Playter. 'Shut up swearing,' said her sister. 'Shut up yourself: I'm not.' People clapped and cheered Glanford's strokes. Charles Bremmerdale now could do nothing with him: to mid-off, two: to mid-on, two: a wide: a strong drive, over cover's head, to the boundary, four: to long-leg in the deep field, two – no – three, while Jack Bailey bungles it with a long shot at the wicket: point runs after it: 'Come on!' – four: the fieldsman is on it, turns to throw in: 'No!' says Margesson, but Glanford, 'Yes! come on!' They run: Bremmerdale is crouched at the wicket: a fine throw, into his hands, bails off and Glanford run out. 'Bad luck!' said Jim Scarnside, standing with Tom and Fanny Chedisford at the scoring table: Glanford had made 91. 'But why the devil will he always try and bag the bowling?'

Glanford walked from the field, bat under his arm, shaking his head mournfully as he undid his batting-gloves. He went straight to the pavilion to put on his blazer, and thence, with little deviation from the direct road, to Mary. 'I am most frightfully sorry,' he said, sitting down by her. 'I did so want to bring you a century for a birthday present.'

'But it was a marvellous innings,' she said. 'Good heavens, "What's centuries to me or me to centuries?" It was splendid.'

'Jolly decent of you to say so. I was an ass, though, to get run out.'

Mary's answering smile was one to smoothe the worst-ruffled feathers; then she resumed her conversation with Lucy Dilstead: 'You can read them over and over again, just as you can Jane Austen. I suppose it's because there's no padding.'

'I've only read *Shagpat*, so far,' said Lucy.

'O that's different from the rest. But isn't it delicious? So serious. Comedy's always ruined, don't you think, when it's buffooned? You want to live in it: something you can laugh with, not laugh at.'

'Mary has gone completely and irretrievably cracked over George Meredith,' Jim said, joining them.

'And who's to blame for that?' said she. 'Who put what book into whose hand? and bet what, that who would not be able to understand what-the-what it was all driving at until she had read the first how many chapters how many times over?'

Jim clutched his temples, histrionically distraught. Hugh was not amused. The match proceeded, the score creeping up now very slowly with Margesson's careful play. General Macnaghten was saying to Mr Romer, 'No, no, she's only twenty. It is: yes: quite extraordinary; but being only daughter, you see, and no mother, she's been doing hostess and so on for her father two years now, here and in London: two London seasons. Makes a lot of difference.'

Down went another wicket: score, 153. 'Now for some fun,' people said as Tom Appleyard came on the field; but Margesson spoke a wingèd word in his ear: 'Look here, old chap: none of the Jessop business. It's too damned serious now.' 'Ay, ay, sir.' Margesson, in perfect style, sent back the last ball of the over. Appleyard obediently blocked and blocked. But in vain. For one of Bremmerdale's master-creations of innocent outward show and inward guile sneaked round Margesson's defence and took his leg stump. Nine wickets down: total 157: last man, 9. Hyrnbastwick, in some elation, were throwing high catches round the field while Dilstead, Anmering's next (and last) man in, walked to the wicket. Margesson said to Tom Appleyard, 'It's up to you now, my lad. Let 'em have it, damn slam and all if you like. But, by Jingo, we must pull it off now. Only 7 to win.' Appleyard laughed and rubbed his hands.

There was no more desultory talk: all tense expectancy. 'If Sir Oliver gets the bowling, that puts the lid on it: never hit a ball yet.' 'Why do they play him then?' 'Why, you silly ass, because he's such a thundering good wicket-keeper.' George Chedisford, about sixteen, home from Winchester because of the measles, maintained a mature self-possession at Lord Anmering's elbow: 'I wish my frater – wish my brother was in again, sir. He'd do the trick.' 'You watch Mr Appleyard: he's a hitter.' By good luck, that ball that had beaten Margesson was last of the over, so that Appleyard, not Dilstead, faced the bowling: Howard once more, a Polyphemus refreshed. His first ball was a yorker, but Appleyard stopped it. The second, Appleyard, all prudent checks abandoned, stepped out and swiped. Boundary: four. Great applaudings: the parson's children and the two little Rustham boys, with the frenzy of Guelph and Ghibelline, jumped up and down jostling each other. The next ball, a very fierce one, pitched short and rose at the batsman's head. Appleyard smashed it with a terrific over-hand stroke: four again – 'Done it!' 'Match!'

Then, at the fourth ball, Appleyard slogged, missed, and was caught in the slips. And so amid great merriment, chaff and mutual congratulations, the game came to an end.

from A FISH DISH IN MEMISON
1941

CAUGHT SUB.

by

L.P. Hartley

Young Leo Colston has been acting as 'go-between' between Marian Maudsley, the local magnate's daughter who is engaged to Lord Trimingham, and Ted Burgess, a small farmer and clandestine lover of Marian. Their affair, and Leo's part in its discovery, are ironically mirrored in the cricket match and its climax.

With Marcus's full approval I put on my school cricket-clothes but when I asked him if I could wear the school cap – a blue one made in segments converging on a crowning button, and having a white gryphon woven on the front – he was doubtful. 'It would be all right,' he said, 'if it was an England cap, or even a county cap or a club cap. But being only a school cap, people might think you were putting on side.'

'They wouldn't if it was to keep the rain off, you old heifer.'

'It won't rain, stomach-pump.'

We argued for some time about the propriety of wearing a cap, heaping ingenious insults on each other.

Sunshine and shadow outside, sunshine and shadow in my thoughts. Since Marcus's return I had become vaguely aware that I was leading a double life. In one way this exhilarated me; it gave me a sense of power and called out my latent capacities for intrigue. But also I was afraid, afraid of making some slip, and at the back of my mind I knew that the practical difficulty of keeping Marcus in the dark about the letters still existed, though

I had been half persuaded to ignore it. I carried about with me something that made me dangerous, but what it was and why it made me dangerous, I had no idea; and soon my thought of it was banished by the imminence of the cricket match, which was making itself felt throughout the house. I caught glimpses of white-clad figures striding purposefully to and fro, heard men's voices calling each other in tones of authority and urgency, as if life had suddenly become more serious, as if a battle were in prospect.

We had a stand-up, buffet luncheon, all going to the sideboard and helping ourselves, and this seemed a tremendous innovation. It relieved the excitement and suspense to be always jumping up, and Marcus and I busied ourselves with waiting on the others. Waiting on, and waiting for them; for we had long ago finished our meal, and were kicking our heels, when Lord Trimingham caught Mr Maudsley's eye and said: 'Ought we to be moving now?'

I remember walking to the cricket ground with our team, sometimes trying to feel, and sometimes trying not to feel, that I was one of them; and the conviction I had, which comes so quickly to a boy, that nothing in the world mattered except that we should win. I remember how class distinctions melted away and how the butler, the footman, the coachman, the gardener and the pantry-boy seemed completely on an equality with us, and I remember having a sixth sense which enabled me to foretell, with some accuracy, how each of them would shape.

All our side were in white flannels. The village team, most of whom were already assembled in the pavilion, distressed me by their nondescript appearance; some wore their working clothes, some had already taken their coats off, revealing that they wore braces. How can they have any chance against us? I asked myself, for though less conventional than Marcus I did not believe you could succeed at a game unless you were dressed properly for it. It was like trained soldiers fighting natives. And then it crossed my mind that perhaps the village team were like the Boers, who did not have much in the way of equipment by our standards, but could give a good account of themselves, none the less; and I looked at them with a new respect.

Most of the members of the opposing sides knew one another already, those who did not were formally made acquainted by Lord Trimingham. The process of successively shaking hands with person after person I found confusing, as I still do; the first name or two held, then they began to trickle off my memory like raindrops off a mackintosh. Suddenly I heard: 'Burgess, this is our twelfth man, Leo Colston.' Automatically I stretched my hand out and then, seeing who it was, for some reason I blushed furiously. He, too, seemed embarrassed but recovered himself more quickly than I did, and said 'Oh yes, my lord, we know each other. Master Colston and I, he comes to slide down my straw-stack.'

'Stupid of me,' said Lord Trimingham, 'of course, he told us. But you should make him run errands for you, Burgess, he's a nailer at that.'

'I'm sure he's a useful young gentleman,' said the farmer, before I had time to speak. Lord Trimingham turned away, leaving us together.

'I didn't see you when I came,' I blurted out, eyeing the farmer's white flannels, which transformed him almost as much as if he had been wearing fancy dress.

'I was with the mare,' he said, 'but she's comfortable now, she's got her foal. You must come and see them.'

'Are you the captain?' I asked, for it was difficult to think of him in a subordinate position.

'Oh no,' said he, 'I'm not much of a cricketer. I just hit out at them. Bill Burdock, he's our skipper. That's him over there, talking to his lordship.' Of course I was used to hearing the servants call Lord Trimingham his lordship, but it seemed odd to me that Ted should, and involuntarily I glanced round to see if Marian was there; but the ladies from the Hall had not appeared. 'Look, they're spinning the coin,' he said, with an eagerness that was almost boyish. 'But it won't signify; his lordship never wins the toss.'

This time he did, however, and we went in first.

The game was already under way when Mrs Maudsley and her train arrived. I could hardly contain my disapproval of their lateness. 'They simply wouldn't start,' Marcus confided to me.

'See you again, old man.' He went down with them to a row of chairs below the steps; I sat with the team in the pavilion.

I have never voluntarily watched a cricket match since, but I realize that conditions at Brandham were exceptional; the Triminghams had always been interested in the game and Mr Maudsley carried on the tradition; we had a score-board, scoring-cards, white sheets, and a chalk line to mark the boundary. All these correct accessories gave the match the feeling of importance, of mattering intensely, which I required from life; had it been conducted in a slipshod manner I could not have taken the same interest in it. I liked existence to be simplified into terms of winning or losing, and I was a passionate partisan. I felt that the honour of the Hall was at stake and that we could never lift our heads up if we lost. Most of the spectators, I imagined, were against us, being members of the village, or neighbouring villages; the fact that they applauded a good shot did not give me a sense of unity with them; had we worn rosettes or colours to distinguish us I could hardly have looked the other party in the eye, while I would willingly have clasped the hand of the biggest blackguard on our side.

Above all I was anxious that Lord Trimingham should do well, partly because he was our captain, and the word captain had a halo for me, partly because I liked him and enjoyed the sense of consequence his condescension gave me, and partly because the glory of Brandham Hall – its highest potentialities for a rhapsody of greatness – centred in him.

The first wicket fell for fifteen runs and he went in. 'Trimingham's a pretty bat,' Denys had said on more than one occasion; 'I grant you he's not so strong on the leg side; but he has a forcing stroke past cover point that's worthy of a county player and I very much doubt if even R.E. Foster can rival his late cuts. I very much doubt it.'

I watched him walk to the wicket with the unconscious elegance of bearing that made such a poignant contrast with his damaged face; the ceremony of taking centre – actually he asked for middle and leg – a novelty in those days – had its awful ritual solemnity. And he did give us a taste of his quality. The beautiful stroke past cover point reached the boundary twice; the late cut, so fine it might have been a snick, skimmed past the wicket, and then came a bumping ball on the leg stump – looking dangerous as it left the bowler's hand – and he was out, having added only eleven to our score.

A round of applause, subdued and sympathetic and more for him than for his play, greeted his return. I joined in the muted clapping and, averting my eyes, muttered 'Bad luck, sir,' as he came by; so what was my surprise to see Marian applauding vigorously, as for the hero of a century; and her eyes were sparkling as she lifted them to his. He answered with the twisted look that served him as a smile. Can she be mocking him? I wondered. Is it another joke? I didn't think so; it was just that, being a woman, she didn't know what cricket was.

Further disasters followed; five wickets were down for fifty-six. These Boers in their motley raiment, triumphantly throwing the ball into the air after each kill, how I disliked them! The spectators disposed along the boundary, standing, sitting, lying, or propped against trees, I imagined to be animated by a revolutionary spirit, and revelling in the downfall of their betters. Such was the position when Mr Maudsley went in. He walked stiffly and stopped more than once to fumble with his gloves. I suppose he was fifty but to me he seemed hopelessly old and utterly out of the picture: it was as though Father Time had come down with his scythe to take a turn at the wicket. He left behind a whiff of office hours and the faint trail of gold so alien to the cricket field. Gnome-like he faced the umpire and responded to his directions with quick, jerky movements of his bat. His head flicked round on his thin lizard neck as he took in the position of the field. Seeing this, the fielders rubbed their hands and came in closer. Suddenly I felt sorry for him with the odds so heavily against him, playing a game he was too old for, trying to look younger than he was. It was as though an element of farce had come into the game and I waited resignedly for his wicket to fall.

But I waited in vain. The qualities that had enabled Mr Maudsley to get on in the world stood by him in the cricket field – especially the quality of judgment. He knew when to leave well alone. It cannot be said that he punished the loose balls – he never hit a boundary – but he scored off them. He had no style, it seemed to me; he dealt empirically with each ball that came along. His method was no method but it worked. He had an uncanny sense of where the fielders were, and generally managed to slip the ball between them. They were brought in closer, they were sent out further, they straddled their legs and adopted attitudes of extreme watchfulness; but to no purpose.

A bowler whose fastish swingers had claimed two wickets earlier in the innings now came on. One of his deliveries hit Mr Maudsley's pads and he appealed, but the appeal was disallowed, and after that his bowling became demoralized and he was taken off. In the next over a wicket fell and Denys joined his father. The score was now 103 of which Mr Maudsley had made 28. The ladies, as I could tell from their motionless hats, were now taking a proper interest in the game: mentally I could see the searchlight beam of Mrs Maudsley's eye on the wicket.

Before he left the pavilion Denys had told us what he meant to do. 'The great thing is not to let him tire himself,' he said. 'I shall not let him run a single run more than I can help. I wanted him to have someone to run for him, but he wouldn't. When a ball comes to me I shall either hit a boundary or I shall leave it alone. I shall leave it absolutely alone.'

For a time these tactics were successful. Denys did hit a boundary – he hit two. He played with a great deal of gesture, walking about meditatively when his father had the bowling, and sometimes strolling out to pat the pitch. But his methods did not combine well with his father's opportunist policy. Mr Maudsley, always anxious to steal a run and knowing exactly when to, was frequently thwarted by Denys's raised arm, which shot up like a policeman's.

Once or twice when this happened the spectators tittered but Denys appeared to be as unconscious of their amusement as he was of his father's growing irritation, which also was visible to us. At last, when the signal was again raised against him, Mr Maudsley called out, 'Come *on*!' It was like the crack of a whip; all the authority that Mr Maudsley so carefully concealed in his daily life spoke in those two words. Denys started off like a rabbit but he was too late; he had hardly got half-way down the pitch before he was run out. Crestfallen and red-faced he returned to the pavilion.

There was now no doubt as to who dominated the field. But oddly enough though I did not grudge my host his success I could not quite reconcile it with the spirit of the game. It wasn't cricket; it wasn't cricket that an elderly gnome-like individual with a string neck and creaking joints should, by dint of head-work and superior cunning, reverse the proverb that youth will be served. It was an ascendancy of brain over brawn, of which, like a true Englishman, I felt suspicious.

Mr Maudsley did not find anyone to stay with him long, however. The last three wickets fell quickly, but they had raised our score to 142, a very respectable total. Tremendous applause greeted Mr Maudsley as he came back, undefeated, having just made his fifty. He walked alone – the footman, his last companion at the wicket, having joined the fieldsmen, with whom no doubt he felt more at home. We all rose to do him honour; he looked a little pale but much less heated than the village team, who were perspiring freely and mopping their faces. Lord Trimingham took the liberty of patting him on the back; gentle as the pat was, his frail frame shook under it.

During the tea-interval the game was replayed many times, but the hero of the hour seemed content to be left out; indeed it soon became as difficult to associate him with his innings as with the financial operations he directed in the City. At five o'clock our team took the field; the village had two hours in which to beat us.

I still have the scoring cards but whereas I can remember our innings in detail, theirs, although the figures are before me, remains a blur, until the middle. Partly, no doubt, because our batsmen were all known to me personally, and theirs, with one exception, were not. Also because it looked such an easy win for us – as the scores, all in single figures, of the first five batsmen testify – that I withdrew some of my attention: one cannot concentrate on a walk-over. The excitements of our innings seemed far away and almost wasted – as if we had put out all our strength to lift a pin. I remember feeling rather sorry for the villagers, as one after another their men went back, looking so much smaller than when they had walked to the wicket. And as the game receded from my mind the landscape filled it. There were two bows: the arch of the trees beyond the cricket field, and the arch of the sky above them; and each repeated the other's curve. This delighted my sense of symmetry; what disturbed it was the spire of the church. The church itself was almost invisible among the trees, which grew over the mound it stood on in the shape of a protractor, an almost perfect semi-circle. But the spire, instead of dividing the protractor into two equal segments, raised its pencil-point to the left of the centre – about eight degrees, I calculated. Why could not the church conform to Nature's plan? There must be a place, I thought, where the spire would be seen as a continuation of the protractor's axis, producing the perpendicular indefinitely into the sky, with two majestic right angles at its base, like flying buttresses, holding it up. Perhaps some of the spectators enjoyed this view. I wished I could go in search of it, while our team was skittling out the village side.

But soon my eye, following the distressful spire into the heavens, rested on the enormous cloud that hung there, and tried to penetrate its depths. A creation of the heat, it was like no cloud I had ever seen. It was pure white on top, rounded and thick and lustrous as a snow-drift: below, the white was flushed with pink, and still further below, in the very heart of the cloud, the pink deepened to purple. Was there a menace in this purple tract, a hint of thunder? I did not think so. The cloud seemed absolutely motionless; scan it as I would, I could not detect the smallest alteration in its outline. And yet it *was* moving – moving towards the sun, and getting brighter and brighter as it approached it. A few more degrees, and then—

As I was visualizing the lines of the protractor printed on the sky I heard a rattle and a clatter. It was Ted Burgess going out to bat; he was whistling, no doubt to keep his spirits up.

He was carrying his bat under his arm, rather unorthodox. How did I feel about him? Did I want him, for instance, to come out first ball? Did I want to see him hit a six and then come out? I was puzzled, for until now my feelings had been quite clear: I wanted everyone on our side to make runs, and everyone on their side not to.

The first ball narrowly shaved his wicket and then I knew: I did not want him to get out. The knowledge made me feel guilty of disloyalty, but I consoled myself by thinking that it was sporting, and therefore meritorious, to want the enemy to put up a fight; besides, they were so far behind! And in this state of uneasy neutrality I remained for several overs while Ted, who got most of the bowling, made several mis-hits including one skier, which the pantry-boy might have caught had not the sun been in his eyes.

Then he hit one four, and then another; the ball whistled across the boundary, scattering the spectators. They laughed and applauded, though no one felt, I think, that it was a serious contribution to the match. More mis-hits followed and then a really glorious six which sailed over the pavilion and dropped among the trees at the back.

A scatter of small boys darted off to look for it and while they were hunting the fieldsmen lay down on the grass; only Ted and his partner and the two umpires remained standing, looking like victors on a stricken field. All the impulse seemed to go out of the game: it was a moment of complete relaxation. And even when the finder had triumphantly tossed the ball down into the field, and play began again, it still had a knock-about, light-hearted character. 'Good old Ted!' someone shouted when he hit his next boundary.

With the score card in front of me I still can't remember at what point I began to wonder whether Ted's displayful innings might not influence the match. I think it was when he had made his fifty that I began to see the red light and my heart started pounding in my chest.

It was a very different half-century from Mr Maudsley's, a triumph of luck, not of cunning, for the will, and even the wish to win seemed absent from it. Dimly I felt that the contrast represented something more than the conflict between Hall and village. It was that, but it was also the struggle between order and lawlessness, between obedience to tradition and defiance of it, between social stability and revolution, between one attitude to life and another. I knew which side I was on; yet the traitor within my gates felt the issue differently, he backed the individual against the side, even my own side, and wanted to see Ted Burgess pull it off. But I could not voice such thoughts to the hosts of Midian prowling round me under the shade of the pavilion veranda. Their looks had cleared marvellously and they were now taking bets about the outcome not without sly looks at me; so spying a vacant seat beside Marian I edged my way down to her and whispered:

'Isn't it exciting?' I felt this was not too much a betrayal of our side.

When she did not answer I repeated the question. She turned to me and nodded, and I saw that the reason she didn't answer was because she couldn't trust herself to speak. Her eyes were bright, her cheeks were flushed and her lips trembled. I was a child and lived in the society of children and I knew the signs. At the time I didn't ask myself what they meant, but the sight of a grown-up person so visibly affected greatly increased my emotional response to the game, and I could hardly sit still, for I always wriggled when excited. The conflict in my feelings deepened: I could not bear to face the fact, which was becoming more apparent to me every moment, that I wanted the other side to win.

Another wicket fell and then another; there were two more to go and the village needed twenty-one runs to pass our total. The spectators were absolutely silent as the new batsman walked out. I heard their captain say 'Let him have the bowling, Charlie,' but I doubted whether Ted would fall in with this; he had shown no sign of wishing to 'bag' the bowling. It was the last ball of the over; the new batsman survived it, and Ted, facing us, also faced the attack.

Lord Trimingham had two men in the deep field, and long on was standing somewhat to our right. Ted hit the first ball straight at us. I thought it was going to be a six but soon its trajectory flattened. As it came to earth it seemed to gather speed. The fieldsman ran and got his hand to it, but it cannoned off and hurtled threateningly towards us. Mrs Maudsley jumped up with a little cry; Marian put her hands in front of her face; I held my breath; there was a moment of confusion and anxious inquiry before it was discovered that neither of them had been touched. Both the ladies laughed at their narrow escape and tried to pass it off. The ball lay at Mrs Maudsley's feet looking strangely small and harmless. I threw it to long on, who, I now saw, was one of our gardeners. But he ignored it. His face twisted with pain he was nursing his left hand in his right and gingerly rubbing it.

Lord Trimingham and some of the other fielders came towards him and he went to meet them; I saw him showing them his injured hand. They conferred; they seemed to come to a decision; then the group dispersed, the handful of players returned to the wicket, and Lord Trimingham and the gardener returned to the pavilion.

Confusion reigned in my mind: I thought all sorts of things at the same time: that the match was over, that the gardener would be maimed for life, that Ted would be sent to prison. Then I heard Lord Trimingham say: 'We've had a casualty. Pollin has sprained his thumb, and I'm afraid we shall have to call on our twelfth man.' Even then I did not know he meant me.

My knees quaking I walked back with him to the pitch. 'We've got to get him out,' he said. 'We've got to get him out. Let's hope this interruption will have unsettled him. Now, Leo, I'm going to put you at square leg. You won't have much to do because he makes most of his runs in front of the wicket. But sometimes he hooks one, and that's where you can help us.' Something like that: but I scarcely heard, my nervous system was so busy trying to adjust itself to my new rôle. From spectator to performer, what a change!

Miserably nervous, I followed the movements of the bowler's hand, signalling me to my place. At last I came to rest in a fairy ring, and this absurdly gave me confidence, I felt that it might be a magic circle and would protect me. Two balls were bowled from which no runs were scored. Gradually my nervousness wore off and a sense of elation took possession of me. I felt at one with my surroundings and upheld by the long tradition of cricket. Awareness such as I had never known sharpened my senses; and when Ted drove the next ball for four, and got another four from the last ball of the over, I had to restrain an impulse to join in the enemy's applause. Yet when I saw, out of the tail of my eye, a new figure going up on the score-board, I dare not look at it, for I knew it was the last whole ten we had in hand.

The next over was uneventful but increasingly tense; the new batsman stamped and blocked and managed to smother the straight ones; the lower half of his body was more active than the upper. But he got a single off the last ball and faced the bowling again.

It was not the same bowling, however, that had given Ted Burgess his boundaries in the preceding over. As I crossed the pitch I saw that a change was pending. Lord Trimingham had the ball, and was throwing it gently from one hand to the other; he made some alterations in the field, and for a moment I feared he was going to move me out of my magic circle; but he did not.

He took a long run with a skip in the middle but the ball was not very fast; it seemed to drop rather suddenly. The batsman hit out at it and it soared into the air. He ran, Ted ran, but before they reached their opposite creases it was safe in Lord Trimingham's hands. It was evidence of our captain's popularity that, even at this critical juncture, the catch was generously applauded. The clapping soon subsided, however, as the boy who kept the telegraph moved towards the score-board. The figures came with maddening slowness. But what was this? Total score 9, wickets 1, Last man 135. Laughter broke out among the spectators. The board boy came back and peered at his handiwork. Then to the accompaniment of more laughter, he slowly changed the figures around.

But funny though it seemed, the mistake didn't really relieve the tension, it added to it by suggesting that even mathematics were subject to nervous upset. And only eight runs – two boundaries – stood between us and defeat.

As the outgoing met the incoming batsman and exchanged a word with him, at which each man nodded, I tried for the last time to sort my feelings out. But they gathered round me like a mist, whose shape can be seen as it advances but not when it is on you, and in the thick, whirling vapours my mind soon lost its way. Yet I kept my sense of the general drama of the match and it was sharpened by an awareness, which I couldn't explain to myself, of a particular drama between the bowler and the batsman. Tenant and landlord, commoner and peer, village and hall – these were elements in it. But there was something else, something to do with Marian, sitting on the pavilion steps watching us.

It was a prideful and sustaining thought that whereas the spectators could throw themselves about and yell themselves hoarse, we, the players could not, must not, show the slightest sign of emotion. Certainly the bowler, digging his heel into the ground, a trick he had before starting his run, and Ted facing him, his shirt clinging to his back, did not.

Lord Trimingham sent down his deceptively dipping ball but Ted did not wait for it to drop, he ran out and hit it past cover point to the boundary. It was a glorious drive and the elation of it ran through me like an electric current. The spectators yelled and cheered, and suddenly the balance of my feelings went right over: it was their victory that I wanted now, not ours. I did not think of it in terms of the three runs that were needed; I seemed to hear it coming like a wind.

I could not tell whether the next ball was on the wicket or not, but it was pitched much further up and suddenly I saw Ted's face and body swinging round, and the ball, travelling towards me on a rising straight line like a cable stretched between us. Ted started to run and then stopped and stood watching me, wonder in his eyes and a wild disbelief.

I threw my hand above my head and the ball stuck there, but the impact knocked me over. When I scrambled up, still clutching the ball to me, as though it was a pain that had started in my heart, I heard the sweet sound of applause and saw the field breaking up and Lord Trimingham coming towards me. I can't remember what he said – my emotions were too overwhelming – but I remember that his congratulations were the more precious because they were reserved and understated, they might, in fact, have been addressed to a *man*; and it was as a man, and not by any means the least of men, that I joined the group who were making their way back to the pavilion. We went together in a ragged cluster, the defeated and the surviving batsmen with us, all enmity laid aside, amid a more than generous measure of applause from the spectators. I could not tell how I felt; in my high mood of elation the usual landmarks by which I judged such things were lost to view. I was still in the air, though the scaffolding of events which had lifted me had crumbled. But I was still aware of one separate element that had not quite fused in the general concourse of passions; the pang of regret, sharp as a sword-thrust, that had accompanied the catch. Far from diminishing my exultation, it had somehow raised it to a higher power, like the drop of bitter in the fount of happiness; but I felt that I should be still happier – that it would add another cubit to my stature – if I told Ted of it. Something warned me that such an avowal would be unorthodox; the personal feelings of cricketers were concealed behind their stiff upper lips. But I was almost literally above myself; I knew that the fate of the match had turned on me, and I felt I could afford to defy convention. Yet how would he take it? What were his feelings? Was he still elated by his innings or was he bitterly disappointed by its untimely close? Did he still regard me as a friend, or as an enemy who had brought about his downfall? I did not greatly care; and seeing that he was walking alone (most of the players had exhausted their stock of conversation) I sidled up to him and said, 'I'm sorry, Ted. I didn't really mean to catch you out.' He stopped and smiled at me. 'Well, that's very handsome of you,' he said. 'It was a damned good catch, anyway. I never thought you'd hold it. To tell you the truth I'd forgotten all about you being at square leg, and then I looked round and there you were, by God. And then I thought, "It'll go right over his head," but you stretched up like a concertina. I'd thought of a dozen ways I might get out, but never thought I'd be caught out by our postman.' 'I didn't mean to,' I repeated, not to be cheated of my apology. At that moment the clapping grew louder and some enthusiasts coupled Ted's name with it. Though we were all heroes, he was evidently the crowd's favourite; and I dropped back so that he might walk in alone. His fellow-batsmen in the pavilion were making a great demonstration; even the ladies of our party, sitting in front, showed themselves mildly interested as

Ted came by. All except one. Marian, I noticed, didn't look up.

As soon as we were back at the Hall I said to Marcus, 'Lend me your scoring-card, old man.'

'Why, didn't you keep one, pudding-face?' he asked me.

'How could I, you dolt, when I was fielding?'

'Did you field, you measly microbe? Are you quite sure?'

When I punished him for this, and extracted his score-card from him, I copied on to mine the items that were missing.

'E. Burgess c.sub.b.Ld.Trimingham 81,' I read. 'Why, you might have put my name in, you filthy scoundrel.'

' "C.sub." is correct,' he said. 'Besides, I want to keep this card clean, and it wouldn't be if your name was on it.'

from THE GO-BETWEEN
1953

THE CUSSEDNESS OF CRICKET

by

J.C. Snaith

John Collis Snaith wrote many novels but Willow the King, *perhaps because it concentrates on a particular subject – 'the story of a cricket match' – seems to be the longest lived. It has many of the attractions of de Selincourt's* The Cricket Match *published twenty-five years later – such as the narrator's superstitious reactions to the prospects for his day's cricket and his eloquent delight when he scores a perfectly timed boundary off a fast bowler* *(see page 316)**. Snaith's knowledge of the game is hardly surprising. As* The Wisden Book of Obituaries *shows, he was a good enough all-rounder to play twice for Nottinghamshire in 1900, and frequently for the county second XI and for Notts Amateurs. In 1914 he took part in a second-wicket stand of 340 for Skegness. He died in 1936.*

Had I been in less of a tottering funk, I might have taken the admirably timed arrival of the Authentics as an omen of good luck. But I was in that suicidal frame of mind when a man wishes that he is anything but what he is, anywhere but where he is, and that he has to do aught but what he has to do. It is a frame of mind that can give for deep-seated torture a long start to nightmares, weddings, sea-sickness, and public speaking. If I were only going in first wicket, I shouldn't care! If I'd only an inkling of what the bowling was like! If only it wasn't Little Clumpton *v.* Hickory! If only the crowd wasn't so beastly big and demonstrative! If only it wasn't such a glaring hot day! If only this abject cap was not two sizes too small! If it was only my own, and it didn't look and feel so supremely ridiculous! If I could only cut away to a prompt and very private death! Cricket is quite a gentle, harmless game, but he is a lucky man who has not to sweat some blood before he's done with it.

'Ready, Dimsdale?' said the Captain.

I followed him sickly, fumbling at my batting-glove with nervous fingers.

'Wish you luck, old man,' said some person of benevolent disposition, as I issued forth. It is never exactly kind, however, to wish luck to the keenly sensitive, as it leads them to think that they'll certainly need luck, and plenty of it, if they're going to stay long. From the Artistic Standpoint (capital letters, please, Mr Printer!), it is a thousand pities that I cannot say that when I stepped from the pavilion on this great occasion to open the innings with my Captain, a man whose name had penetrated to the remotest corners of the cricket world, I held my head up with an air of conscious power. Why was I not, as the Hero of this story, prepared to do the thing in style, in the manner of the most accepted writers? Of course I ought to have marched to the wicket, my heart big with courage, calm in the knowledge that the Hero never does get less than fifty. I ought to have been ready to chastise Villainy in the person of the Demon Bowler, by hitting his length balls for six on the slightest provocation. I am sure that no less than this is expected of me by every right-minded reader. Nor am I blind by any means to my obligations; yet somehow it is so much easier to get runs with the pen than with the bat. At least I have always found it so!

I daresay that, except for being a trifle pale, I looked quite happy to all but the trained observer. I don't suppose that ten persons of the shouting thousands present had the faintest notion that the trim-built chap of medium height who walked in with H.J. Halliday, his bat tucked beneath his arm, as he fastened on his glove, had limbs of paper and a heart of fear. There was nought to indicate that there was a dreadful buzzing in his ears, a black mist before his eyes, that his knee-joints were threatening to let him down at every step, and that he was praying to be bowled first ball, to be put out of his misery at once.

When you go in to bat, it is not that you dread aught special and particular. You would cheerfully endure anything rather than your present ordeals. You are not afraid of getting a 'duck'. On the contrary, you'll be almost happy if you get one. It is the mere sensation of an impending something, you know not what, that plays skittles with your impressionable nature.

' 'Mind taking first ball, Halliday?' I said hoarsely.

'If you like,' said he; then added, 'just play your usual, and you're bound to get 'em.'

True cricketers are the soul of kindness.

Carefully noting at which end the wicket-keeper was, I just as carefully went to the one at which he was not. The mighty H.C. Trentham was loosening his arm, and sending down a few preliminaries. I watched him as keenly as the black mists before my eyes allowed. He brought his long brown arm right over with a beautiful, easy, automatic swing. The ball slipped from his fingers at an ordinary pace, but as soon as it took the ground it spun off the pitch with an inward twist at three times the rate one would expect. He looked every inch a bowler, powerfully built in every part, his body supple as a cat's, a remarkable length of limb, and, better still, a pair of extremely strong and heavy-timbered legs.

However, the man preparing to resist him looked every inch a batsman, too. Lithe, alert, calm, he seemed quietly happy that he had got to face a bowler worthy of his artifice. The manner in which he asked for his guard, and took it, the elaborate process he went through to ensure the maintenance of 'two leg', the diligent way in which he observed the placing of the field, and the freedom with which he ordered the screen about, all pointed to the conclusion that if Hickory got him out for under fifty on that wicket, they would be able to congratulate themselves. There is as much difference between the first-class cricketer and the ordinary club-man as there is between a professional actor and the gifted amateur. The club-man may be a marvel of conscientiousness, discretion, and enthusiasm, and able to recite Steel and Lyttelton from the preface to the index at a moment's notice, but he has not that air of inevitableness that emphasizes the county man scoring off the best of Briggs and Richardson, and apparently able to compass any feat in the batting line but the losing of his wicket.

The terrific H.C. Trentham was now ready to deal destruction. Anxiously had I observed the placing of the field, the most noticeable items of which were the wicket-keeper standing a dozen yards behind the sticks, and the four men in the slips still deeper, with their hands on their thighs, and their noses on a level with the bails. The bowler measured his distance, and scratched up the turf at his starting-point. The batsman set himself. The bowler walked a couple of yards, then broke into a trot, that gradually grew into a run, and when he arrived at the crease, with the velocity of a locomotive he hurled the ball from his hand, and his body after it, almost faster than the eye could follow. The Captain fairly dug his bat into his block-hole, and the ball came back straight down the pitch, whizzing and rotating in half-circles. It was a most determined and barefaced attempt to 'york' the captain, and the bowler smiled all over his countenance in a very winning manner. The Captain set himself again. The next ball was of perfect length, a few inches on the off, and turned in suddenly, with the ungenerous idea of hitting the top of the off stump; but the Captain, watching it all the way, met it very warily, his right leg well against his bat, and blocked it gently back again to the bowler. The third had a very similar design, but happening to be pitched a little farther up, it came back as though propelled from a gun. The bowler neatly picked it up with one hand, and drew the first cheer from the crowd. The fourth was full of guile. It was a trifle on the short side, wide of the off stump, and instead of turning in, was going away with the bowler's arm. The Captain drew himself erect, held up his bat, and never made the least attempt to play it. The bowler smiled more winningly than ever. A London critic unburdened his mind by shouting 'Nottingham!' The fifth was wickedness itself. The bowler covered his fifteen yards of run with exactly the same action and velocity, hurled down the ball with the same frantic effort of arms and body, but, behold, the ball was as slow as possible, and the eye could distinctly follow it as it spun in the air with a palpable leg-bias. Even the great batsman who had to receive it was at fault. He played a little too soon, but, happily for

Little Clumpton, the ground was so hard and true that it refused to take the full amount of work, and instead of its curling in and taking the Captain's middle, as the bowler had intended, it refused to come in farther than the leg stick, which was conscientiously covered by the Captain's pad. There it hit him, and rolled slowly towards the umpire, whilst the wicket-keeper pelted grotesquely after it.

'Come on!' I cried, seizing the opportunity, for I was very, very anxious for the Captain to take first over from the other end. Accordingly, we scuttled down the pitch, and I got home just as the wicket-keeper threw down my citadel.

'Well bowled, Charlie!' said the Captain. But I think there was more in this than may appear, as I believe the thoughtful Captain wished to attract my careful attention to that particular ball. Meantime the bowler had been grinning so violently at his own exceeding subtlety that mid-off politely requested him to to commit such an outrage on the handiwork of nature.

'Tom, you have a try that end,' said Captain George, throwing the ball to T.S.M. Trentham. 'Set the field where you want 'em.'

'Left-hand round the wicket!' the umpire announced to the batsman; 'covers 'em both, sir.'

It was plain, by the irregular arrangement of the field, which had three men out, that T.S.M. was slow.

'You don't want a third man; send him out into the country, and bring point round a bit!'

Now as these commands were issued most distinctly from the top of the coach, and as Miss Grace Trentham was at that moment the sole occupant of the same, she must be held responsible for them. A wide smile flickered in the face of every fielder, including that of the happy-go-lucky Hickory captain. But let it be observed, in passing, that there are captains to whom this advice, however Pallas-like, would not appear 'good form'. It was evident that Miss Grace knew her man.

'By Jove! she's right,' said the good-humoured soldier; 'get round, Jimmy.'

'She always is,' said the Harrow captain, her youngest brother; 'and I wish she wasn't. She knows a jolly sight too much.'

'Why don't she qualify for Kent,' said J.P. Carteret, as he waddled off to deep square-leg.

The Harrow boy began with a singular sort of movement that must have had a resemblance to the war-dance of the cheerful Sioux, or the festive Shoshanee, which developed into a cork-screw kind of action that was very puzzling to watch, and imparted to the ball a peculiar and deceptive flight. He was quite slow, with a certain amount of spin and curl. The Captain played right back to him every time, and, like the old Parliamentary hand he was, there was very little of his wicket to be seen, as his legs did their best to efface it. The Captain had come in with the determination to take no liberties. He meant to play himself thoroughly well in before turning his attention to the secondary matter of making runs. If T.S.M. had been a Peate, his first over could not have been treated with a more flattering respect. The consequence was that he opened with a maiden also.

My turn had now arrived. I was called on to face the finest amateur bowler in England. Judging by the one over of his that I had had the privilege of witnessing, he appeared to combine the pace of a Kortright with the wiles of a Spofforth. Taking him altogether, he did not seem to be the nicest bowler in the world for a man of small experience and ordinary ability to oppose. But I remembered vaguely that the wicket was perfection, and that a straight bat would take a lot of beating. Besides, the black mists had lifted somewhat from my eyes, and the beastly funk had considerably decreased, as it often does when one is actually at work. All the same, I took my guard without knowing exactly what I did; I observed the field without knowing precisely how it was arranged, yet could see enough of it to be aware that point was looking particularly grim, and half inclined to chuckle, as though saying to himself, 'Oh, he's a young 'un, is he?'

It was perhaps the sardonic countenance of point that stirred the old Adam in me, for suddenly I took heart of grace, recollected the Captain's 'Play your usual, and you're bound to get 'em,' and made up my mind to play out at H.C. Trentham as though my life depended on it. All the same, I could have wished that the cap I wore was my own, and not two sizes smaller than it should be, and that I could divest my brain of Miss Grace's earlier sinister remark anent Charlie's arm getting over the screen, at the end at which (doubtless at her suggestion) he had gone on to bowl. Besides, he was grinning in a way that, though surely very self-satisfied and ridiculous, was disconcerting to a high degree. I certainly think that if in the umpire's opinion a bowler takes too great liberties with his face at any period of his delivery of the ball, the said umpire should be empowered to 'no-ball' the said bowler. Probably the counties will petition M.C.C.

I planted my right foot on the edge of the crease with mathematical care, and set myself to meet the best bowler at either 'Varsity since Sammy Woods. My straining eyes never left him for an instant as he picked the ball up, worked his thumb up and down the seam, rubbed it on the ground, and then walked jauntily to his starting-point. I could see him all the way; the beautiful clear sunlight, the bright new red ball, and my own intentness almost enabled me to read the maker's name on the cover as he held it in his hand whilst he walked, trotted, galloped to the crease. As he brought his arm high over his head, despite the cessation of the screen's assistance, I could see the thumb and two fingers in which he grasped the ball and every bit of his powerful wrist work. I had no time to think or to know where the ball was, however. But as it came humming from his hand instinct said, 'Go forward hard!' and forward I went, leg, bat, and elbow, for all that I was worth. There was a delicious vibration that told me the ball was timed to the second full in the middle of the bat. It flew like a streak to mid-off all along the carpet; but mid-off happened to be a county man, and it was back in the bowler's hands and threatening the Captain's wicket just as 'No!' had left my mouth. And there was a personal compliment implied in the blinking eyes of H.C. Trentham and the benevolent smile of H.J. Halliday that was a recompense for all the pains I was enduring and many hours of 'duck'-requited toil. I was conscious of an elated thrill running through my fibres as I awaited number two. Again I watched it eagerly as it came spinning through the sunlight and humming like a top; again I could not say exactly where it was, but out went bat, and leg, and elbow as before, and mid-off was afforded another opportunity for the exhibition of his skill. I set myself defiantly for number three. Let H.C. Trentham bowl his heart out. The third came along humming, and whizzing, and spinning in the manner of the other two, but I had a vague sort of idea that it was a little wider and a little farther up. It was faster than an express train, but it merely appeared delicately to kiss the middle of the bat in the gentlest, sweetest way.

'Oh, well hit!' came the voice of the Captain down the wicket. The crowd broke into a roar, and in a perfect ecstasy I looked into what I guessed should be the direction of the ball. Behold! there was cover-point on the verge of the boundary waiting whilst a spectator officiously returned it. It was merely the force of habit that was responsible for that fourer, but the sensation of pure rapture was incomparable. As there is nothing in the whole range of poetry or prose with which to point a parallel, it must be allowed that beside a perfectly-timed boundary hit, on a hard ground, from fast bowling, all other delights of this life are as nothingness.

The fourth ball came along in much the same way as the third, yet was appreciably shorter and slower. I left it severely alone. The fifth was a regular uprooting yorker, but I got my bat down in time and chopped it away. So much for the crack's first over. I had broken my duck in the most handsome manner; I could see the ball; I was beginning to feel alarmingly happy; I never felt so fit and so much like making runs. And I had only to continue as I'd started to be sure of a trial for the county next week against Somerset. But I must restrain my eagerness, play steady, and keep cool.

The Captain adopted the same tactics of masterly inactivity in regard to the second over of the youthful T.S.M. He was quite an ordinary club bowler compared to his great brother at the other end. A shortish one was hooked quietly round to leg for a single, and it was my turn to meet him. There was not a hint of my previous vacillation in the way I took my guard. The buzzing in my head had altogether gone; my eye was as clear and keen as possible. I had had my baptism of fire already. This was very common stuff; indeed, so much so that I took the liberty of turning the second ball I had of it to leg for three.

It being the last ball of the over, I had again to face H.C. With a bowler of this quality it requires a man of very great inexperience to be quite at ease or to think of attempting liberties. Therefore, again I concentrated the whole of my attention on every ball; and the billiard-table pitch and a straight, unflinching bat enabled me to cope with his second over. It was a maiden, but it called for brilliancy on the part of mid-off, and a magnificent bit of fielding by Carteret in the slips, who saved a keen late cut from being a boundary to make it one. Each ball was timed to the instant; my wrists and the rare old blade with the wrapping at the bottom seemed to be endowed with magic; the sun was just in the right place; I had forgotten all about my cap, the screen, the might of the attack – forgotten everything but the joy of achievement, so supreme was the sense of making runs with certainty and ease from county bowling, in the presence of an appreciative crowd, on a great occasion. Here was Elysium. It was a sufficient recompense for a hundred failures. If I kept playing this game I couldn't help but get 'em. Fifty was assured, perhaps; who knew— ? But no man can be sanguine in regard to his first century. That is a bourn that few travellers ever reach.

The Captain played T.S.M. gently for another single. I trotted down blithely to the other end. He was still bowling his slow leg-breaks, but it would be folly to attempt to drive him, as his flight was so deceptive; besides, he had three men out. One ball which he delivered a full two yards behind the crease was tossed up so high that it was difficult to resist, as it appeared to be almost a half-volley at first sight. It actually dropped shorter than his others, however. This was the ball with which he usually got his wickets; and although, crude as it was, it might do well enough for schoolboys, it was to be hoped that he didn't expect a man who intended to appear next week for his county to fall a victim to it! If he did, he would very probably be disappointed. The feel of that three to leg was still lingering in my wrist, and I was certain that this stroke could be played with impunity on this wicket. Besides, it would show the Captain at the other end that I was by no means content to follow his lead, but had resources of my own. Again, if I persevered in getting T.S.M. away to leg, he would be certain to pitch them up a bit, and if he could only be persuaded to do that, sure as fate I should go out to him and lift him clean over the ring! It wasn't such a very big hit; besides, I felt capable of doing anything with ordinary club bowling. Really, I never felt so fit, and on such excellent terms with everybody and everything! When I received the first ball of T.S.M.'s next over I had a plan of the positions of the on-side fielders in the corner of my eye. But it was such an excellent length that I had to play defensively. To my infinite pleasure, I immediately saw that the second was his usual shortish one. I promptly prepared to help myself to another three, stepped into my wicket so to do, but was so anxious to seize my opportunity that I had not troubled to note exactly how short it was. Therefore it rose a little higher than I expected, and I was also a little bit too soon. It hit me just above the pad with an almost caressing gentleness.

'How *was* that?' said the bowler, turning round to the umpire.

This didn't bother me in the least. I merely felt a trifle annoyed that my ardour had caused me to let off so bad a ball. But my pleasant meditations were suddenly disturbed by adjacent voices —

'Chuckerrupp!'

It never entered my head that I could be out by any possibility. The ball was a very vulgar long hop. I looked at the umpire with an air of bewilderment. He had a stolid solemnity that was funereal. I saw his hand go up. Thereon, with the blood buzzing into my ears, I made tracks for the pavilion. All the way I went I could not realize that I was out. My only sensation was the not unpleasing one of walking swiftly. Dead silence reigned as I marched in head down, thinking of nothing in particular. But the vision of the umpire's upthrown hand seemed to be painted on my retina.

The Ancient was in the dressing-room brandishing his bat.

'Rough luck, old man!' he said.

Thereupon he went out to take my vacant place at the wicket, while I sat down, slowly mopped my wet face, rinsed my parched mouth, and then proceeded to take my pads off in the dullest, most apathetic manner.

from WILLOW THE KING
1899

FRIENDS FOR LIFE

by

George Meredith

Meredith, a highly admired man of letters in his day (1828–1909), has too intricate, even finicky, a style to be broadly popular. But with it went also a strong narrative gift too, vivid dialogue, perceptive portrayal of women and an ability to paint brief, sharp portraits of background characters and events such as cricketing scenes. There are several of these in The Ordeal of Richard Feverel *(1859),* Evan Harrington *(1861),* Diana of the Crossway *(1885), and the two episodes which follow from* The Adventures of Harry Richmond *(1871). Meredith is not describing the game itself so much as treating it as part of the country scene or social background; and he is thinking essentially of the pre-overarm period before 1864. Somehow 'cricketing', rather than 'cricket', sums it up. Incidentally, his son, William Maxse Meredith, like his father a reader for Chapman & Hall, used to turn out for J.M. Barrie's Allahakbarries.*

I had a day of rollicking laughter, puzzling the girl, who could only grin two or three seconds at a time, and then stared like a dog that waits for his master to send him off again running, the corners of her mouth twitching for me to laugh or speak, exactly as a dog might wag his tail. I studied her in the light of a harmless sort of unaccountable creature; witness at any rate for the fact that I had escaped from school.

We loitered half the morning round a cricketers' booth in a field, where there was moderately good cricketing. The people thought it of first-rate quality. I told them I knew a fellow who could bowl out either eleven in an hour and a half. One of the men frightened me by saying, 'By Gearge! I'll in with you into a gig, and off with you after that ther' faller.' He pretended to mean it, and started up. I watched him without flinching. He remarked that if I 'had not cut my lucky from school, and tossed my cap for a free life, he was—' whatever may be expressed by a slap on the thigh. We played a single-wicket side game, he giving me six runs, and crestfallen he was to find himself beaten; but, as I let him know, one who had bowled to Heriot for hours and stood against Saddlebank's bowling, was a tough customer, never mind his age.

This man offered me his friendship. He made me sit and eat beside him at the afternoon dinner of the elevens, and sent platefuls of food to the girl, where she was allowed to squat; and said he, 'You and I'll tie a knot, and be friends for life.'

I replied, 'With pleasure.'

from THE ADVENTURES OF HARRY RICHMOND
1871

WHY DON'T MORE GENTLEMEN TAKE TO CRICKET?

by

George Meredith

Unlike most writers when they use cricket or cricket matches as background, George Meredith would always present character in a lively way and give a proper emphasis to the cricket. Siegfried Sassoon, in his biography Meredith *(1948) pointed out this quality: 'His obvious imperfections as a story teller were caused by the irrepressible energy and obtrusiveness of [Meredith's] nature. His novels were vehicles propelled by an engine which was too highly powered for the passengers whom he invites to travel in them. One cannot accuse him of being a reckless driver; but the running of the machine is boisterous and unequal; and he has an uncomfortable habit of turning his head to shout something at us just when he is approaching a sharp corner.'*

We rolled down to the masts among the chimneys on the top of an omnibus. The driver was eloquent on cricket-matches. Now, cricket, he said, was fine manly sport; it might kill a man, but it never meant mischief: foreigners themselves had a bit of an idea that it was the best game in the world, though it was a nice joke to see a foreigner playing at it! None of them could stand to be bowled at. Hadn't stomachs for it; they'd have to train for soldiers first. On one occasion he had seen a Frenchman looking on at a match. 'Ball was hit a shooter twixt the slips: off starts Frenchman, catches it, heaves it up, like his head, half-way to wicket, and all the field set to bawling at him, and sending him, we knew where. He tripped off: "You no comprong politeness in dis country." Ha! ha!'

To prove the aforesaid Frenchman wrong, we nodded to the driver's laughter at his exquisite imitation.

He informed us that he had backed the Surrey Eleven last year, owing to the report of a gentleman-bowler, who had done things in the way of tumbling wickets to tickle the ears of cricketers. Gentlemen-batters were common: gentlemen-bowlers were quite another dish. Saddlebank was the gentleman's name.

'Old Nandrew Saddle?' Temple called to me, and we smiled at the supposition of Saddlebank's fame, neither of us, from what we had known of his bowling, doubting that he deserved it.

'Acquainted with him, gentlemen?' the driver inquired, touching his hat. 'Well, and I ask why don't more gentlemen take to cricket? 'Stead of horses all round the year! Now, there's my notion of happiness,' said the man condemned to inactivity, in the perpetual act of motion; 'cricket in cricket season! It comprises —count: lots o' running; and that's good: just enough o' taking it easy; that's good: an appetite for your dinner, and your ale or your Port, as may be the case; good, number three. Add on a tired pipe after dark, and a sound sleep to follow, and you say good morning to the doctor and the parson; for you're in health body and soul, and ne'er a parson'll make a better Christian of ye, that I'll swear.'

As if anxious not to pervert us, he concluded: 'That's what *I* think, gentlemen.'

Temple and I talked of the ancient raptures of a first of May cricketing-day on a sunny green meadow, with an ocean of a day before us, and well-braced spirits for the match. I had the vision of a matronly, but not much altered Janet, mounted on horseback, to witness the performance of some favourite Eleven of youngsters with her connoisseur's eye; and then the model of an English lady, wife, and mother, waving adieu to the field and cantering home to entertain her husband's guests. Her husband!

Temple was aware of my grief, but saw no remedy. I knew that in his heart he thought me justly punished, though he loved me.

from THE ADVENTURES OF HARRY RICHMOND
1871

HOW THE DINGLEY DELL CRICKET CLUB PLAYED ALL-MUGGLETON

by

Charles Dickens

Mr Winkle has just accidentally wounded Mr Tracy Tupman in the left arm when firing at pigeons.

'Are you a cricketer?' inquired Mr Wardle of the marksman.

At any other time Mr Winkle would have replied in the affirmative. He felt the delicacy of his situation, and modestly replied, 'No.'

'Are you, sir?' inquired Mr Snodgrass.

'I was once upon a time,' replied the host; 'but I have given it up now. I subscribe to the club here, but I don't play.'

'The grand match is played today, I believe,' said Mr Pickwick.

'It is,' replied the host. 'Of course you would like to see it.'

'I, sir,' replied Mr Pickwick, 'am delighted to view any sports which may be safely indulged in, and in which the impotent effects of unskilful people do not endanger human life.' Mr Pickwick paused, and looked steadily on Mr Winkle, who quailed beneath his leader's searching glance. The great man withdrew his eyes after a few minutes, and added: 'Shall we be justified in leaving our wounded friend to the care of the ladies?'

'You cannot leave me in better hands,' said Mr Tupman.

'Quite impossible,' said Mr Snodgrass.

It was therefore settled that Mr Tupman should be left at home in charge of the females; and that the remainder of the guests, under the guidance of Mr Wardle, should proceed to the spot where was to be held that trial of skill, which had roused all Muggleton from its torpor, and inoculated Dingley Dell with a fever of excitement.

As their walk, which was not above two miles long, lay through shady lanes and sequestered footpaths, and as their conversation turned upon the delightful scenery by which they were on every side surrounded, Mr Pickwick was almost inclined to regret the expedition they had used, when he found himself in the main street of the town of Muggleton . . .

[He] gazed with an air of curiosity, not unmixed with interest, on the objects around him. There was an open square for the market-place; and in the centre of it, a large inn with a sign-post in front, displaying an object very common in art, but rarely met with in nature – to wit, a blue lion, with three bow legs in the air, balancing himself on the extreme point of the centre claw of his fourth foot. There were, within sight, an auctioneer's and fire-agency office, a corn-factor's, a linen-draper's, a saddler's, a distiller's, a grocer's, and a shoe-shop – the last mentioned warehouse being also appropriated to the diffusion of hats, bonnets, wearing apparel, cotton umbrellas, and useful knowledge. There was a red-brick house with a small paved court-yard in front, which anybody might have known belonged to the attorney; and there was, moreover, another red-brick house with Venetian blinds, and a large brass door-plate, with a very legible announcement that it belonged to the surgeon. A few boys were making their way to the cricket-field; and two or three shopkeepers, who were standing at their doors, looked as if they should like to be making their way to the same spot, as indeed to all appearance they might have done, without losing any great amount of custom thereby. Mr Pickwick having paused to make these observations, to be noted down at a more convenient period, hastened to rejoin his friends, who had turned out of the main street, and were already within sight of the field of battle.

The wickets were pitched, and so were a couple of marquees for the rest and refreshment of the contending parties. The game had not yet commenced. Two or three Dingley Dellers and All-Muggletonians were amusing themselves with a majestic air by throwing the ball carelessly from hand to hand; and several other gentlemen dressed like them, in straw hats, flannel jackets, and white trousers – a costume in which they looked very much like amateur stone-masons – were sprinkled about the tents, towards one of which Mr Wardle conducted the party.

Several dozen of 'How-are-you's?' hailed the old gentleman's arrival; and a general rising of the straw hats, and bending forward of the flannel jackets, followed his introduction of his guests as gentlemen from London, who were extremely anxious to witness the proceedings of the day, with which, he had no doubt, they would be greatly delighted.

'You had better step into the marquee, I think, sir,' said one very stout gentleman, whose body and legs looked like half a gigantic roll of flannel, elevated on a couple of inflated pillow-cases.

'You'll find it much pleasanter, sir,' urged another stout gentleman, who strongly resembled the other half of the roll of flannel aforesaid.

'You're very good,' said Mr Pickwick.

'This way,' said the first speaker; 'they notch in here – it's the best place in the whole field;' and the cricketer, panting on before, preceded them to the tent.

'Capital game – smart spot – fine exercise – very,' were the words which fell upon Mr Pickwick's ear as he entered the tent; and the first object that met his eyes was his green-coated friend of the Rochester coach, holding forth, to the no small delight and edification of a select circle of the chosen of All-Muggleton. His dress was slightly improved, and he wore boots; but there was no mistaking him.

The stranger recognized his friends immediately; and, darting forward and seizing Mr Pickwick by the hand, dragged him to a seat with his usual impetuosity, talking all the while as if the whole of the arrangements were under his especial patronage and direction.

'This way – this way – capital fun – lots of beer – hogsheads; rounds of beef – bullocks; mustard – cart loads; glorious day – down with you – make yourself at home – Glad to see you – very.'

Mr Pickwick sat down as he was bid, and Mr Winkle and Mr Snodgrass also complied with the directions of their mysterious friend. Mr Wardle looked on in silent wonder.

'Mr Wardle – a friend of mine,' said Mr Pickwick..

'Friend of yours! – My dear sir, how are you? – Friend of *my* friend's – give me your hand, sir,' – and the stranger grasped Mr Wardle's hand with all the fervour of a close intimacy of many years, and then stepped back a pace or two as if to take a full survey of his face and figure, and then shook hands with him again, if possible more warmly than before.

'Well; and how came you here?' said Mr Pickwick, with a smile in which benevolence struggled with surprise.

'Come,' replied the stranger – 'stopping at Crown – Crown at Muggleton – met a party – flannel jackets – white trousers – anchovy sandwiches – devilled kidneys – splendid fellows – glorious.'

Mr Pickwick was sufficiently versed in the stranger's system of stenography to infer from this rapid and disjointed communication that he had, somehow or other, contracted an acquaintance with the All-Muggletons, which he had converted, by a process peculiar to himself, into that extent of good fellowship on which a general invitation may be easily founded. His curiosity was therefore satisfied, and putting on his spectacles he prepared himself to watch the play which was just commencing.

All-Muggleton had the first innings; and the interest became intense when Mr Dumkins and Mr Podder, two of the most renowned members of that most distinguished club, walked, bat in hand, to their respective wickets. Mr Luffey, the highest ornament of Dingley Dell, was pitched to bowl against the redoubtable Dumkins, and Mr Struggles was selected to do the same kind office for the hitherto unconquered Podder. Several players were stationed, to 'look out', in different parts of the field, and each fixed himself into the proper attitude by placing one hand on each knee, and stooping very much as if he were 'making a back' for some beginner at leap-frog. All the regular players do this sort of thing – indeed, it's generally supposed that it is quite impossible to look out properly in any other position.

The umpires were stationed behind the wickets; the scorers

were prepared to notch the runs; a breathless silence ensued. Mr Luffey retired a few paces behind the wicket of the passive Podder, and applied the ball to his right eye for several seconds. Dumkins confidently awaited its coming with his eyes fixed on the motions of Luffey.

'Play!' suddenly cried the bowler. The ball flew from his hand straight and swift towards the centre stump of the wicket. The wary Dumkins was on the alert; it fell upon the tip of his bat, and bounded far away over the heads of the scouts, who had just stooped low enough to let it fly over them.

'Run – run – another. – Now, then, throw her up – up with her – stop there – another – no – yes – no – throw her up, throw her up!' – Such were the shouts which followed the stroke, and at the conclusion of which All-Muggleton had scored two. Nor was Podder behindhand in earning laurels wherewith to garnish himself and Muggleton. He blocked the doubtful balls, missed the bad ones, took the good ones, and sent them flying to all parts of the field. The scouts were hot and tired; the bowlers were changed, and bowled till their arms ached; but Dumkins and Podder remained unconquered. Did an elderly gentleman essay to stop the progress of the ball, it rolled between his legs or slipped between his fingers. Did a slim gentleman try to catch it, it struck him on the nose, and bounded pleasantly off with redoubled violence, while the slim gentleman's eyes filled with water and his form writhed with anguish. Was it thrown straight up to the wicket, Dumkins had reached it before the ball. In short, when Dumkins was caught out, and Podder stumped out, All-Muggleton had notched some fifty-four, while the score of the Dingley Dellers was as blank as their faces. The advantage was too great to be recovered. In vain did the eager Luffey, and the enthusiastic Struggles, do all that skill and experience could suggest, to regain the ground Dingley Dell had lost in the contest – it was of no avail; and in an early period of the winning game Dingley Dell gave in, and allowed the superior prowess of All-Muggleton.

The stranger, meanwhile, had been eating, drinking, and talking, without cessation. At every good stroke he expressed his satisfaction and approval of the player in a most condescending and patronizing manner, which could not fail to have been highly gratifying to the party concerned; while at every bad attempt at a catch, and every failure to stop the ball, he launched his personal displeasure at the head of the devoted individual in such denunciations as – 'Ah, ah! – stupid' – 'Now, butter-fingers' – 'Muff' – 'Humbug' – and so forth – ejaculations which seemed to establish him in the opinion of all around as a most excellent and undeniable judge of the whole art and mystery of the noble game of cricket.

'Capital game – well played – some strokes admirable,' said the stranger, as both sides crowded into the tent at the conclusion of the game.

'You have played it, sir?' inquired Mr Wardle, who had been much amused by his loquacity.

'Played it! Think I have – thousands of times – not here – West Indies – exciting thing – hot work – very.'

'It must be rather a warm pursuit in such a climate,' observed Mr Pickwick.

'Warm! – red hot – scorching – glowing. Played a match once – single wicket – friend the Colonel – Sir Thomas Blazo – who should get the greatest number of runs. – Won the toss – first innings – seven o'clock a.m. – six natives to look out – went in; kept in – heat intense – natives all fainted – taken away – fresh half-dozen ordered – fainted also – Blazo bowling – supported by two natives – couldn't bowl me out – fainted too – cleared away the Colonel – wouldn't give in – faithful attendant – Quanko Samba – last man left – sun so hot, bat in blisters, ball scorched brown – five hundred and seventy runs – rather exhausted – Quanko mustered up last remaining strength – bowled me out – had a bath, and went out to dinner.'

'And what became of what's-his-name, sir?' inquired an old gentleman.

'Blazo?'

'No – the other gentleman.'

'Quanko Samba?'

'Yes, sir.'

'Poor Quanko – never recovered it – bowled on, on my account – bowled off, on his own – died, sir.' Here the stranger buried his countenance in a brown jug, but whether to hide his emotion or imbibe its contents we cannot distinctly affirm. We only know that he paused suddenly, drew a long and deep breath, and looked anxiously on, as two of the principal members of the Dingley Dell club approached Mr Pickwick, and said,—

'We are about to partake of a plain dinner at the Blue Lion, sir; we hope you and your friends will join us.'

'Of course,' said Mr Wardle, 'among our friends we include Mr—;' and he looked towards the stranger.

'Jingle,' said that versatile gentleman, taking the hint at once. 'Jingle – Alfred Jingle, Esq., of No Hall, Nowhere.'

'I shall be very happy, I am sure,' said Mr Pickwick.

'So shall I,' said Mr Alfred Jingle, drawing one arm through Mr Pickwick's, and another through Mr Wardle's, as he whispered confidentially in the ear of the former gentleman,—

'Devilish good dinner – cold, but capital – peeped into the room this morning – fowls and pies, and all that sort of thing – pleasant fellows these – well-behaved, too – very.'

from THE POSTHUMOUS PAPERS OF
THE PICKWICK CLUB
1837

EPILOGUE

A FAREWELL TO ARMS

by

Eric N. Simons

In Friendly Eleven *Eric N. Simons gives an affectionate yet realistic account of cricket in a Derbyshire village after the Second World War. This chapter, under this same title, is the final one in his book for, as the writer says, 'the saddest day in a cricketer's life had come to me, as come it must to us all'.*

I had had a shocking season. Nothing had gone right for me. My batting, never brilliant, had been a miserable failure, and my bowling like weak tea. Then, one day, I disgraced myself by muffing a couple of simple catches.

So egotistical, so tenacious in his grip upon the game, is your ageing cricketer that I might have been shameless enough to pretend to myself and others that this was a mere 'bad patch', a temporary lapse such as may come in any player's career. That same evening, however, sitting in the bus that takes our villagers to the 'pictures' in the market town on Saturdays, I overheard two sentences that told me the truth.

Walt and Bill got in and sat down, never seeing me in my shadowy corner. They began to discuss the afternoon's game. At first their voices were low, but in the interest of the discussions rose a trifle. Walter mentioned my name, saying:

'Ay, th'old chap's past it. They'd drop him, I reckon, if it weren't for hurtin' his feelings. You might get your place in the team regularly then, Bill. You've done well this season, considering the few chances you've had.'

What Bill replied I shall never know, for at that moment Jenny, behind them, leaned over and whispered something. I suspect she warned them I was on the bus, for they gave a hasty look round, their voices fell again, and I heard no more. I had heard enough. I pretended to have heard nothing, of course, and when I got out smiled kindly at the two young men, bidding them good evening in what I hope was my pleasantest manner.

I knew now what I had to do. All my life I had said that when I fell away, and found myself keeping a good youngster out of the side, I would retire. I had still the bitterest memories of old Garber, who for years when I was a youth kept me out of the side because he would not admit decrepitude. Yet like him, like thousands before me, like the Bishop in *Gil Blas*, I had refused in my turn to admit waning powers, the onset of old age. I had ignored those rheumaticky twinges in my knee; the pain in the chest that sometimes came over me when I ran a sharp three; the weariness after and sometimes during the game; the stiffness that from time to time, when I bowled, made my shoulder stick a little, so that my arm, instead of coming well over, seemed to be checked half-way, the ball flying out of my hand in a direction totally different from my desire. I had ignored the frequent 'ducks' against my name; the mounting tally of wides; the fours I was not fast enough to stop; now the catches my dimming eyes made me let fall were yet another signal.

I repeat, I knew what I had to do, and when I returned home went straight to my desk and did it. I wrote to old John Bowles:

'Dear John, – After next Saturday's match, if I am picked for it despite my deplorable exhibition today, I intend to retire permanently from the game. I have realized at last what I ought to have realized long ago, that I am not now worth my place in the side. In fairness to our younger men, it is time I gave up. You will know what this decision means to a cricketer, having had to make it yourself. All I need add is that I have loved my games with the team, and shall take with me into retirement only the happiest memories of you all. I shall continue, of course, to support the Club in every possible way. Henceforward you will see me, I hope, every Saturday in the watchers' bench with the old men under the wall, for a seat among whom I have by now surely qualified. Yours sincerely, —.

On the Wednesday evening my telephone rang, and the gruff voice of John Bowles sounded:

'I got your letter,' he announced baldly.

'Oh, yes?'

'Ay, well, am I to take it serious?'

'Of course, John!'

'Has t'Club offended you in any way?'

'No, no! Every word of my letter's sincere, John. It's just *anno domini*, old man! It comes to us all, and I've had a good innings. Saturday taught me my lesson.'

'Well, I'm very sorry! All t'Committee will be when I put this before them.'

'Nice of you to say so, John!'

'You're sure you won't change your mind; sure it's nothing someone's been sayin'? 'Cause you don't want to take any notice of—'

'My mind's quite made up, and it isn't pique or anything.'

'Oh, well, I'm glad of that! You'll play o' Saturday, though, if you're picked?'

'Like a shot! I want to turn out once more with the team, and have a last knock.'

'Ay, well, I reckon that'll be all right. I'm very sorry. It'll not be like t'same team without you.'

Poor old John! It was difficult for him on the one hand to express his genuine personal regret at the ending of a cricketer's career – an event whose painfulness he understood only too well – and on the other to conceal the relief he, as a competent Secretary, must have felt at this solution of what was rapidly becoming a problem. Village cricketers are too kindly to drop you with abruptness at the end of your career. If I had not forestalled them, what would have happened, I believe, is this.

I should have been allowed to play through the season. Then, at our annual 'do', two or three of the older members: John, Frank, Old George, and possibly 'Captain' Jim, would have constituted themselves an unofficial deputation. They would have come and sat beside me, stood me a drink, offered me a cigarette and a light, and talked to me for a time about the weather, the crops, my neighbours and theirs. Then, by degrees, they would have brought the conversation round to cricket, and gently, kindly, insinuated into my mind the suggestion that Bill and Walt were much improved players; that I hadn't had a great deal of 'luck' this season past; that it was difficult nowadays to know whom to leave out; and at last, delicately: Might it not be advisable for me, next year, to take more frequent 'rests'; 'save myself' for the really big matches?

I should have known what they meant, and they would have known that I knew, and been terribly embarrassed. I had saved them all that, and John was grateful.

On the Saturday of my last game, it seemed to me that ironically the sun shone as it had never shone before, sharpening and intensifying my grief. I dressed slowly for the game. My wife had put out my very best flannels, beautifully clean and smart. To my surprise she had whitened boots and belt for me also, which touched me deeply, for it showed she knew what I was feeling, and was in sympathy with me. I went to thank her, but she must have heard me coming, for she promptly slipped away into a neighbour's house, knowing I would not follow.

I took my bat out of its bag, and looked at its poor old face, scarred and dented, yet good for many a hundred in the right hands. For the first time I appreciated it as a superfluity, a luxury to which I no longer had a right. My flannels I could still use after cricket was over. My spiked boots would serve, perhaps, in the garden. But my bat? Is there anything more useless to a man than his bat when all his innings are over? To sell it would go against the grain, and to keep is as a memento would be a waste. No, I would give it to one of the lads who replaced me. That, I felt, would be fitting, and with so good a weapon he might surpass even his present promise, for a good bat, as this was, often serves its master better than he knows.

At the usual time I walked gravely with my bag out into the lane. Truly the sun was magnificent, and the sky a lucent blue. There was a zizzing of grasshoppers and a twittering of birds. A scythe was swishing in a meadow, and a little boy was whistling somewhere out of sight. I looked back, and saw my wife, the neighbour behind her, peeping at me through the window of the next house. She saw I had detected them, waved and smiled, her upper lip a shade stiff, so that I knew she understood, and was trying to hide the effect understanding had upon her. I waved back, and made my wave as careless and casual as I could, knowing all the time the pretence deceived nobody.

When I reached the cricket field, it seemed to me, though perhaps I was wrong, that everyone greeted me with unusual warmth. In the pavilion my team-mates looked at me, looked away again, made trivial comments about the wicket and the day, then found excuses for going outside.

'Captain' Jim came in presently, and said: 'We're batting!'

'Good!' I responded. 'It's a real batsman's wicket today. We ought to get a couple of hundred easily.'

Jim seemed to be struggling to express some unusual idea.

'Get your pads on!' he blurted out at last.

I looked round thinking Bob or Young George must have come in, but we were alone, and I gasped: 'Do you mean *me*?'

'Yes. I've had a word with Bob and Young George, and the rest, and as it's your last game, we'd all like you to open for us.'

It was something I had wanted to do all my life, and never been good enough to achieve. In what moment of rashness and to whom had I confided this deep desire? Village memories are long, and someone had stored up that random remark in his mind, not in scorn or cynicism, but to pleasure me in my old age. The hut blurred suddenly. I turned my back and began to put on my pads.

When Bob and I walked out together there was an unusually prolonged burst of clapping from all sides of the ground. Even the old men under the wall were smacking their palms together with unwonted energy and unanimity.

'This is for *thee*, tha knows!' said Bob, half-smiling, but discreetly averting his eyes.

Some unknown, aged throat cried out: 'good owd —! Glog 'em, owd lad!'

'I shall be out first ball if this goes on,' I said. 'I can hardly see a thing.'

'Tha'll be all reight when t'time cooms,' Bob replied. 'Ah'll tak' t'battin' end, an' that'll gi'e thee time.'

If I were a liar, I should relate how youth returned to me, and I smote the bowling hip and thigh, returning to the pavilion with a glorious fifty to my credit. No such thing happened. I did not make fifty. On the other hand, I did not get a duck. Actually my score was ten, a ten whose shakiness the numerals in the scorebook will never reveal. Then I received a fast one that swung late and sent my off stump flying. So ended my last 'knock'.

'Hard luck, owd lad!' said a spectator as I came away. There were more handclaps, and some shy, fleeting smiles from my pals. A little boy cried: 'That wer' thi last innin's, warn't it, mester?'

'Not a bad little last effort, that, I must say!' said Johnny, and Arthur, the wag, added: 'Shall I shove a o after it in t'book? Then tha can tear t'sheet out after t'game, an' frame it.'

I wasn't needed for bowling, because Harry and Bowler Jim, Sam and Young George did all that was necessary in that way. 'Captain' Jim 'hid' me very successfully at point, and by the grace of God, no chances came my way, so that I did not suffer shame in this my last match. We won the game; Old George put the bails in his pocket; and all at once our fellows ran for the stumps, each tearing one out of the earth and bolting with it back to the hut. I was left alone to move slowly off the pitch, Old George in my wake.

I did not understand this sudden flight, but began to walk back hoping I looked reasonably dignified and not too ancient, and feeling my heart sink at every step.

As I drew near the pavilion there was a scurry and scutter. My team-mates, with old John Bowles, Frank, Old Norman, and even old Webb, lined up in two rows, creating a kind of triumphal arch with elevated stumps and bats. Through this I was compelled to walk. There was a final outbreak of clapping, and as I emerged from the arch and passed into the hut, my colleagues, the Committee, some small boys, and an indeterminate number of spectators, started to give me three cheers . . .

I don't wish to dwell unduly on that last gesture, nor on the farewells that were said to me, the handshakes and pats on the back. I remember that I sat on the narrow bench in the pavilion, while one by one my friends drifted off homewards, leaving me there. Old Norman came to lock up, took a look at me, and said quietly:

'Lock t'door when th'art ready, will ta? An' let me 'ave t'key later on.'

I nodded, and saw his head go by the aperture as he went on his way down the hill. After a time I could tell I was alone. I picked up my bag, locked the door of the hut behind me, and stood looking at the pitch and the ground, green and tranquil in the soft light.

Happy memories came into my mind: that Saturday when, rising on tiptoe, I brought my bat down on a fast ball to the off, and cracked it past point for a four along the ground, leaving the fielders standing; the match in which I did the hat-trick, all three clean bowled, and four wickets in five balls; the day when I bowled unchanged for an hour against a Yorkshire Council batsman who had had a trial for Yorkshire, and though I did not get his wicket had negligible runs scored off me, and received his praise as we walked off at the end of the innings.

Over yonder was the very spot where, running at full speed on the boundary, I once brilliantly caught out Z, an old County player, at the top of his form that day. That bare patch on the far side of the pitch had actually been made by my heels in bowling. On this stretch of smooth turf I had stood and chatted, chaffed Old George, run and sweated and toiled. And it was all over.

When next I appeared on the ground I should be in ordinary clothes, moving without urgency, having no part in the drama; one of the 'old 'uns', soon to be a decaying recollection. It did not seem possible!

I had only to look inwards, and the entire field became alive again with white, and I important in it. That inward re-creation was all I had to look forward to now. From this day on cricket for me would be pure spectacle, something that went on without me, influenced in no way whatsoever by my personality and will. Never again should I feel that slight qualm, that tremor of uncertainty, when put on by the Captain, with six runs wanted to win, and two good last men well set at the wickets, the spectators tensely silent, all their hope and desire centred on me as I ran up to bowl; never again return to the pavilion, bat under arm, with a crackle of applause running like a moorland fire round the ground, touching my cap in acknowledgement, and watching a delighted urchin fumble for a nine to put after the three of my 39. Never again should I see out of the corner of my eye the ball hit terrifically hard to one side of me, fling my hand out, feel my fingers close over it, and hold, Oh God, *hold* it! Never again sit in the doorway of the hut with my pads on, the sun warm on my face, waiting to bat; never feel the smooth surface of a new ball under my crisping fingers, and the hard impress of the seam upon my flesh; never fret and fume at rain-clouds drifting over the hill . . .

There may have been tears in my eyes, for I remember putting my hand in my pocket and bringing out a grubby handkerchief, which I applied to them. I looked and looked, unable to tear myself away; but at long last I turned and walked through the stile, out of that home of joyous memories, out of our cricket field with all it held for me of life and laughter and rich recollections, out of our greatest game, and so, regretfully, out of this book.

from FRIENDLY ELEVEN
1950

APPENDIX

CRICKET IN FICTION

A checklist compiled by
Gerald Brodribb

This list – which is a revised, updated version of Gerald Brodribb's publication 'Cricket in Fiction' (the Mountjoy Press, Canford, 1950, Limited Edition) – is not exhaustive or complete, but it does aim to represent fairly what has been written and published. For an explanation of the different sections, please see the Editor's Introduction above, pages vii – xi.

CRICKET NOVELS

Adrian Alington *The Amazing Test Match Crime* Chatto & Windus 1939
Phoebe Allen *The Cricket Club, or warned just in time* SPCK 1884
Stella Bingham *Charters & Caldicott* BBC 1985
Dudley Carew *The Son of Grief* Arthur Barker 1936
J. L. Carr *A Season in Sinji* Alan Ross 1967
Dennis Castle *Run out the Raj* Constable (reissue) 1986
Douglas Clark *The Libertines* Gollancz 1978
Robert Crampsey *The Run-Out* Richard Drew 1985
Hugh de Selincourt *The Cricket Match* Cape 1924
Hugh de Selincourt *The Saturday Match* Dent 1937
Ted Dexter & Clifford Makins *Testkill* Allen & Unwin 1976
Richard Digance *Run out in the Country* Macmillan 1984
Justin Dowling *Clean Bandage* Elek Books 1963

William Godfrey *Malleson at Melbourne* Museum Press 1956
William Godfrey *The Friendly Game* M. Joseph 1957
Sir Home Gordon *That Test Match* Duckworth 1921
Francesca Grant *Caught and Bowled* Wright 1888
Bruce Hamilton *Pro: An English Tragedy* Cresset Press 1946
Mollie Hardwick *Willowwood* Methuen 1980
Charles Hatton *Maiden Over* Long 1955
Jack Hobbs *The Test Match Surprise* Readers Library 1926
Harold Hobson *The Devil in Woodford Wells* Longmans 1946
Horace G. Hutchinson *Peter Steele, the Cricketer* Arrowsmith/Simpkin 1895
M. D. Lyon *A Village Match and After* Nash & Grayson 1929
Mike Marqusee *Slow Turn* Michael Joseph 1986
Alan Miller *Close of Play* St Hugh's Press 1949
Maurice Moiseiwitch *A Sky-Blue Life* Heinemann 1956
Christopher Nixon *The Tour: a novel* Reed (Sydney) 1973
Barry Norman *Sticky Wicket* Hodder & Stoughton 1984
'An Old Boy' *Adventures of a Cricket Ball* Ward, Lock 1860
John Parker *The Village Cricket Match* Weidenfeld 1977
John Parker *Test Time at Tillingfold* Weidenfeld 1979
John Parker *Tillingfold's Four* W.H. Allen 1986
John Parker *First Wicket Down* W.H. Allen 1988
D. Petri *Horton's Test* Rotabook 1983
Susan Pleydell *Jethro's Mill* Collins 1974
Simon Raven *Close of Play* Blond 1962
Denys Roberts *The Elwood Wager* Methuen 1957
Stanley Shaw *Sherlock Holmes at the 1902 Fifth Test* W.H. Allen 1985
Eric N. Simons *Friendly Eleven* T. Werner Laurie 1950
A.C.H. Smith *Extra Cover* Weidenfeld 1981
J.C. Snaith *Willow the King: the story of a cricket match* Ward, Lock 1899
Frank Stuart *Never so Young Again* Stanley Paul 1953
Allen Synge *Bowler, Batsman, Spy* Weidenfeld 1985
G. Appleby Terrill *Out in the Glare* Chambers 1927
Paul Wheeler *Bodyline, the novel* Faber & Faber 1983
Peter Stanley Williams *The Pantybont Challenge* New Horizon 1984

NOVELS CONTAINING ELEMENTS OR EPISODES OF CRICKET

Cyril Alington *Blackmail in Blankshire* Faber 1949
Cyril Alington *Mr Evans: a cricketo-detective story* Macmillan 1922
Anthony Armstrong *Patrick, Undergraduate* Stanley Paul 1926
Frank Baker *My Friend, the Enemy* Boardman 1948
R. C. Gorell Barnes *Warrior's Way* John Murray 1945
J. M. Barrie *The Little White Bird* Hodder & Stoughton 1902
Denzil Batchelor *The Test Match Murder* Angus & Robertson 1936
Cuthbert Bede *Mr Verdant Green* Blackwood 1853
Josephine Bell *Death at Half-term* Longman's 1939
Vicars Bell *Death has Two Doors* Faber 1950
E. F. Benson *David Blaize* Hodder & Stoughton 1916
J. D. Beresford *The Hampdenshire Wonder* Sidgwick & Jackson 1911
Nicholas Blake *A Question of Proof* Collins 1935
Ivor Brown *Years of Plenty* Martin Secker 1915
Edward Bucknell *Linden Lea* Williams & Norgate 1925
Alan Clutton-Brock *Murder at Liberty Hall* John Lane 1941
John Creasey *The Mark of the Crescent* Melrose 1935
John Creasey *A Six for the Toff* Hodder & Stoughton 1955
David Scott Daniel *Morning's at Seven* Cape 1940
Charles Dickens *The Posthumous Papers of the Pickwick Club* Chapman & Hall 1837
E. R. Eddison *A Fish Dinner in Memison* Dutton 1941
George Macdonald Fraser *Flashman's Lady* Barrie & Jenkins 1977
B. & C. B. Fry *A Mother's Son* Methuen 1907
Roy Fuller *The Ruined Boys* Deutsch 1959
Andrew Garve *Death and the Sky Above* Collins 1953
Michael Gilbert *The Night of the Twelfth* Hodder & Stoughton 1976
John Hadfield *Love on a Branch Line* Hutchinson 1959
L. P. Hartley *The Go-Between* Hamish Hamilton 1953

Ian Hay *Pip: A Romance of Youth* Blackwood 1907
Ronald Hingley *Up Jenkins!* Longmans 1956
Eileen Hollands *Never Marry a Cricketer* Quill Publications 1974
Christopher Hollis *Death of a Gentleman* Burns, Oates 1943
Chistopher Hollis *Fossett's Memory* Hollis & Carter 1944
Christopher Hollis *Letters to a Sister* Hollis & Carter 1944
E. W. Hornung *Fathers of Men* Smith, Elder 1912
E. W. Hornung *Mr Justice Raffles* Smith, Elder 1909
Thomas Hughes *Tom Brown's Schooldays* Macmillan 1857
Geoffrey Household *Fellow Passenger* Michael Joseph 1955
H. G. Hutchinson *Creatures of Circumstance* Longmans 1891
R. C. Hutchinson *The Unforgotten Prisoner* Cassell 1933
Herbert Jenkins *The Return of Alfred* Herbert Jenkins c. 1920
James Joyce *Portrait of the Artist as a Young Man* Egoist Press 1917
James W. Kenyon *Peter Trant, Cricketer-Detective* Methuen 1944
Lou King-Hall (Mrs Desmond Eagar) *Fly, Envious Time* Peter Davies 1944
Shane Leslie *The Oppidan* Chatto & Windus 1922
A. G. Macdonell *England, Their England* Macmillan 1933
A. G. Macdonell *How Like an Angel!* Macmillan 1934
Denis Mackail *The Flower Show* Heinemann 1927
Denis Mackail *We're Here* Hutchinson 1947
J. J. Marric (John Creasey) *Gideon's Sport* Hodder & S. 1970
Bruce Marshall *Prayer for the Living* Gollancz 1934
J. C. Masterman *Fate cannot Harm Me* Gollancz 1935
Helen Mathers *Comin' Thro' the Rye* Bentley 1875
George Meredith *The Ordeal of Richard Feverel* Chapman & Hall 1859
George Meredith *Evan Harrington* Bradbury 1861
George Meredith *The Adventures of Harry Richmond* Smith, Elder 1871
George Meredith *Diana of the Crossways* Chapman & Hall 1885
Laurence Meynell *Hooky and the Prancing Horse* Macmillan 1980

Osmington Mills *No Match for the Law* Bles 1957
John Moore *The Blue Field* Collins 1948
John Moore *Brensham Village* Collins 1946
John Moore *The White Sparrow* Collins 1954
Charles Morgan *Portrait in a Mirror* Macmillan 1929
R. K. Narayan *Swami and Friends* Hamish Hamilton 1935
Bernard Newman *Death at Lord's* Gollancz 1952
E. Phillips Oppenheim *The Missioner* Ward, Lock 1908
Eric Parker *Playing Fields* Philip Allan 1922
Hal Pink *The Test Match Mystery* Hutchinson 1940
Lionel Portman *Hugh Rendal* Alston Rivers 1905
James Pycroft *Elkerton Rectory* Booth 1860
E. & M. A. Radford *Murder isn't Cricket* Melrose 1946
Simon Raven *Fielding Gray* Blond 1967
Ernest Raymond *Tell England* Cassell 1922
Ernest Raymond *To the Wood No More* Cassell 1954
Talbot Baines Reed *The Fifth Form at St Dominic's* Religious Tract Society 1881
Randal Roberts *Curb and Snaffle* F. V. White 1888
Michael Sadleir *Desolate Splendour* Constable 1923
Siegfried Sassoon *Memoirs of a Fox-hunting Man* Faber 1928
Dorothy L. Sayers *Murder Must Advertise* Gollancz 1933
Osbert Sitwell *Before the Bombardment* Duckworth 1926
C. P. Snow *Death Under Sail* Heinemann 1932/1959
Nancy Spain *Death before Wicket* Hutchinson 1946
Julian Symons *Bland Beginning* Gollancz 1949
Alfred Tack *The Test-Match Murder* Herbert Jenkins 1948
A. A. Thomson *The Exquisite Burden* Herbert Jenkins 1935
Edward Thompson *Lament for Adonis* Benn 1932
Edward Thompson *Introducing the Arnisons* Macmillan 1935
Anthony Trollope *The Fixed Period* Blackwood 1882
Charles Turley *Godfrey Marten, Undergraduate* Heinemann 1904
H. A. Vachell *The Hill* John Murray 1905
Rex Warner *Escapade* Bodley Head 1953
Alec Waugh *The Loom of Youth* Grant Richards 1917
H. G. Wells *You Can't be too Careful* Secker & Warburg 1941
P. G. Wodehouse *Psmith in the City* Black 1910

Barbara Worsley-Gough *Alibi Innings* Michael Joseph 1954
Dornford Yates *The Berry Scene* Ward, Lock 1947

STORY COLLECTIONS BY A SINGLE AUTHOR

C. W. Alcock *Cricket Stories: Wise and otherwise* Arrowsmith 1901
A. E. Bayley and Walter Briscoe *Chronicles of a Country Club* Sands 1900
Horace Bleackley *Tales of the Stumps* Ward, Lock 1901
Horace Bleackley *More Tales of the Stumps* Ward, Lock 1902
Walter Briscoe *Cricket Love and Humour: Tales told of balls bowled* Grafton 1921
A. Clitheroe *Silly Point* Duckworth 1939
A. H. J. Cochrane *Told in the Pavilion* Arrowsmith 1896
Anthony Crouch *Memoirs of a Twelfth Man* Crowood Press 1984
Hugh de Selincourt *The Game of the Season* Chapman & Hall 1931
Horace G. Hutchinson *Cricketing Saws and Stories* Longmans 1889
Charles Igglesden *The Demon Eleven, and other cricket stories* Kentish Express 1901
R. T. Johnstone *Century of a Lifetime* Macmillan 1956
G. H. Milner-Pugh *The Bowler of the Season* Simpkin Marshall 1907
Barry Perowne *Raffles of the M.C.C.* Macmillan 1979
Dal Stivens *The Demon Bowler and other cricket stories* Outback Press 1979
Peter Tinniswood *Tales from a Long Room* Arrow 1981
Peter Tinniswood *More Tales from a Long Room* Arrow 1982
Peter Tinniswood *Collected Tales from a Long Room* Hutchinson 1982
Peter Tinniswood *The Brigadier Down Under* Macmillan 1983
Peter Tinniswood *The Brigadier in Season* Macmillan 1984
Peter Tinniswood *Tales from Witney Scrotum* Joseph 1987

Graham White *Cricket on Saturday* Sporting Handbooks 1947
Graham White *Cricket in Benfield* Stanley Paul 1960
E. B. V. Christian (ed.) *The Light Side of Cricket* Bowden 1898
(no editor) *Twenty-five Cricket Stories* Newnes 1909

INDIVIDUAL STORIES

Jeffrey Archer 'The Century' from *A Quiver Full of Arrows* Hodder & Stoughton 1980
John Arlott 'A Cup of Cold Tea' from *Great Short Stories from the World of Sport* Heinemann 1960
John Arlott 'Not 'Arf a Blooming Game' from *Best Cricket Stories* (ed. Denzil Batchelor) Faber 1967
Anthony Armstrong 'Our Cricket Match' from *Warriors at Ease* Methuen 1926
Stacy Aumonier 'The Match' from *Miss Bracegirdle, and others* Heinemann 1929
H. C. Bailey 'The Young God' from *Mr Fortune's Casebook*, printed in *Sporting Detective Stories*, ed. Ellery Queen Faber 1946
Denzil Batchelor 'Outsider and Son' from *Days without Sunset* Eyre & Spottiswoode 1949
Denzil Batchelor 'The Greenford Novice' and 'The Novice: Down Under' from *The Game Goes On* Eyre & Spottiswoode 1947
Hon. Arthur Bligh 'A Draco of Cricket' from *Crotchets and Foibles* Arrowsmith/Simpkin 1903
James Bridie 'The Cricket Match' The Spectator 1950
W. A. Darlington 'The Guardian Angel' from *My Funniest Story* Faber 1932
Arthur Conan Doyle 'How He Triumphed in England' from *Adventures of Gerard* Newnes 1903
Arthur Conan Doyle 'The Story of Spedegue's Dropper' from *The Maracot Deep* John Murray 1929
Lord Dunsany 'How Jembu Played for Cambridge' from *Best*

Sporting Stories ed. J. Wentworth Day   Faber 1942

Herbert Farjeon 'Herecombe v. Therecombe' and 'More about Herecombe and Therecombe' from *Herbert Farjeon's Cricket Bag*   Macdonald 1946

J. S. Fletcher 'Won on the Last Wicket' from *Best Sporting Stories* ed. J. Wentworth Day   Faber 1942

Brian Glanville 'Up She Jolly Goes!' from *Love is not Love*   Blond 1985 (Titled here, 'Keeping a straight bat')

Harry Graham 'Biffin on Acquaintances' from *A Century of Humour*   Hutchinson 1934

Frederick Grisewood 'The Village Cricket Match' from *Our Bill*   Harrap 1934

E. W. Hornung 'Gentlemen and Players'; 'The Ides of March'; and 'Le premier pas' from *Raffles: The Amateur Cracksman*   Methuen 1899

E. W. Hornung 'Chrystal's Century'; 'The power of the game'; and 'A Bowler's Innings' from *Old Offenders and a few old scores*   John Murray 1923

(C. F. Johnstone) 'Eton v. Harrow' (story) from *Recollections of Eton, by An Etonian*   Chapman & Hall 1870

Margaret Hughes 'Alice at Lord's, 1952' from *All on a Summer's Day*   Stanley Paul 1953

H. R. F. Keating 'Caught and Bowled, Mrs Craggs' from *John Creasey's Crime Collection 1981*   Gollancz 1981

E. V. Lucas 'The Wager' from *Landmarks*   Methuen 1914

A. G. Macdonell 'A Love Match'; 'Dingley Dell v. All-Muggleton'; and 'Those Were the Days' from *The Spanish Pistol and other stories*   Macmillan 1939

A. A. Milne 'A Few Wires' from *The Day's Play*   Methuen 1910

Reginald Ottley 'An Outback Cricket Match from *A Question of Horses*   Collins 1973

Ian Peebles 'A Question of Policy' from *Batter's Castle*   Souvenir Press 1958

Ian Peebles 'The Double-cross Bat' from *Talking of Cricket*   Museum Press 1953

N. S. Phadke 'Thy Name is Burden' from *Best Cricket Stories* ed. Denzil Batchelor   Faber 1967

Maurice Richardson 'Engelbrecht and the Demon Bowler' from

Exploits of Engelbrecht Phoenix House 1950
Richard Stilgoe 'The Cricket Match' from *The Richard Stilgoe Letters* Allen & Unwin 1982
Julian Symons 'Test Match Murder' from *Murder! Murder!* Fontana 1961
A. A. Thomson 'The Pride of the Popping Crease' from *Bumbledinky* Mills & Boon 1925
Byron Webber 'Pigskin and Willow' from *Pigskin and Willow* James Hogg 1883
A. M. Wells 'Last Over!' from *All This is Ended* Melrose 1936

NOVELS AND STORIES WITH SCHOOL SETTINGS AND INCIDENTAL CRICKET

A) Written mainly for adult readers
E. F. Benson *David Blaize* Hodder & Stoughton 1916
Nicholas Blake *A Question of Proof* Collins 1935
Ivor Brown *Years of Plenty* Secker 1915
J. L. Carr *The Harpole Report* Quartet Books 1973
Nigel Foxell *Schoolboy Rising* Dobson 1973
Roy Fuller *The Ruined Boys* Deutsch 1959
Michael Gilbert *The Night of the Twelfth* Hodder and Stoughton 1976
E. W. Hornung *Fathers of Men* Smith, Elder 1912
Thomas Hughes *Tom Brown's Schooldays* Macmillan 1857
Helen Mathers *Comin' Thro' the Rye* Bentley 1875
Eric Parker *Playing Fields* Philip Allan 1922
Lionel Portman *Hugh Rendal* Alston Rivers 1905
Esmond Quinterley *Ushering Interlude* Fortune Press 1936
Simon Raven *Fielding Gray* Blond 1967
Ernest Raymond *Tell England* Cassell 1922
Randal Roberts *Curb and Snaffle* F. V. White 1888
A. A. Thomson *The Exquisite Burden* Herbert Jenkins 1935
H. A. Vachell *The Hill* John Murray 1905
Alec Waugh *The Loom of Youth* Grant Richards 1917
H. G. Wells *You Can't be too Careful* Secker & Warburg 1941
P. G. Wodehouse *Mike: A Public School Story* Black 1909

B) Written mainly for younger readers

Robert Bateman *Young Cricketer* Constable 1959
Tom Bevan *One of the Awkward Squad* Nisbet 1912
Edmund Boyd *Wanderlust's Third Innings* Collins 1953
Dorita Fairlie Bruce *The Best Bat in the School* Oxford U.P. 1931
Mary Grant Bruce *Mates at Billabong* Ward, Lock 1913
Anthony Buckeridge *According to Jennings* Collins 1954
Rob Childs *Sanford in to Bat* Blackie 1985
Hylton Cleaver *The Harley First XI* Oxford U.P. 1920
Hylton Cleaver *The Old Order: a public school story* Oxford U.P. 1922
Hylton Cleaver *Lawson for Lord's* Warne 1950
Frank Elias *The Shadow on the School* Lutterworth 1922
John Finnemore *Teddy Lester, Captain of Cricket* Chambers 1916
Brian Flynn *Tragedy at Trinket* Nelson 1934
Antonia Forest *The Cricket Team* Faber 1974
Jeff Granville *The Schoolboy Test Cricketer* Patrick Johns 1958
Gunby Hadath *Schoolboy Grit* Nisbet 1913
Gunby Hadath *The Bridgehead* Oxford U.P. 1945
Michael Hardcastle *The Gigantic Hit* Pelham Books 1982
Michael Hardcastle *Caught Out* Methuen 1983
Edward R. Home-Gall *A Prince of the Willow* Hennel Locke 1950
J. B. Hobbs *Between the Wickets* Black 1926
G. A. Hope *Kerr of Castleburgh* Shaw 1913
Harry Huntingdon *An Uphill Game* Warne 1913
John C. Hutcheson *Our Scratch Eleven* Blackie 1896
Gilbert Jessop *Arthur Peck's Sacrifice: A Tale of Leckenham School* Nelson 1920
Gilbert Jessop *Cresley of Cressingham* Cassell 1924
(C.F. Johnstone) *Recollections of Eton, by An Etonian* Chapman & Hall 1870
J. H. Byron Lewis *Molly's Chance* Nelson 1926
Eric Leyland *The Cricket Week Mystery* Ward, Lock 1950
George Mills *King Willow* Harrap 1938
Dorothea Moore *The New Girl* Nisbet 1918

David Morris *A Name Dishonoured* Edmund Ward 1946
Gareth Owen *The Final Test* Gollancz 1985
St John Pearce *Off His Own Bat* Ward, Lock 1921
Michael Pearson *Splashers* Methuen 1987
Patrick Pringle *The Missing Cricketer* Evans 1952
Talbot Baines Reed *The Fifth Form at St Dominic's* Religious Tract Society 1887
Jo Rice *Mortimer Also* World's Work 1968
Frank Richards *Cardew's Catch* Spring Books 1960
Gary Sobers *Bonaventure and the Flashing Blade* Pelham 1967
Howard Spring *Darkie & Co.* Oxford U.P. 1932
John Sweet *Bellamy Comes Back* Oxford U.P. 1930
Reginald Taylor *Wings over Tewkesley* Bodley Head 1955
Charles Turley *Godfrey Marten, Schoolboy* Heinemann 1902
Charles Turley *The Left-hander* Oxford U.P. 1930
Rowland Walker *Pepper's Crack Eleven* Nelson 1925
P. G. Wodehouse *A Prefect's Uncle* Black 1903 n.e.1924

BOYS' MAGAZINES AND SERIALS

There are a great number of cricket stories, often very lively and unusual, in the serials such as those issued by the Amalgamated Press. I have made a list of some sixty of these, and the authors include 'Richard Randolph' (J. N. Pentelow), Charles Hamilton (the real name of 'Frank Richards'), and there is even one story attributed to 'Walter Hammond, England's famous Test cricketer'.

There are also many stories to be found in such productions as *The Captain*, *C.B. Fry's Magazine*, *The Magnet* and *The Gem*. See the article by L.E.S. Gutteridge in *The Cricketer*, 25 April 1959. See also Chapter 5 of *A Walk to the Wicket* by Ted Dexter and David Lemmon (Allen & Unwin, 1984); *Sing all a Green Willow* by Ronald Mason (Epworth Press, 1967); *At the Sign of the Wicket: Essays on the Glorious Game* by E.B.V. Christian (Arrowsmith, 1894); and *Play Up and Play the Game* by Patrick Howarth (Eyre Methuen, 1973).

Acknowledgements

The editor and the publishers would like to thank the following authors and publishers for permitting the reproduction of copyright material in this book:

Mr Jeffrey Archer and Hodder & Stoughton Ltd for 'The Century' from *A Quiver Full of Arrows*;

Mr E. R. Dexter and Mr Clifford Makins, and Unwin Hyman Ltd, for 'Byron's faultless strokeplay' from *Testkill*;

Mr Mike Marqusee and Michael Joseph Ltd for 'A very personal form of attack' from *Slow Turn*;

Pitman Publishing for 'The Double-cross bat' from *Talking of Cricket* by the late Ian Peebles;

The estate of the author and Chatto & Windus Ltd for the extract from *The Amazing Test Match Crime* by Adrian Alington;

The estate of the late Dudley Carew for 'Northshire v. Downshire: first day' from *The Son of Grief* (Arthur Barker Ltd);

The estate of Bruce Hamilton for the extract from *Pro: An English Tragedy* (The Cresset Press);

Mr Nigel Hollis and the estate of the late Christopher Hollis for 'My hour on the stage' from *Death of a Gentleman* (Burns, Oates);

Macmillan, London and Basingstoke for 'A Lancashire Triumph' by the late Cyril Alington from his novel *Mr Evans*;

Sidgwick & Jackson Ltd for 'Ginger Stott's Genius' from *The Hampdenshire Wonder* by the late J.D. Beresford;

John Farquharson Ltd for 'We want Jessop!' from *The Exquisite Burden* by the late A. A. Thomson;

W. H. Allen Publishers for 'I took up Rhodes' bat' from *Sherlock Holmes at the 1902 Fifth Test* by Mr Stanley Shaw;

Methuen & Co. Ltd for 'Versus Australia' by the late B. and C.B. Fry from *A Mother's Son*;

Mr George Macdonald Fraser for 'Rugby v. Kent' from *Flashman's Lady* (Barrie & Jenkins/Pan Books);

Herbert Jenkins Ltd, now Century Hutchinson, for 'Mike at the nets' by the late P.G. Wodehouse from *Mike: A Public School Story*. The first part of this book was later retitled and reissued as *Mike at Wrykyn*; the second part as *Mike and Psmith*, and later *Enter Psmith.*

The estate of the author, and the Hogarth Press, for 'Ten to make. . .' from *David Blaize* by the late E.F. Benson;

The Tessa Sayle Agency for the extract from 'The Magnet' no. 914. Copyright © 1988 Fleetway Publications Ltd;

Mr Alec Waugh and Methuen London for the extract from *The Loom of Youth*;

Mrs Sheila Ferrar for 'Return of a hero' from *Prayer for the Living* by the late Bruce Marshall;

Mr R.K. Narayan and William Heinemann Ltd for 'The "M.C.C." ' from *Swami and Friends*;

John Murray Ltd for 'The Last of the grand old series' from *Warrior's Way* by Lord Gorell;

Mr Brian Glanville and Anthony Blond Ltd for 'Keeping a Straight Bat' (originally titled 'Up she jolly goes') from *Love is not Love*;

Mr A.C.H. Smith and George Weidenfeld & Nicolson Ltd for 'Cricket is a confidence trick' from *Extra Cover*;

Mr J.L. Carr and Alan Ross Ltd for the extract from *A Season in Sinji*;

Mr Dal Stivens and The Outback Press for 'The Ring-in' from *The Demon Bowler and other cricket stories*;

To A.D. Peters & Co Ltd for permission to reproduce the extract from *Brensham Village* by the late John Moore (William Collins Sons & Co Ltd);

To David Higham Associates Ltd for 'The Novice: Down Under' by the late Denzil Batchelor from *The Game Goes On* (Eyre & Spottiswoode);

Macmillan, London and Basingstoke for the extract from *England, Their England* by the late A.G. Macdonell;

The executors of the late Hugh de Selincourt, Jonathan Cape Ltd and Oxford University Press, for 'Gauvinier's last game' from *The Game of the Season* originally published by Chapman & Hall;

Mrs J.G.R. Latham and E.P. Dutton Inc. for 'A Country-house match and some lookers-on' from *A Fish Dinner in Memison* by the late E.R. Eddison;

Hamish Hamilton Ltd for 'Caught sub.' from *The Go-Between* by the late L.P. Hartley;

The Bodley Head Ltd for 'A Farewell to Arms' from *Friendly Eleven* by Mr Eric N. Simons;

Mr Gerald Brodribb for permission to reprint in a revised and updated version 'Cricket in Fiction' originally published by The Mountjoy Press, Canford, in a Limited Edition.